D0256585

OUTBURSTS

OUTBURSTS

Oliver Walston

Farming Press
Ipswich

Published 1988

British Library Cataloguing in Publication Data

Walston, Oliver
Outbursts.
1. Arable farming
I. Title
631

ISBN 0–85236–177–7

Photoset in Bembo by
CAS Typesetters, Southampton

Printed by
MacKays of Chatham PLC, Chatham, Kent

Contents

Foreword by Simon Gourlay · ix
Preface · xi

Farmer's Glory · 1
Bitter Harvest · 3
Living on Borrowed Time? · 5
The Smithfield Show 1976 · 9
Puffed Wheat · 11
The Eleventh Commandment · 14
Sugar Beet Stakes · 17
My Heart Bleeds for Me · 19
Seed Growing Ain't the Same Any More · 23
Damascus in Schleswig-Holstein · 26
Two Weeks in China · 29
Knowing When to Stop · 31
Garbage In, Garbage Out · 34
Discovering Discs · 37
Down with Plant Breeders · 40
Prospects for the 1980s · 42
Private . . . Come In · 45
Fertilise by Computer · 49
Microchips on My Shoulder · 52
Dear Landlord · 54
The Best Farmer · 57
Mississippi Rip-off · 60
A Subsidy for Cannabis · 62
The Great Combine Test · 65
Starting Sheep · 68
John Cherrington · 71
Ten Tonnes of Wheat · 74
The Case Against Burning · 76
The New Farm Worker · 79
Why Grow Sugar Beet? · 82
Hard Cheese · 84
Bloated Sheep? · 87

Memorandum 90
What Can We Do with Straw? 92
A New Deal for Tenants? 95
One Farm – Two Computers 97
Importing Chemicals from France 100
NFU – Members and Memos 103
Harvest 1981 106
It's Not Much Fun Being a Hypocrite 109
Red-hot Buyers? 111
Revolting Farmers 113
Why Not Simplify Your Farm? 115
Just Figure This Out 118
The Bottom Rung 120
Buying a Seed Drill 122
Bad News 124
Experiences with a Computer 126
Open Letter to a Pension Fund Manager 128
Harvest 1982 130
The Price of Wheat Is Too High 133
Commuters Rule, OK? 136
The Lure of Urea 138
New Combines – Old Problems 141
To Hell with Co-operatives 143
Rip-off 145
Kansas Cornucopia 148
Farmers – Unlike TV Producers – Live in the Real World 151
Weighing Up a Problem 154
A Few Seed Merchants Are Honest 157
Farming at Its Frozen Limits 160
Bad Debts 167
Buying More Land 170
Be Nice to a Conservationist – Plough Up an SSSI 172
Be Patient – If You Possibly Can 175
Livestock in East Anglia 177
Richard Butler for President 179
The Sodbuster 182
Boy's Land 186
Walston's First Law of Gastronomy 188
Open Up Your Farms to the Public 191

Contents

Send a Tonne to Africa   194
Welcome to the Real World   196
The Common Ground   199
Stubble Digesters – and Other Quack Remedies   201
Hybrid Wheat   203
The New Villager   206
Harvest 1984   209
No Burning – Post Mortem   211
Send a Tonne to Africa – Looking Back   214
Eritrea – Diary from a Starving Land   217
We Got Ourselves into This Mess   224
Survival Plan   226
Bad News from British Sugar   229
Buying a Combine   231
The Bankrupt Farmers of Nebraska   234
Pre-harvest Round-up   238
An Open Letter to My Landlord   240
Harvest 1985   243
Talking to the Bank Manager   246
Why I'm Not an Organic Farmer   248
New Year Wishes 1986   251
In France the Lunatics Run the Asylum   252
Gluttony in Paris   254
Bad Debt Nightmare   256
Don't Buy Certified Cereal Seed   258
An Open Letter to Patrick Tory   260
No More Cereal Surpluses   262
Noble Savage   264
The Ministry Cocks It Up   267
The Tenants' Revolt   269
A Year of Fiascos   272
Harvest 1986   274
Managing to Survive . . . or Surviving to Manage   277
All I Want Are Some Greengages   287
Wunderbar – If You Happen to Be a German Farmer   289
SSSI Dream   291
Open Letter to Jonathan Porritt – Friend of the Earth   293
Garbage from Britain   296
Harvest 1987   299

Contents

Salaries for All   301
A Born-again Whinger   303

Index   305

Foreword

When you meet Oliver Walston, you can't help being struck by his physical presence. Short and wide; not built for speed or agility.

It will not be long before he opens his mouth. An enthusiastic talker, it is immediately clear that his mind is the antithesis of his body. Fast, agile and irrepressibly full of a highly idiosyncratic way of looking at things. He writes as he talks.

For a part-time journalist he must have infuriated more people than anyone else in the business. At one time or another he must have upset every regular (if there is such a thing) reader of his articles. Certainly that applies to me. But his novel approach, gutsy style and ability to criticise and laugh at himself as much as others make for refreshing and often compulsive reading.

Over the twelve years spanned by this book, many sacred cows have disappeared. Others, less sacred, have come and gone. Fashions have changed. A sheep flock was introduced at Thriplow as recently as 1980, but today the farm is stockless. The first generation of computers has given way to the second, and the second (now that the instructions have been properly read) has already spawned a third. Lucerne has suffered the same fate as the Jersey cows and over half the labour force. They became no longer profitable to keep.

Although he is an ideas man, Oliver Walston also has a strong practical streak. He gets things done. Send a Tonne to Africa in 1984 was his initiative and he was the motor force behind it. It raised over £2 million. And he combined his flair for the offbeat with his practical organising ability when he organised on his own farm the world record for the fastest loaf ever to be made from a standing wheat crop.

Sit back; enjoy the hyperbole, the tales of the biggest, the fastest, the shiniest, the greatest, the least and the worst. You may have to grit your teeth and bite your tongue occasionally, but I challenge you to get through this collection of Outbursts without at least some wry smiles and having learnt something about yourself and your farming.

Simon Gourlay
January 1988

To my Father
who gave me the chance

and

Lionel Dawes
who gave me good advice

Preface

The following collection of articles was written over a twelve year period which started a few months before the Great Drought of 1976. At that time I had been a farmer for only five years; little did I guess that they were probably the most prosperous years British Agriculture has ever known.

Looking backwards, which is an occupation I have never found arduous, it is clear that the farming industry had hit the jackpot on a never-ending fruit machine. Yet at the time influential voices were insisting that agriculture was in danger of imminent ruin unless prices were raised, and raised again. This habit of farmers to bemoan their fate, even while they are making fortunes, is a recurring theme in this book. I make no apology. Quite the contrary.

Today, as the same farmers face a future which will be as hard as the last decade was easy, some of them may now regret that they did not shut up and sit tight during the prosperous 1970s and early 1980s. But they didn't. And they have nobody to blame but themselves.

The temptation to re-write some of these pieces has been enormous; it has been resisted. All my prejudices, inaccurate predictions and just plain stupidities are here to be mocked. I have, however, sometimes added explanatory footnotes or brief post-scripts which appear in italics.

Conservationists will be overjoyed (but the timber industry will be sad) to learn that not a single tree or shrub was felled to produce the manuscript since no paper was used. Instead the text was written on an APPLE MACINTOSH computer using WORD software. It was then typeset with a Linotronic 100 machine. If only farming were as simple.

I thank the editors of *The New Statesman*, *The Observer*, *Big Farm Weekly*, *Farmers Weekly* and (the late) *Big Farm Management* for giving me permission to reprint these pieces. Roger Smith and Julanne Arnold of Farming Press take the credit for putting the book together and Jake Tebbit, who comes from another Cambridgeshire farming family, for the cartoons. But most of all I must thank my wife, Anne, for acting as proofreader, psychiatrist and gastronomic adviser. Without her, this slim volume would never have seen the light of day. There, I feel better now. I've always wanted to say that.

O.W.
Thriplow Farm
January 1988

Farmer's Glory

APRIL 1976

Discriminating members of the public who appreciate silence in a noisy world are savouring a moment which they will recount to disbelieving grandchildren in decades to come. The British farmer has recently been so busy taking advantage of the superb weather of the past six months that he has had neither the time nor the inclination to complain. Even the NFU, whose skill at making mountains (usually beef) out of molehills could teach Clive Jenkins* a thing or two, is at a temporary loss for words. Rarely has the short term future for agriculture looked so hopeful, even if the longer term problem of capital taxation, the tied cottage and tenancy succession remain to worry the farmer.

The livestock men in the west have discovered that, contrary to all predictions made last year, milk production did not decline last winter. The supposed hay and straw shortages did not materialise, albeit thanks only to the export from East Anglia of vast quantities of straw and a mild autumn in which grass grew faster than at any time during the summer. Mastitis, the dairy industry's most serious disease, is gradually declining and even the feared increase in the price of concentrates was less than had been predicted.

For the cerealistes of the east, the weather has been even kinder. Conditions last autumn were so good that the acreage of winter wheat, the most profitable cereal crop, was a record 2.8 million acres, 1.2 million acres more than in the previous year, and 4.5% higher than the previous record for the harvest year 1973-74. A brief period of frost this winter was enough to break down the clods of ploughed land into a fine tilth, and the recent dry spell has enabled even the farmers on the heavy clay soils to finish their spring drilling earlier than ever before.

Sugar beet growers, after two of the worst years ever known because of drought and disease, have been attracted by a price of over £19 per ton, which should give them a return of at least £220 per acre. Although some growers have given up beet completely after their recent experiences, the British Sugar Corporation are confident that this year's crop of 510,000 acres will produce enough

* Trade Union leader, General Secretary of ASTMS.

— 1 —

to fulfil the UK's basic EEC white sugar quota of 1,040,000 tons. Conditions for planting have been ideal and most growers are well ahead of schedule. Potato planting is equally advanced, and even though a 350% increase in seed cost over last year has frightened off some of the less successful growers, there should be no danger of the price falling anywhere near the guarantee of £40 per ton.

Beef and pig producers, who last year faced bankruptcy, are today considering the relative merits of Tenerife and Majorca for their holidays. Both commodities are approaching their cyclical peaks, which should last at least until the end of the year. Sheep numbers continue to fall slowly and, while the outlook for both meat and wool is not very exciting, there should at least be modest profits to be made.

The only two sectors of the industry which have reason to be gloomy are poultry and horticulture. The chicken and egg producers (neither came first) have been in a trough for a year and the increased price of foodstuffs, exacerbated by the Community's clumsy attempt to reduce the powdered milk surplus, has not made them optimistic. The horticulturists, who received nothing in the recent Price Review except a vague promise of increased capital grants, are in particularly bad shape. Hit by increased heating costs, appalling storm damage to the greenhouses and now the recent spell of dry weather, they must now be doubting whether it is worth spending a lot of money duplicating climatic conditions which occur naturally in other parts of the Common Market.

But normality, which in farming is usually synonymous with despair, will return any day now. Already the dry weather is becoming a curse and not a blessing. After this brief and welcome respite, we shall once again be hearing a lot about such wondrous problems as Glume Blotch (an aptly named disease affecting wheat), Sheep Scab, Swine Vesicular Disease, Aphids, Blight and that most talked-about agricultural ailment of all which is usually defined as What-the-hell-do-those-people-in-Brussels-think-they're-doing-anyway? So hurry. Take a farmer out to tea quickly. You will find him quite human, but this may not last for long.

Written just before the Great Drought of 1976 really made itself felt. There is, I note, a passing reference to "the recent dry spell". Little did I realise it was due to last for a further four months and we would experience the worst harvest since the war.

Bitter Harvest

AUGUST 1976

Farmers are reverting to type. After a brief flirtation with optimism during last winter and spring, they now face the most difficult conditions they have ever known. Taking a farmer to tea these days would be a depressing exercise. Even a concussed undertaker would be a more stimulating companion with whom to share a crumpet. What makes the farmer particularly frustrated is that there is nobody he can blame. The agnostics regard weather as a sequence of scientific interactions and the churchgoing members of the NFU know that to blame Him invites the retribution of eternal damnation. Grumbling about the Green Pound and guillotined tied cottages may distract their minds for short periods, but the sight of shrivelled corn and brown pastures is infinitely more worrying.

The flood of drought news put out by the media has ensured that even people who spend their waking hours on the Bakerloo Line are probably aware that a crisis exists. North of a line between Grimsby and Bristol (this Crosland–Benn axis is one of the more unlikely consequences of the drought) the situation is better. The grass did manage to grow and crops, though poorer than anticipated, are better than in the south.

Arable farmers, some of whom have done exceptionally well for the past three years, have received the biggest shock. Yields are down by 25% or more and the smallness of the grain shows the effect of a two-pronged attack from the weather and an invasion of aphids (the greenfly on roses) which sucked what little moisture remained in the growing plant. Another by-product of the dry weather has been to ensure that the nitrogen fertilisers have been absorbed by the plant itself rather than the soil. The resulting high level of nitrogen in the grain is bad news for the maltsters who need low nitrogen barley to produce good malt. The premium paid for good malting barley has risen sharply and is now 30% over the price of barley used for cattle fed. Seed merchants are equally disturbed. The sieves over which they pass the grain to remove impurities are losing up to 40% of the crop because the small grains fall through. This fact, in addition to the low yields, will create an acute shortage of seed next year. High prices will encourage many farmers to keep back their own grain for sowing, which is a risky operation because the presence of weed seeds, particularly wild oats, will reduce the size of next harvest.

In the Good Old Days, somewhere between Turnip Townshend and John Maynard Keynes, a small harvest would at least have resulted in high prices. But in today's Global Village, it is what happens in Nebraska and the Ukraine that matters. To the chagrin of East Anglia, things are looking good in Nebraska, where a record harvest is being gathered. Although prices to British farmers have risen since last year, they in no way compensate for the drastic fall in yields and increase in costs.

If, as seems unlikely, we have a wet autumn, the sugar beet crop will be better than in the past two years (not a difficult achievement) and the arable outlook will improve slightly. But at present the beet look a sorry sight. Already yellowing with virus (those aphids again) and wilting in the sun, a continuation of the drought will result in yields which will fall well below the United Kingdom's production quota and many farmers will finally decide that after three years' losses on beet, they will have to find a replacement crop. The snag is that there really is not a satisfactory alternative, a fact that the British Sugar Corporation knows is the trump card.

So the prudent arable farmer will have to live off his fat for the next year. In fact, it looks as if the new Volvo will have to be cancelled and the baler will be asked to do another season. The Bank Manager will be sympathetic but stern in his demand for retrenchment.

The livestock men have seen it all before and, rightly, have little sympathy for their arable colleagues. Their grass has not grown for two months and hay and silage crops are being eaten into long before the winter begins. Paradoxically, the efficient dairy farmer has been hit hardest because his skill (and a lot of fertiliser) has enabled him to keep large herds on small acreages. But this summer no amount of skill and fertiliser could persuade grass to grow. So the older cows are weeded out and become part of the Beef Mountain and the farmer prays for rain and Petrus Lardenois★.

If the meteorologists are right about the weather pattern changing permanently, the implications for farming are obviously serious. Techniques will have to alter, new varieties must be bred, and water conservation will have to be taken a lot more seriously

★ EEC Agricultural Commissioner.

than it is today. But all of this takes years not months. In the meantime we may have to face the fact that this country's agricultural productivity, of which we have recently been so proud, is not so much because we are superb farmers, but simply because it rained a lot.

> *Written at the height of the Great Drought of 1976. I am singing a very different song to the previous* New Statesman *article written in April. Note the reference to the Crosland-Benn axis. These two pillars of the right and left wings of the Labour Party represented Grimsby and Bristol respectively.*

Living on Borrowed Time?

AUGUST 1976

My knowledge of cart horses is limited to a hazy memory of Suffolk Punches standing patiently between the shafts while mangolds were loaded into the cart. As a child, it always struck me as unfair that these horses wore blinkers and thus could not enjoy the scenery. But the reason was clear; it was to prevent them noticing the ever-increasing number of tractors which were rapidly making them redundant.

Today, some thirty years later, the manufacturers of the same tractors are also wearing blinkers which ensure that they do not notice the increasing number of imported machines which are liable to consign British farm machinery to the obscurity of the Suffolk Punch. With the exception of a handful of companies in Britain today, the entire industry appears to be happily unaware that they are living on borrowed time by refusing to adapt to the conditions of farming in the 1970s, and what may happen in the eighties.

We hear a lot about the export achievements of the tractor manufacturers, and it is undeniable that this country has a fine record. But a closer look at the situation reveals a disturbing trend. The larger tractors of 100hp or above are either imported or depend to a large extent on imported components being assembled here. Yet it is precisely this type of tractor which is increasing its market share on the big farm at the expense of the smaller models.

The trend towards more power has been continuing for the whole of this century and is, if anything, actually accelerating. The manufacturers have so far generally kept tractors' horsepower rising in line with the increasing demand for higher power, but are they all alive to the likely pace of development? Of course there are exceptions, and certainly in the field of large four wheel drive machines, our products are as good or better than most. But even this achievement rests on the presence of two smaller companies using their inventiveness to modify the products of the large manufacturers.

This refusal to admit that the scene is changing rapidly is the single most important difference between British and foreign manufacturers. We apparently feel that it is worth spending hundreds of thousands of pounds re-tooling for a new radiator grille and re-positioned toolbox, but stronger drawbars and tyres to take today's increased weights are thought to be unnecessary luxuries.

Four-furrow mounted reversible ploughs and ten tonne trailers are hardly new on the scene, and yet the tractor manufacturers have deliberately ignored the problem these weights pose. At least one has to assume that the inaction has been deliberate, since the alternative explanation is that manufacturers are unaware of the existence of this sort of tackle. Compare this attitude to the situation in Europe where tyres and drawbars to cope with the problem are readily available either as factory-installed options or from the dealer.

The situation in the rest of the industry is no better. We all know the sad saga of the Ransomes combine★, and it would be nice to say that it was an isolated incident, but the fact remains that German and Belgian combines are the market leaders. They sell in their hundreds each year in spite of, rather than because of, their price. The reason is simple. They are well-designed, strongly built and backed by an excellent spares and service network.

British trailer manufacturers are perhaps even more prone to the blinkered approach, surviving simply because imported trailers are so much more expensive and certainly not because our products are in any way superior. Far from it. The normal British trailer was, is, and shows every sign of remaining, a box on wheels.

★ The last combine manufactured by a British-owned company. It had recently gone out of production.

Over the years the size has increased by scaling up a design which was adequate for a three ton model pulled by a Standard Fordson, but is simply ludicrous for the loads of today's farms. Brakes are usually optional extras, hydraulic oil requirements are far in excess of what a tractor can safely pump, and sideboards and tailgates are so flimsy that within a short time they flap about so much it is impossible to prevent grain from leaking out.

Neither tractor nor trailer manufacturers appear to have spoken to each other for the last ten years, since it is impossible to imagine two machines more unsuited to each other. Each party blames the other for the situation, and the only person to suffer the consequences is the farmer himself.

The British plough, which used to be the finest in the world, today relies on the efforts of one large and one small company to stem the flood of imports from the Continent. In most of the

modern developments, like the stubble plough, we lag behind the rest of Europe and look like remaining in that position.

The situation in forage machinery is even worse, as anyone who went to last year's Grassland Demonstration will remember. Self-propelled forage harvesters, pickup trailers and (with one notable exception) mobile crop driers remain the exclusive territory of foreign companies who have risked the time, money and effort to produce machines suited to a capital-intensive industry in which men are fewer but more skilled. One of my dealer friends tells me that they have to go to the Paris Show or the DLG★ to keep in touch with new machinery.

The comments of the industry are all too often verging on the complacent. "We are meeting market demands already" and "There just is not sufficient demand to make production worthwhile" are comments which could equally have been made by Ferguson about his three-point linkage. But thankfully he had faith in his idea and we have been benefiting enormously as a result. One has only to look at the once-great textile industry in this country to see what happens when we depend on old techniques, old markets and old attitudes.

British farmers are a patriotic lot who would prefer, all things being equal, to buy British. But all things are very far from being equal, and show every sign of becoming still less equal. The agricultural engineering industry has a past to be proud of, but it is time to forget the past and think of the future. Unless this is done quickly, British farm machinery will join the *Suffolk Punch* as an object of affectionate nostalgia.

> *Written largely as the result of my discovery earlier in 1976 that no tractor drawbars were actually strong enough to support the larger trailers of the day. Neither tractor nor trailer manufacturers appeared to have noticed this rather crucial fact. I was also very depressed about the direction in which the British agricultural engineering industry was going. For once (in hindsight at least) I was right. However, this article so upset that year's President of the Agricultural Engineers Association that he invited me to Smithfield to show me that I was misguided.*

★ German Agricultural Society which organises the annual Farm Show.

The Smithfield Show 1976

JANUARY 1977

During the past year I have become increasingly depressed about the state of the British farm machinery industry; it seems as if it is in danger of falling asleep on its feet while competitors from abroad come up with all the new ideas. The machines we bought for the farm this year were almost invariably foreign and this was not because we were prejudiced against British tackle. Far from it.

The snag is that this country does not produce a single example of a shallow plough, self loading trailer, pneumatic fertiliser spreader, large trailed sprayer with 24 metre boom or a self-propelled forage harvester. And as if that weren't enough, the 100hp tractor we ordered in February still had not arrived by September. Hence our first foreign tractor.

My experiences with heavy trailers and drawbar loadings had already convinced me that tractor and trailer manufacturers lived in different worlds and spoke different languages. But more importantly, it showed that the industry as a whole had not thought about the problems posed by the ever-increasing size and weight of new machinery.

The traditions of the village blacksmith may have their virtues, but the "If it looks right it is right" school of design is a luxury we cannot afford. Thus I came to Earls Court feeling a bit pessimistic about agricultural engineering in this country.

The first thing I saw was not a machine but a piece of paper full of figures. It showed our tractor manufacturers had an export record which would make any other industry, except possibly scotch whisky, very envious indeed. Tractor exports had risen by 24% over last year. This may explain where my 100hp tractor has gone to, and I take comfort from the thought that my loss is a German farmer's gain. Tractor imports, by the way, had gone up by 44%.

The export performance of other agricultural machinery (i.e. everything but tractors) did not look so good. It had improved by 7% which, with inflation, meant we sold less than the year before. So much for the figures. We are great at producing tractors, not so good at the things that the tractors pull, and foreign sales here are increasing faster than ours abroad.

After fighting my way through the statistics, the Smithfield crowds looked less daunting. I went in search of good ideas and machines which would make life easier and the farm better. It soon became clear we make better drills than any country in the world. Last year it was the MF 30 and this year the Bettinson. But even more exciting is the appearance of Stanhay's precision cereal drill. Here is a superb example of what this country should be doing by having the guts and the foresight to persevere with a good idea. There still seem to be a few snags before the drill appears on many farms (I wouldn't like to fill those small hoppers with a 50kg sack on my back) but precision drilling must be the system of the future and Stanhay are a long way ahead of their competitors.

Rough terrain forklift trucks are another area in which we are supreme. Incredibly expensive to buy, especially after you have kitted them out with the necessary forks and buckets, they are the most addictive items since the invention of alcohol. Hours after you start using one you become completely hooked and life is never the same again.

So far so good. The Dowdeswell ploughs, the Ransomes Hunter beet combine and an excellent tramlining device on the Bettinson stand show that here and there we are keeping up the best traditions of the industry. Unfortunately, the single most important development was the sole property of one country – Denmark. Taarup and JF both displayed their versions of the on-farm straw processors which will inevitably revolutionise livestock and arable farming. The technique of treating straw with caustic soda is far from new, but hitherto it has been possible only in large and complicated factories. Here are two machines which enable a small farmer to convert straw into a feedstuff only slightly less valuable than grain itself. The implication is clear; straw will become a crop in its own right instead of just being an arable by-product.

The rest of the exhibits contained little which could be considered new; most were developments of existing ideas. The Claas big baler promises to solve some of the handling problems inherent in the round bale system. Howards continue to develop their own square baler and the battle of the bigs, littles, rounds and squares appears to be hotting up nicely.

But overall, my misgivings about the future were not completely allayed. If your requirements are for big machines and the latest techniques, the chances are that you will have to buy foreign. If you want to lift more than three rows of sugar beet at a time you will have to buy a French machine. If you want a trailer that loads itself, you won't be able to buy a British one. If you want to retain the advantages of mouldboard ploughing with the workrate of a chisel plough, neither Ransomes nor Dowdeswell can help you. The very large and sophisticated trailed sprayer – which will become increasingly common because of tramlines – is not manufactured in this country.

Perhaps it is a sensible commercial decision to cater for the small-to-medium-sized market because it is certainly the biggest in terms of volume. Perhaps it is too expensive to develop new techniques, and this should be left to foreigners. Certainly we are doing well enough at the present time. But the lurking fear remains that behind the impressive export figures of today, we are eating the seed corn of tomorrow. And you don't have to be a farmer to know this is a dangerous thing to do.

If ever there was an example of bad forecasting this was it. The precision cereal drill which I was so excited about never made the grade. Neither did the Taarup or JF straw treaters. The Ransomes Hunter was hardly the greatest success either. But I was right to be keen on Dowdeswell ploughs, Claas big balers and rough terrain fork lift trucks.

Puffed Wheat

JULY 1977

"Let me say right away that I do not consider existing conditions likely". Thus spoke Peter Sellers's Macmillanesque politician some fifteen years ago. He was, of course, referring to the situation facing farmers today. On the thin chalk hills of south Cambridgeshire where water drains away before you realise that it is raining, the old-timers say that "a ruined hay crop means a good harvest". Constant rain in May and late June never allows the hay to dry – but it does fill out the grains of wheat and barley. This year the hay crop has been magnificent and there is every indication that the harvest will be one of the best for a long time.

This time last year the harvest was almost finished as combines sliced through fields which would not have looked amiss in the Kalahari Desert. Today, the start of harvest is still two weeks away. Only the earliest sown winter barleys, which have been in the ground since last September, look even faintly golden. But – another rustic adage coming up – "Long in the bed, long in the head" (i.e. the longer the plant is in the earth the heavier will be the head of corn), and so farmers are not worried at the prospect of having to wait longer than usual before they unleash their 25,000 machines for three or four weeks of frenetic combining.

Needless to say, even with what the press always calls a "bumper harvest" (farmers talk of "big" or "heavy" harvests but never use the word "bumper") staring them in the face, those involved in Britain's agriculture still cling to their professional pessimism. It may, they warn, be be a wet harvest which will involve break-downs and expensive drying of the corn. It is still not too late, they add with a certain melancholic satisfaction, for disease to strike and cover the leaves with brown or yellow rust. Furthermore, it will certainly be a late harvest; and this (with a strong shake of the head) will not allow enough time to prepare the land for sowing in the autumn. As if these bogies were not enough, there remain the economic factors. The price of barley is already dropping in anticipation of the record 17 million ton cereal harvest that the experts (i.e. merchants who want to see low prices) are predicting. Little wonder, then, given their psychological tendencies, that even the most bullish farmers remain cowed.

Most other sectors of agriculture are also enduring the prospect of prosperity with the sort of fortitude you would expect from the self-styled Yeomen of England. Livestock men have enjoyed an excellent hay and silage season, with the grass growing fast and plentiful. The high hay prices of the past two winters will not be repeated this year, and motorists trying to escape from the West Country will not be baulked by the endless convoys of lorries carrying straw from Suffolk to Cornwall. Beef producers can be confident of the future but are uneasy about the present because consumer resistance is now a very real factor with steak selling for more than £2 per pound. Pig farmers are, and have been for the past year, exceptions to the trend. Common Market farm policy has subsidised Danish pork and bacon imports into this country so that English producers have been unable to compete. As is so often the case, the efficient man with his modern, labour-saving setup, has been losing more money than the man with a few old sows scratching round in the mud and farrowing in in a rusty Nissen hut. The latter has not borrowed money at high interest rates, and is probably self-employed, so he rarely charges for his own time and labour.

The biggest question mark in farming today hangs over the sugar beet fields which litter the eastern side of England and have, for the past fifty years, provided a profitable break crop between cereals. The last three years have been disastrous for beet growers because of drought and disease. This year looks better, but many farmers have had enough and are determined to give up the crop completely. A mounting sugar surplus in Europe, the new process by which sugar (isoglucose to be precise) can be extracted from maize and wheat, and alternative break crops like oilseed rape, have all combined to put the pressure on sugar beet. The British Sugar Corporation, a state monopoly which buys and processes sugar beet, is caught between the need to modernise its factories and the declining acreage of beet. It is a prospect which will excite the northern French farmers who will be only too happy to take up any additional acreage and grow extremely heavy yielding crops of beet on a scale which only a few areas in this country can match. So those who are bad on agronomy but good on colours should watch out for more yellow (rape) and less green (beet) next year. Maybe there will be even a bit more blue (linseed is very pretty at this time of year) than in the past, and there is just an outside chance that before long southern England will resemble Yugoslavia with rolling fields of gorgeous sunflowers.

In the political sphere, farmers are increasingly unhappy about the Government's performance – or lack of it. The White Paper, "Food from Our Own Resources", now has ivy climbing up it as it stands for all to admire. The latest Minister pays lip service to its aims without being prepared to put his money remotely near where is mouth is believed to be. It is hardly surprising that farmers are more than ever convinced that he is Minister of Food but not Agriculture. or a brief moment of recorded time pig producers thought he was on their side when he managed to introduce a subsidy to reduce their losses. But bearing in mind the inherent conflict between a sow's ear and a Silkin★ purse, it was not surprising that the subsidy was removed at the request of Brussels.

★   Silkin, the current (Labour) Minister of Agriculture.

The dialogue between farmers and consumers invariably resembles the England Rugby trial with the Improbables playing the Impossibles (lots of tries but no conversions). In spite of the fact that most farmers vote conservative or not at all, there is little belief that things would be any different under a Thatcher regime. Indeed, the only Ministers of Agriculture in the postwar period who are remembered with any reverence at all are Tom Williams and Fred Peart. For the latter it is quite an achievement because Beatification of Ministers is almost invariably a posthumous award. But then rigor mortis is an occupational hazard in their Lordships' House.

You would never believe it from reading this rubbish, but 1977 was a lovely year. Harvest was good, profits were high and all was well with the world. Or so it seems today. But in those days we were still whingeing even though we were all making fortunes. Did steak really ever cost £2 per pound, and could I really buy a combine for £25,000? Today they cost more than three times this amount. But most surprising of all, was a 17 million ton harvest really a record? The 1987 harvest of 22 million tonnes is considered to be disastrously small by farmers today. Sugar beet is today one of the few crops which makes a profit, and oilseed rape did expand as I had predicted. But Linseed never really caught on and even today there are almost no sunflowers grown in Britain. So much for my prescience.

The Eleventh Commandment

JANUARY 1979

There is a lot to be said for having a Rembrandt on the wall. It looks pretty, impresses your friends and might even make the bank manager less nervous when it comes to increasing your overdraft. But above all, there is the knowledge that Rembrandts are not made any more, so in addition to the pleasures of ownership, you also have an excellent hedge against inflation. The same applies to the diamond as big as the Ritz on your wife's finger or – to a lesser extent – the Rolls Royce in the garage. But not even the Rembrandt

Owners Club or the Country Diamond Wearers Association would waste their time in trying to persuade a sceptical British public that these things are in any way essential to life in 1979. A house is perfectly habitable without a Rembrandt on the wall and a car will still get you places without a winged lady on the bonnet.

But when one or more farmers are gathered together, as they were at the last Oxford Farming Conference, you very soon get the impression that a farm is only a farm if the farmer owns the land. Moses, it seems, came down from Mount Sinai with eleven tablets, one of which has been mislaid until recently. Biblical scholars, working in close co-operation with the Country Landowners Association, have succeeded in interpreting the hieroglyphics on this relic of early agriculture (when manna was the staple crop). It reads

> *There shalt be owner-occupation, without which farming and all those engaged therein shall perish from the land.*

It is perhaps lucky that this Commandment has only recently come to light because, until 60 years ago, there wasn't very much owner-occupation in this country. And nobody seemed to mind.

The landlord–tenant system had worked pretty well for a long time until the Great Families found that they needed a bit of extra cash. They sold some farms to the tenants which made everybody happy. However, the grandchildren of these tenants have either very short or highly selective memories about what happened to farms before the First World War. Widespread owner-occupation is not even as old as the motor car. It is not one of the great traditions of this country, nor was it the cornerstone of British agriculture.

I do have great sympathy with owner-occupiers today who seek to preserve their land and pass it on to the next generation. Regardless of the rights and wrongs of capital taxation, one can neither argue with nor be surprised by the desire of an individual to hold on to his possessions. This is true for farmland as much as, but no more than, the aforementioned Rembrandt. Where I do part company with owner-occupiers is when they claim that it is actually necessary for them as farmers to own their own land. This lack of distinction between what is desirable and what is necessary is a common feature of the human race. If one wants something badly enough, it is all too easy to convince oneself – and hopefully others too – that what may appear to be a luxury is, in fact, a necessity.

If this deliberate woolliness can be used for the trivial things of life, how much more is it needed when the object of our desire is land. Nothing on earth arouses the emotions, stirs the viscera and gets the adrenalin pumping as much as the ownership of land. As an owner-occupier myself, I am only too well aware of the utterly indefinable pleasure which comes from walking over, looking at or even thinking about the land which you own. As if this were not enough, we also have the additional pleasure of actually farming it.

The quite staggering prices paid for farm land these days, 80% of which is bought by neighbouring farmers, is sufficient proof (as if proof were needed) of the inexplicable mania which seizes even the most cautious of men when he hears that the neighbouring field is up for sale. Virgil must have been writing about owner-occupiers when he said "Lucky beyond all bliss are farmers, if only they knew their own happiness." In the intervening two thousand years, we have learnt only too well how lucky we are.

The man who confuses what he would like to see happen with what he thinks will actually happen, is doomed to disappointment and failure. Regrettably, there can now be no doubt that the owner-occupier of today is the tenant of tomorrow. The sacrifices necessary to preserve even 300 acres of land will be more than the most successful farm will be able to bear. Our efforts can be used to delay or modify this inevitable process by fighting a rearguard action against overwhelming odds. But if we were to divert ourselves to ensure that the new Institutional landlords of tomorrow will be as good as our Noble landlords of yesterday, we would be doing ourselves and our industry a great deal more good.

Back in 1979 it really did look as if the private owner-occupier was doomed and the City Institutions were about to buy every acre in the country. Today, in 1988, the outlook for the owner-occupier is pretty bright (always provided he has not borrowed too much money to to pay for his land) and every City Institution I know is desperately (but usually unsuccessfully) trying to sell its land.

Sugar Beet Stakes

APRIL 1979

*Deep in the Malayan jungle the American stepped from his
helicopter. The entire village had been assembled to hear about
the new variety of rubber tree which gave double the yield of the
old variety. At the end of his talk the agronomist sat down to
perfunctory applause. The village chief rose and said: "On
behalf of the village I would like to thank our friend from the
United States for his most interesting talk. It is wonderful that
his new tree produces twice as much rubber as our old trees,
because it means that I shall only have to have half as many trees
and work half as hard as I used to." Loud cheers.*

The laws of economics sometimes appear to be suspended for
farmers. When the price of a commodity goes down, ostensibly to
reduce the supply, farmers frequently redouble their efforts to
ensure that their income is maintained. The attitude of the Malayan
chief towards increased profitability is not, however, repeated very
often in this part of the world.

In my case it is sugar beet and not rubber which appears, at first
glance, to have defied these laws of economics. Of all the crops we
grow, sugar beet has been the most consistently unprofitable
during the past five years. Logic and economics therefore dictate
that if there was any crop on the farm which did not merit massive
investment, it was sugar beet. And yet it is sugar beet which will,
next season, make use of the largest and most expensive piece of
machinery we have ever bought. The six-row self-propelled sugar
beet harvester which we have ordered costs roughly £50,000 –
enough to have bought a 150 acre farm less than a decade ago.

Before we took the decision to buy this machine, we had first to
answer a rather fundamental question: should we continue to grow
sugar beet at all? On the face of it, the arguments against beet are
overwhelming. Our yields on the thin, south Cambridgeshire
chalks are poor compared to the national average, which is itself
poor compared to the sugar beet growers on the Continent. The
mounting sugar surplus in Europe, and the spectre of isoglucose,
could well mean that only the most profitable sugar beet growers

will survive a narrowing of margins. It is probable that, in real terms, the price of beet will not rise next year. As if this were not enough, two other pressures have been building up on the farm for the past two years.

Our acreage of winter corn has been rising steadily, which means there is now great pressure to get the beet off so that the winter wheat and barley can be drilled by the end of November at the latest. The labour force is still shrinking slowly, and we try not to replace men who retire.

But we need break crops, and sugar beet is the least unsatisfactory of a dismal bunch. Our reasons for using breaks are simply because we grow cereals for seed and therefore need the breaks between changes of variety. Of course, sugar beet is the not the only weapon in our armoury. Oilseed rape is increasing, but we don't want to grow it on the same field more often than every six years. Beans, peas, tares, mustard and herbage seeds all have roles to play, but their problems outweigh their advantages, and ensure that they are grown only on a small scale.

Our sugar beet acreage hovers around 300 acres, which is an awkward size. It is too big for the Standen Multibeet which we have been using for the past four years, and is too small for one of the various French three-stage systems. The self-propelled six row combine could not possibly be justified unless we persuaded our neighbours to allow us to lift their beet for them. A total of 500 acres would make the operation barely feasible, and we set ourselves a target of this amount in the first year, rising to 1000 acres in three years' time. At this level we would be enjoying greatly reduced costs per acre, and all the benefits of being able to lift and cart nearly three acres an hour with only three men. Our two 12 tonne trailers will enable us to cart to a pile up to half a mile from the field, which means that we can make use of our existing network of concrete pads.

The snags will only come to light during the next campaign, but there are already eighteen of these machines at work in England, so we are hardly blazing a trail. The British Sugar Corporation have certain misgivings about the quality of topping which flail systems produce, but they admit that they can find no other faults.

On paper it all looks very hopeful – always assuming we can find enough acres on our neighbours' farms. They do not appear to feel that the price we have quoted them for beet lifted and carted to a heap is excessive.

I am convinced that we must be moving in the right direction because, with each passing year, the cost of replacing the beet machinery rises and the labour force dwindles. The trend towards bigness has been running strongly and shows no signs of slowing down, so the solution must lie in many farmers either sharing or hiring a high capacity machine. But even if I am wrong, the next season is going to be both interesting and fun. And that is what farming should be all about.

We stuck with sugar beet. Eventually our yields went up to reasonable levels, but this was written at a time when I was very gloomy about the crop. Today I am overjoyed that I did not give it up completely.

My Heart Bleeds for Me

MAY 1979

I sometimes feel like a man attending his own funeral – or at least the funeral of British agriculture. With each passing week I read about the desperate plight of farming and farmers from men whose talents and energies are only surpassed by the size of their farming enterprises. If it isn't Anthony Rosen★ telling us what an uphill struggle the dairymen are facing, it is Dick Bilborough★★ , who farms 20000 acres in East Anglia, proving quite conclusively that if things were bad in the bad old days, they are even worse today, and will become still more terrible tomorrow.

Do they or don't they? Only their accountants know for sure. I can well imagine that anyone who felt it sensible to buy land at the peak of the market, or rent it from someone who did – and then to erect vast and expensive buildings – could well be feeling the pinch today. But if this is the case, it is hard to see where governments,

★   Founder of Fountain Farming, a dairy-based mega farming empire which was the first to prosper and the first to go bust.
★★   Founder of Hallsworth Ltd, another farming empire, but this time built on an arable foundation. The company still survives, albeit without the participation of Mr. Bilborough.

common markets or even consumers are to blame for what is clearly a victory of enthusiasm over prudence. The man who builds an expensive ice cream factory at the South Pole should not necessarily blame his failure on the lack of subsidies for ice cream.

But it is not only farming tycoons who tell us that things are bad and getting worse. The Ministry itself has shown that real incomes fell by 11% in 1978. What further proof do we need that we are a doomed industry in sharp decline? All this is, of course, grist for the NFU's mill, and they lose no time in letting the world know that farming is about to go the way of the motorcycle industry, unless. Unless the Green Pound is devalued. Unless Danish bacon is kept out of Britain and British lamb is allowed into France. And above all, unless the Minister of Agriculture stops behaving like a Minister of Food by molly-coddling that irrelevant 97% of the population who only eat food, and instead turns his attention to the 3% who really matter. These are the ones who actually produce the food – or at least some of it.

But that's not all. The poor farmer, faced with ever-diminishing margins and ever-rising overdrafts, now faces a new threat. When he wants to buy some land he has to pay astronomic prices, or equally ludicrous rents if he wants to be a tenant. How, it is asked in plaintive tones, can he possibly afford to pay over £2000 an acre in competition with the loathsome City Institutions that don't have to worry about such things as Capital Transfer Tax, and whose coffers are bursting with money looking for a safe haven against inflation?

The position facing tenants is even more dire. On the rare occasions when a tenancy does become available, the rent offered breaks new records with a large amount of key money added to what is nostalgically called the "real rent". These rents are used by the hard-hearted arbitrators to force up all the other rents in the area out of all proportion to what the land is "really worth".

No, there's no doubt about it, British Agriculture is on its last legs. The wonder of it is how we farmers have managed to keep afloat for so long. Here we are, minding our own business as we eke out a simple living from the thin soil. We are attacked by plague, pestilence and politicians, and it is only a combination of providence (the divine sort) and sheer hard work which has enabled us to survive at all. This, at least, is the Gospel According to the NFU, and many of today's pundits. There's just one snag; it happens to be unadulterated rubbish. And if you don't believe me, you should take a close look at a pundit when you next see one. Mark the

threadbare clothes, the sallow complexion on the gaunt and emaciated frame. Notice the rusty Cortina which won't quite make the next MoT. Likewise, keep your eyes open when you are next outside Agriculture House, and look at the crumbling masonry and the air of faded respectability of the district in London in which the building stands.

Today's price of land, and the level of rents, are the direct result of the actions of a tightly knit group of commercially motivated men★. They are the men who actually buy 80% of the farmland which comes on the market. They are the same men who actually offer the astronomic rents whenever a tenancy is available. They are

★ Harold Wilson once accused the striking Seamans Union of being "A tightly knit group of politically motivated men".

the men who drive rather bigger cars than they used to, and they are the men whose purchases of farm machinery (rather than paying taxes) have actually kept the agricultural engineering industry afloat these past few years. These are the men who are our friends and neighbours. These men are called Farmers.

As you drive around Britain today, the signs of prosperity are there for anyone to see. Unlike the annual accounts, new buildings and machinery cannot be hidden away. Farmers in East Anglia have done better in the past five years than they, their fathers or their grandfathers ever dreamed possible. Their counterparts in the West Country with cows and sheep have done less well, but have still managed to make good profits. Pigs and beef are as erratic as ever, but no farmer should ever pretend to be surprised by this. Looked at overall, there can be no doubt that British farming is in good heart today. And long may it stay that way.

But the day may well come when this is no longer the case. If the going gets rough, like it did between the wars, we shall need to muster all our reserves of strength and we shall need to tell the politicians and the public loud and clear that farming is in trouble. If this day ever does come, we should not be surprised if a cynical public replies, "We've heard all that before."

1979 was the high water mark of the Farming Boom. Never before or since had farmers been so prosperous. Yet there were people who felt that prices were too low, profits too small and life too hard. Messrs Bilborough and Rosen were two of the three largest farmers in Britain at the time. Maybe there is a lesson to be drawn. At all events, this is one of the few articles I have no regrets about. The final sentence is, I regret, all too true today.

Seed Growing
Ain't the Same Any More

JUNE 1979

Do you remember the days when you didn't have to think about cereal varieties? Your only problem was from which merchant to buy the Proctor and Cappelle Dezprez. In those days everybody was happy. Everybody, that is, except for the plant breeders; they behaved like a cross between a Charity and a Gentleman's Club. When in 1953 Dr. Bell eventually succeeded in breeding Proctor, a letter went out to the fellows of the NIAB★ beginning "Gentlemen" and containing an offer of 4 bags of Foundation Seed at 50/- per bag. Those gentlemen wise enough to take up this offer benefited from the sort of breakthrough which comes all too rarely in farming. Quite what Dr. Bell and the PBI★★ got out of Proctor is hard to quantify. They made a bit of money from the sale of Foundation Seed and gained a lot of prestige from plant breeders the world over.

Other breeders were in the same position but, not having funds to rely on, found that it wasn't really worth their while spending ten years producing a new variety if at the end of the day they received nothing more than a round of applause. But something was stirring in the Westminster woodwork and in 1964 there appeared the Plant Varieties and Seeds Act which gave protection, and hence royalties, to plant breeders. From that moment on there was money to be made in plant breeding. The commercial companies started work in earnest and the results can be seen in the varieties in this year's Recommended List.

Farmers should not complain about a system which has given us the likes of Maris Huntsman, Ark Royal and Jupiter and there can be no doubt that our yields and profits would today be lower than they are without the varieties which have come onto the market in the past few years. But this New Deal for plant breeders has not been an unmitigated success; it has created a whole range of problems which the seed trade is only just beginning to face. Indeed

★ National Institute of Agricultural Botany.
★★ Plant Breeding Institute, then government-owned but now privatised and part of the Unilever empire.

the breeders and merchants may well fall victims to their own
success.

The new varieties which appear on the scene each year are all
competing for sales in an already overcrowded market. The Basic
seed is sold to the trade for multiplication at least one year before the
NIAB decides whether or not to include them on the Recommended List and therefore there is a very important risk to be taken
by merchants in deciding which of the new varieties to grow. But
even after a variety does get onto the Recommended List the
problems are a long way from being over. This year we had the
spectacle of Mink, an excellent spring barley, being dropped from
the list after one year because of its poor resistance to yellow rust.
All over the country seed growers have realised that they won't be
able to get a seed crop from the fields which grew Mink last year.
The merchants will probably have cancelled their contracts for the
variety and will themselves be wondering what to do with last
year's crop.

But if the merchants make the right decision and their variety
gets a good rating from the NIAB, there is a lot of money to be
made, particularly in the first two years of a variety's life. By the
same token the wrong decision can be an expensive matter. When
this happens the reputable merchants pay the grower the agreed
premium even though they know that they will find it hard to sell
the crop for seed and its eventual destiny will be for grinding.
However, it is all too common that in this situation the merchant
tries very hard to reject the crop for technical reasons and there can
be no doubt that at the very least they take a particularly long hard
look at samples in the hopes that a piece of ergot or runch seed will
give then legitimate grounds for rejection. Few growers will
endure the endless problems of arbitration which is the only
alternative to accepting a dubious rejection and it is as a result of
these situations that the recently formed Cereal Seed Growers
Association more than doubled its membership last year.

So the risks are increasing all the time. By the laws of capitalism
the rewards should increase in direct proportion to the risks but for
seed growers the opposite is the case. Premiums are being reduced,
tonnage limits are being introduced and open contracts, which give
the merchant no obligation to purchase, are becoming common.
These measures have one purpose only, to increase the merchant's
margins and to ensure that the risks of growing new varieties are,
wherever possible, offloaded onto the grower without at the same

time allowing the grower to share in the very substantial profits which result from choosing the right variety.

The farmer who buys seed at the end of the chain is also caught in this squeeze because the merchant has raised his prices to cover himself against the day when a variety comes unstuck. The only thing the farmer can do to protest is the one thing which the entire seed trade dreads more than anything else: he can stop buying seed and use his own instead.

But as if the problems caused by too many varieties are not enough, it now looks as if the seed trade have themselves made a very serious miscalculation. The past two good harvests with their exceptional yields took the trade by surprise no less than the rest of the farming community. Surpluses built up and, as a result, the contract acreage of seed crops was reduced by more than 15% last autumn. I suspect that this reduction was the result of an overreaction to the recent good yields and even without the frost damage which we have experienced this winter (which can only make the situation worse) there could well be a shortage of winter corn seed this coming autumn. In the old days the merchants would now be praying for a wet back-end to ensure a reduced demand for winter seed, but today this would cause even greater problems. In fact the spectre of a wet autumn is the one thing which makes even the most hard-headed merchant reach for his Accountant.

The swing away from spring corn and the new fashion of drilling in the third week of September have combined to make life very difficult indeed. Instead of having a leisurely eight weeks between combining the seed and delivering it to the customer, the merchant now has to process double the quantity in half the time. And for the rest of the winter his machines are barely ticking over cleaning the small amount of spring seed which is needed. It's Catch 22 all over again. A wet autumn will be difficult because it will expose the shortage of spring corn seed but a dry autumn may be no better if the trade has been panicked into cutting back the acreage too much. So be nice to your friendly neighbourhood seed merchant. He's only doing his best. But is it good enough?

A sickening whinge about the difficulties of being a cereal seed grower. We had recently formed the Cereal Seed Growers Association and this was clearly at the front of my mind.

Damascus in Schleswig-Holstein

JULY 1979

"It must be the cold winds," we used to say when the barley turned a nasty yellowish colour. "It'll get over it when the nights come warmer." As years passed, we became terribly scientific and sometimes in the early summer we would notice mildew on the leaves. "It'll get over it," we reassured ourselves. Then along came fungicides and we used to have endless arguments about whether it was worth spraying the crop. Would the damage done by the mildew outweigh the damage done by the wheelings and the cost of the spray?

Three years ago I found myself huddled in the back of a Unimog early one misty June morning. I had squeezed into a group who were accompanying the Duke of Schleswig-Holstein on his annual inspection of the estate. Accompanying the Duke were his general manager, three farm managers, a private adviser and a government adviser. For eleven hours we drove across the 2000 hectare farm visiting each field by driving smack into the middle of the crop. The relevant farm manager would describe what had been done to the particular field, drilling date, seed rate, fungicides, herbicides and what yield he anticipated. He was interrogated by the others and only when they were satisfied did the Unimog move on to the next field. After a cold lunch and a break for tea – which consisted of champagne at one of the manager's houses – we finally returned to the schloss as darkness fell.

I supposed that day was my version of St Paul's road to Damascus. It became clear to me that the traditional approach to cereal growing was obsolete. Field after field of winter wheat and barley were of a standard that I had rarely seen in England. The amount of care which had gone into this very large farm was unlike anything I had experienced before. Back in England the arguments were just beginning. The disciples of Laloux and Schleswig-Holstein were sparring gently and a few really progressive farmers were doing their own trials. ADAS, of course, was still recovering from the shock of Jethro Tull and Turnip Townshend.

The sensible thing would have been to try a field or two under a high input regime; but we decided to be foolhardy and commit the entire farm to what was in fact a hybrid Laloux/Schleswig-Holstein system, making use of the former's low seed rates and the latter's high nitrogen inputs. A wholly prophylactic spraying programme would be used in which the fields would receive their fungicides whether or not any disease was actually visible. The nitrogen would be split and would increase 80% over our traditional doses to a maximum of 190kg per hectare. We decided to stop using hormone weedkillers altogether, and instead to use Tribunil in the autumn followed by a contact herbicide in the spring.

This was most interesting to plan in theory, but in practice it involved a lot more work. It soon became clear that the ancient sprayer would have to go because it only had just been able to cope with our old system. The nitrogen was to be applied in liquid form, enabling us to have a large tramline of 27 metres. The sprayer was going to cover each field at least five times in the course of a season and possibly as many as eight times. We would need a pretty big machine. The smart operators seemed to be going for the self-propelled sprayers and this was superficially attractive. They certainly left fewer wheelings on the headlands and they looked compact. But on closer inspection they had two big disadvantages. The amount of money needed to buy one would have given us a 75 horsepower tractor, a 3,000 litre trailed sprayer and enough change left over to go on a couple of world cruises. In addition to their vast price, they lacked a very important technical feature which the new generation of trailed sprayers now used; this is a pump driven by the landwheel which, once set for the correct dose, applies the right amount of liquid regardless of forward speed. The choice of a large trailed sprayer was not difficult. As usual, we looked first for a British made sprayer but there was no machine made in this country. We eventually settled on a 3000 litre Berthoud model with 24 metre booms. These were lengthened by 3 metres to fit the tramlines from our thirty-row Massey drill, and we were ready to go. Or so we thought.

A big sprayer is lovely to think about. Visions of entire fields being covered with a single tankful are the sort of things which make me linger in the bath for those few extra minutes. Life would be easier and better in every way. The problem, again like my bath, was one of water. A big sprayer uses lots of the stuff. A bowser only makes things more difficult, because a fulltime man is needed to fill it and ferry it to and from the fields. It was the old story of the bottleneck. Get a bigger combine and the grainstore bungs up. Get a bigger grainstore and you don't have enough trailers. Maybe we should have kept small.

And then I remembered how the railways used to manage in the steam age. We built a series of tanks holding a total of 30,000 litres, and put them up on piers 3 metres high. Out of these tanks comes a huge pipe with a stopcock big enough for a North Sea oil rig. The sprayer pulls up beside the tank and is refilled in less than four minutes. While the machine is back in the field the tanks refill themselves. Today when the two sprayers (we bought a new 4,000 litre model this spring) come in to refill at the same time it looks like a mixture of Waterloo Station at rush hour and a pit stop at Le Mans. But we can cover over 200 hectares per day without running during lunchtime and in a wet spring such as we have had this year I find it hard to see how we could manage without two machines.

Three years and two harvests have passed since my day in the Unimog. They have been the best years we have ever had (but the weather had been almost perfect for our light land) so I can't claim that the system has been the only cause for the good yields but I am sure it has helped. We shall continue using the high input approach even though costs have risen faster than prices. The facts that all our corn is grown for seed does help the economics of the system and I would not suggest that what makes sense for us necessarily applies to everybody. Each farmer must make his own calculations. When the cereal boom for the past few years does finally come to an end we shall have to take a long hard look at the high input approach. But in the meantime we shall continue paying money and attention; the one to our chemical supplier and the other to the crops themselves. I prefer the latter.

The analogy with the road to Damascus is not exaggerated. From that day onwards I was hooked on high input farming. For the following eight years I had no regrets at all. Today, I am beginning to wonder if it still makes sense.

Two Weeks in China

AUGUST 1979

After a lifetime of prayer and meditation the old monk's ambition was about to be realised. He was going to be allowed to see what God looked like. Outside in the cathedral close a vast crowd had gathered to hear the news. The old man emerged, cleared his throat, paused for a moment and then said in a barely audible whisper, "She's Chinese." They shouldn't have been surprised because one in three people on this earth is Chinese.

Two weeks in a small corner of north-western China with a group of English farmers may not be enough to qualify me as an Old China Hand, even though I had visited the country five years earlier. But a combination of looking at the farms, listening to our interpreters and talking with my fellow travellers (who were all wiser and better farmers than me) has left a few strong impressions. The most striking thing about this huge and extraordinary country is what we did not see. We did not see any hungry people, nor did we see any beggars. Nobody asked for chewing gum or cigarettes, and nobody seemed to want to know about the Beatles or Margaret Thatcher and Trudeau. Hotel bedroom doors were never locked, and tipping was considered to be insulting. Go to any other underdeveloped country in the world – and China is as underdeveloped as any – and you will be assaulted by the poverty, squalor and longing for material belongings. The Chinese attitude was as refreshing as a cold bath, though I still prefer my baths warm.

But above and beyond all the normal tourist reactions, we did not see a single bad farm. Before you all leap for your typewriters and accuse me of having been shown only what the authorities wanted us to see (which is perfectly true), you should realise that when farmers travel by bus, car and train as we did, they examine each and every field as they pass. There can be no doubt that the standard of crops was very high indeed. Mind you, it jolly well should have been with the number of people they employ on the land.

Throughout the world the story of agriculture under communism has been one of failure and decline. Even today only Yugoslavia and Hungary have what could possibly be described as efficient farming, and they leave a lot to be desired when compared to the West. But China is a different story altogether. Compare her with the other Third World countries and the achievement of being able to feed nine hundred million people is set into perspective. The floods and famines which used to wipe out millions have long since been controlled. Would that the same could be said for Bangladesh and other parts of South-East Asia.

The system of communes isn't really terribly original, in spite of what Mao Tse-tung used to claim. They are roughly a collection of villages which in English terms would make up a Rural District Council. The chairman of the RDC is the head of the commune and the villages are referred to as "Brigades", each with its own elected chairman.

But in spite of the system the work gets done and the farms look good. The buildings are invariably shoddy, with peeling paintwork and little spent on repairs. Machinery, where it exists at all, usually consists of the small two-wheeled tractors so beloved of market gardeners in this country. Trailers are horse drawn and oxen provide the motive power for the simple single-furrow ploughs. Fertiliser comes mainly from the communal lavatories and, to a very small extent, from plastic bags. The organic farmers in our group admired the principle but seemed to find that the actual practice left a little to be desired. Herbicides are never used and crops are kept spotlessly clean by constant hand weeding. Fungicides, we were told, are used "when necessary", but how often this is never became clear.

But more than anything else in northern China, water held the key. A brief wet season during July and August means that for the remaining ten months of the year the farmers work under desert conditions, so irrigation is the first priority. Not for them the complexities of sprinklers, guns, reels or centre pivots. The complications and expense of sophisticated equipment would not fit into the Chinese style of farming. Instead they rely on gravity to bring the water to the crops. The fields are small, no more than a couple of acres, and are surrounded by low mud banks to retain the water during flooding. This means that large equipment could not possibly work unless field sizes were increased and the irrigation system discarded. And yet, like farmers all over the world, the Chinese wanted bigger machines.

When we asked what they would do with the surplus labour that a few tractors would cause, they smiled and said that they would start up small factories to produce non-agricultural goods. There is some logic here, and I have a dim inkling of why they feel this way. One afternoon after watching gangs of men and women planting out rice in the paddy fields, I decided to try my hand. Rolling up my trousers, I plunged into the mixture of mud, water and night soil. Five minutes later my backache told me more about the need for machines in Chinese agriculture than all the lectures we received could possibly have done. It may not make sense to the economists, but then they don't plant rice.

As usual after excursions like this, everyone came to his or her conclusions which reflected their own particular interests. The energy-conservers drew inspiration from the way in which the Chinese didn't waste fuel like we do. The livestock men admired the economy of animal feeding. The organic farmers seemed happy to have nine hundred million allies in their fight against chemicals. I myself am sceptical about what we can learn from China except in the broadest sense that there is simply no substitute for attention to detail and old-fashioned good husbandry. It needed China to remind me of this, so the trip was worth while as well as being fun.

Hew Watt, that Confucius of British farming, was (inevitably) with us on this expedition. The highlight of the trip was our visit to Tachai, the pet commune of Mao's widow, Chiang Ching. These were the days when that lady was at the height of her brief career, presiding over the Gang of Four. Today China seems to be a different country. I'm not sure which I prefer.

Knowing When to Stop

SEPTEMBER 1979

It was all very well for Harry Truman to say that "If you can't stand the heat, stay out of the kitchen," but I've never been able to figure out how hot is too hot. The question of when to stop has always given me problems. When to stop seeing a girlfriend, when to stop eating asparagus or indeed when to stop writing opinionated rubbish for this distinguished journal (cries of "Now" from readers). All of these questions are easier to ask than to answer and all of them are far more straightforward than the problems which face us farmers.

Last year we sold our Jersey herd. It had been in existence for over 70 years and had gone, as they say in Yorkshire, from clogs to clogs in three generations. But in between, it had a glittering period of showing successes in the '40s and '50s, and the smallest afterglow of this glamour still lingered in our imaginations. Yet in spite of the fact that most of the evidence showed that we were mad to continue with the herd, we persisted. We argued and talked and called in experts and spoke to ADAS and listened to the Bank Manager (God bless him) and agreed to disagree, and disagreed about what we had agreed. But we were not helped by the fact that options were never unanimous and we always came back to the same sticking point that maybe things would get better. Maybe our milk yields would go up, maybe our calving index would improve, maybe cholesterol would become the smart new drink, maybe our labour problems would ease and above and beyond all else maybe this was simply not the right time to make this decision. It wasn't even a simple matter of nostalgia – though God knows that was important – it was more like good old-fashioned inertia.

A year and a half has passed and I don't any longer believe what I have written in the paragraph above. With the wonderful gift of hindsight (which comes to us all if we wait patiently) it was clearly the right thing to have done and I'm sure we didn't really spend all those years discussing such a straightforward problem. I must be imagining all the arguments because nobody in his right mind could conceivably have wasted more than a minute on a matter of such stunning simplicity. Surely we didn't really agonise about it at all. In other words, everything fitted into place after the decision had been taken; all the advice from friends, experts and expert friends can now be seen to have been right. So why didn't we get out of milk years before?

Today I find myself in a kitchen which gets hotter and hotter with every OPEC price rise, and once again I'm having difficulties in recognising what everyone else can see from miles away. Some six years ago in the balmy carefree days of the 9p gallon of diesel oil we went out and bought a mobile crop drier to take care of our lucerne surplus. It was a sensible thing to do and the past five years have fully justified the decision. Now the age of dried grass is over. The crop drier must be as dead as the steam plough, the Smythe drill or the Range Rover (memo: sell Range Rover before next article is due). So the solution is simple; stop the crop drier.

Stop the crop drier? You must be out of your mind. It's working perfectly well today and there won't be a secondhand market for it. And what about the new self-propelled forage harvester we bought this year? We'd lose a fortune if we sold that. And anyway, what on earth are we going to do with all that lucerne if we can't dry it? Haymaking is the fastest way to ulcers known to man – except running a crop drier. Even if the price of fuel does go up again perhaps we shall be able to sell the dried lucerne at an equally high price. We mustn't rush a decision on this. At all costs we should take our time and think about all the ramifications. Wait for another year. Or another four years. Maybe natural gas could be used instead of oil. Or maybe heavy oil which is even cheaper. Have you thought about wilting? Why not? Don't jump to rash conclusions just because the price of fuel goes up a bit. Or a lot.

Without our 170 hectares of lucerne what would we use for break crops? Would the long term fertility decline and what would the effect be on the following wheat yields? Beans and peas are far too unreliable. Rape isn't too bad but we shouldn't overdo it by growing it too often, and it's a favourite on the menu of the billions of pigeons who now find us a better wintering spot than St Tropez or Casablanca. The food's better, they say. The prospect of more sugar beet gives me conniptions and so, once again, we call in the experts. As usual, they have no doubts at all but give conflicting advice. When summoned to the Imperial Presence they clear their throats, take a deep breath and begin "Within the current agronomic parameters of an ongoing crop drier situation the dynamics of the cost-price squeeze leaves the discounted cash flow negative after de-emphasising the downside risk energywise." Very helpful. That young man will go far in ADAS.

I imagine that sooner or later – probably sooner – we shall have to stop drying lucerne because of the price of fuel. But until that moment comes we shall continue to procrastinate. Then all of a sudden the decision will be taken and, just as with the dairy herd, we shall all feel a lot happier. In a few years we shall buy a nuclear-powered pocket-sized crop drier which will be operated by a PhD behind a plate glass window. Everyone else on the farm will wear white overalls, lead boots and green face masks and each tractor will be fitted with a mobile Geiger counter. The system will work wonderfully well until someone rediscovers silage. The process will then begin all over again as we decide whether to sell our secondhand uranium – always assuming we know how to stop the chain reaction inside the machine.

These tortured ramblings of a fevered mind irritate me because I always rather pride myself as being a rational man whose actions are motivated by all the normal causes like greed, lust and the profit motive which is a combination of both. I grow Brigand wheat because the NIAB tells me that it yields very well, and I use lots of nitrogen because I believe that I make more money that way. Like my friends (most of whom prefer to be called acquaintances) and neighbours, I like to think that I sell for the highest price and buy at the cheapest. When a new technique comes along I'm quick off the mark to look at it and when a new machine appears I find no difficulty in making a quick decision. I've never had a problem about when to start; it's just knowing when to stop which gives me trouble.

We eventually did stop the crop drier which, together with stopping the dairy herd, were the two wisest things I ever did. I haven't regretted either for a single second. But even today I still don't know when to stop. The question now is whether to stop high input cereal growing and return once again to the simpler days of when only one top dressing went on the crop in springtime and we only used a fungicide if the crop was in danger of dying altogether.

Garbage In, Garbage Out

OCTOBER 1979

Have you ever wanted to know how many pink and black striped ones there are in 27 tonnes of liquorice allsorts? Or how many perfectly spherical stones there are on the Norfolk coast between Hunstanton and Cromer? I realise only too well that these questions, along with how old is Joan Maynard and what is an MCA, are never far from the minds of today's serious farmer.

The solution to these problems was found by a Frenchman with the distinctly unagricultural name of Poisson. This, possibly charming and probably talented, mathematician realised that you don't have to sort through the mountain of liquorice allsorts to count the pink and black ones. All you need to do is to take a sample or two. The trick is in how many you take and where you take them from. Monsieur Poisson worked out a complicated formula that is today bedtime reading for all self-respecting samplers who make a living out of sticking spears in bags of seed – and opening random boxes of liquorice allsorts.

As my farm becomes ever more complicated, and as this magazine* is always urging us to become ever more scientific, I find that I have to quantify what my poor father only guessed at. I feel that I really ought to know how many plants and ears to a square metre, how many sugar beet seeds to a hectare, how much humidity in the atmosphere and moisture in the barley, how much phosphate is in the soil and how much easier things were in the old days.

I am, to misquote the old American cigarette advertisement** , sampling more and enjoying it less. At the end of the day I'm precious little the wiser than my aged father was when he used 63% hunch and 37% guesswork to decide if a field needed more nitrogen. It all reached a peak of idiocy during harvest this year. The crops had ripened very unevenly and the samples were speckled with bright green berries oozing moisture. Each time I did a moisture test the result was at least 2% different from the one before. On one occasion this variation was over 4%. The decision of whether or not to dry became a lottery depending on the last sample. I might just as well have tossed a coin.

Every year after harvest, reps call on us to sell their sugar beet fertiliser services. As part of the package they promise spreaders with tyres rather larger than the fields themselves, womb to tomb supervision of most details and, above all else, a soil analysis done for nothing. Who was it who once said that there's no such thing as a free soil analysis? Anyway, the theory is that each field can have a tailor-made fertiliser application to take into account its very special needs. This is a very good idea and one which no beet grower can afford to ignore. The system had worked excellently for some years until the day came when three different firms all asked to be allowed

*   Big Farm Management (now deceased) which was edited by George Macpherson (who today is flourishing mightily).
** "Smoking more but enjoying it less?"

to quote for the job. I decided to have them all test the same fields without knowing that their competitors were duplicating their work. I should add that the actual soil analysis was done by ADAS so the only different factor was the actual sampling of the soil. The result was completely chaotic; the same field produced three sets of results which were wildly out of line with each other. The recommended fertiliser applications differed in price to the extent that the cheapest was £15 per acre and the most expensive was double this figure. I ended up needing a psychiatrist more than an agronomist.

The same problem applies to the new scientific way of growing cereals. In the old days my ancestors, some of whom are happily still living, would go into a field and say that the plant looked at bit thin. They might give it a bit of nitrogen. If it looked a bit thick and lush they might put a few sheep on it for a few days. But today I march around loaded down with pocket calculators, measuring squares and leaflets with Belgian or German postmarks. In addition, I have to remember the rainfall, bear in mind what Ken Hubbard★ says about the adaptability of wheat, and wonder if there isn't a trace element deficiency. The relevant information is then fed into the brain and after a few days of number crunching I decide to increase the chlormequat dose by a bit. And these delicate adjustments are based on a sample or two which I took at random spots on the field.

But if you think that this is bad news, just wait until the new fashion reaches us which is now the rage of Lower Saxony in Germany. There a whole new group if disciples has been formed around the agricultural cult figure of Professor Wehrmann at the University of Hanover. (Remember that name and drop it when you next meet an ADAS man.) The good professor has devised a system so that it is now possible to assess the precise amount of available mineralised nitrogen in the soil. This calculation is done in late winter and so enables the farmers to give only as much top dressing as is actually needed. There is, of course, a small snag but it is one which the Wehrmann followers tend to pooh-pooh. You have to dig holes in the fields and then take your samples from three different depths. These small packets of soil have to be rushed off at great speed to the lab because results vary if too long a period elapses between taking the sample and testing it. But, at all events,

★ Then Chief ADAS Agronomist in the Eastern region.

the farmers of Lower Saxony love it and there can be no doubt that it makes great sense in theory. I just keep coming back to the problem of what happens if you dug the hole in the wrong part of the field? Your entire top dressing programme would be based on a false premise – albeit a highly scientific and most impressive one.

What with Professor Wehrmann on the one hand, and Monsieur Poisson on the other, life should be foolproof. But it isn't, and the computer people were the first to realise why. Amongst all the awful jargon of the computer world there remains one single phrase which sums up the reason why computers or, come to that, soil analysis is not foolproof: GIGO, which, being translated, means Garbage In, Garbage Out.

Discovering Discs

NOVEMBER 1979

I've never been very keen on direct drilling. It's probably my innate conservatism which readers of this column will have identified some months ago. It's a pity really because the autumn bottleneck is my biggest problem and seems to get worse every year as the amount of winter corn grows steadily. This year we shall only be growing 5% of our cereal acreage in spring varieties – a far cry from the 70% which was the case as recently as five years ago.

So why, in spite of all those free meals, demonstrations, colour brochures which ICI reps shower upon us, do I remain sceptical of direct drilling? I suppose the real reason is that I have had a lingering love affair with the Massey Ferguson MF 30 drill for some years now. The old twenty-row model gave way to the thirty-row machine four years ago and since then it has proved quite conclusively that once in a while British agricultural engineers can beat the world when they put their mind to the job. Our MF 30 drills 80 acres per day in the autumn, providing we don't put fertiliser down the spout which knocks 20 acres off this figure. The work rate is terrific and that is critical in the autumn. It's also the one thing which the direct drills can't match – even the four metre Bettinsons – simply because they are not big enough. It's all very well saying that you are saving on ploughing but if you lose on work rates you can still get in a muddle. Last harvest convinced me that early drilling paid even if it did mean Bayleton before Christmas and more barley yellow dwarf virus visible in the spring. The frost left the well-established plants unharmed and only the crops which had not begun to tiller or put down secondary roots suffered when the soil heaved around the turn of the year.

Once my prejudices – never far below the surface – had made me decide against direct drilling when all my trendy neighbours had started a few years ago, it was necessary to think again about cultivations. We'd always been wedded to the mouldboard plough and yet we'd never actually managed to bury much of the stubble. Try as we would by setting coulters and discs, the result always looked a mess. Then along came the chisel plough. My neighbour, who had not only taken up direct drilling but had actually won a prize from ICI for it, chiselled for all he was worth. His fields looked like graveyards as clods bigger than tombstones came to the surface but he seemed to manage perfectly well. Heaven knows how he wore these clods down to manageable sizes. Dynamite seemed to be the only solution but I never heard any bangs so he must have found another method.

I rejected the chisel plough because at that time I had fallen under the spell of the Cultivations Department at Silsoe. These were in the days before they had freaked out on the Rotary Digger. What was exciting them, and hence me, was the shallow plough. We bought two Lemken shallow ploughs with eight furrows each and started to work them. The first problem was that everyone had become so used to reversible ploughing that they had forgotten how to set out lands. But eventually even this problem was solved and for an entire autumn we fiddled around before deciding that a good old fashioned Dowdeswell five-furrow reversible took a lot of beating. So the next year we bought a couple of Dowdeswells and had a wonderful time.

Our ploughing became most respectable and the drivers loved the ploughs. There was one snag, however. We simply couldn't plough enough to keep in front of the drill.

The solution was plastered all over the farming press and had been for a couple of years. I'd just been asleep and so had not noticed the arrival of the flexitine cultivator. This slight oversight was soon corrected with the arrival of two 19 feet Flexitine cultivators made by Cousins of Emneth and strong enough to rip up Piccadilly Circus if necessary. But of course the golden rule of cultivating is first get a Good Burn. Getting a Good Burn means having nerves of steel, ice water in your veins and some very good friends in the Fire Service. A Good Burn means standing with your back to the wind and trying to stop your hand shaking so much it can't light the match. At the precise moment the match touches the straw you should dial 999 because within a couple of minutes the hedge, your neighbour's wheat and his neighbour's oats are likely to be a sheet of flame. If this does not, in fact, take place it means that you have not had a Good Burn.

By the time the autumn had come and gone we had learnt about burning but it was too late. Our flexitined field looked even messier than our ploughed ones used to do and the loose stubble made drilling a nightmare. Dry ground conditions still caused large and hard lumps to be thrown up and wet land meant that we cut narrow slits up and down the field. There just had to be another way.

There was. Heavenly choirs started to sing, rainbows appeared from nowhere and the voice of the advertising man came booming down from the Mount Sinai whence all good farmers get their orders. The voice said "How about discs?" And lo, there was a huge set of Bush Hog discs sitting on the farm waiting to be demonstrated. They weighed in at four tons and were 21 feet wide. Our two 160 horsepower Schluter tractors were itching to do something more arduous than to toy with the flexitine but it came as a shock when the Man from Opico (the importers) took one look at the tractors and said "They're not big enough. They'll never pull the discs. We've been using a 240 horsepower Case." But they did and life has never been the same again. This year we bought a second set of Bush Hog discs, this time 25 feet wide. Together the two machines can cover 20 acres per hour and more than keep up with the drill. They prepare a seedbed with a single pass in all but the wettest conditions and the drivers love using them. They are faster than chisels, make a better tilth than flexitines and use far less energy than mouldboard ploughing. All you need is a reasonably big tractor and a kind Bank Manager who is prepared to let you spend around £10,000. Your machinery dealer will pretend that he can only give you 10% but you'll be able to talk him down to 12.5% and it will be at least three years before you have to renew the discs. At that point you should sell the tackle to your neighbour and hope he doesn't notice how small they are. In the meanwhile you'll realise how much you've been missing. Autumn can be fun. Get hooked on discs and find out for yourself.

For once in my life I did not get carried away by the latest farming fad. Direct drilling has come and gone. Even my neighbour who won the direct drill as a prize has long since given up the technique. I would still be using discs to this day if only I hadn't taken the decision to stop burning straw. So now the wheel has turned a compete circle and we are once again back where we started – with the mouldboard plough.

Down with Plant Breeders

DECEMBER 1979

The polite ones think I'm unwise, the frank ones think I'm irresponsible and the rude ones think I'm just downright stupid. If there's one thing plant breeders dislike more than low royalty rates, it's farmers like me who use lots of fungicides. Their argument is nothing if it's not simple, and it goes like this. For the past umpteen years, plant breeders have been going to enormous lengths to ensure that new varieties have inbuilt disease resistance. Their entire breeding programme, which lasts up to 15 years for a single variety, is concerned quite as much with disease resistance as it is with yield. You only have to visit a Breeding Station to see the replicated trials, the artificial introduction of mildew, rusts and eyespot to be aware of how seriously the geneticists take the problem of disease. Each year the NIAB comes out with its list of new varieties and their rating for resisting the various diseases, and each year a few old varieties get consigned to the scrapheap of history because of their susceptibility to disease.

It is hard to open a page in the farming press without having to look at an advertisement proclaiming Variety X's outstanding resistance to Glume Blotch (an aptly named disease for pessimistic farmers). I'm sure that claims made for a certain variety are fundamentally true, and I would not for an instant doubt the scientific integrity of Bill Fiddian and his colleagues at the NIAB. The snag is that I am far from convinced that these factors are at all relevant to a practical farmer in today's world.

I know that plant breeders have come a long way from the days of Squarehead Masters and Plumage Archer and the yields are there for anyone to see. But when it comes to breeding for disease resistance, they have not been too successful. Even those varieties which are awarded 9 by NIAB (showing that they are very resistant to a disease) invariably seem to suffer. In my experience, the only difference between a susceptible and a resistant variety is that the former gets the disease first and the latter last. In the end they both have it, if it happens to be going around that year.

This fact is not lost on scientists, and none of them would ever claim that any variety is totally resistant. But I do get the strong impression that too much is made of these minute variations in resistance which may seem important in the labs or on the trial plots, but don't count for much on the farm. What has changed the scene in the last few years is the fact that the chemical manufacturers have really started giving the farmer what he needs: an entire arsenal of fungicides which have revolutionised cereal growing. The arrival of Bayleton on the scene three years ago was at least as important as the advent of Maris Huntsman, and credit should go to the backroom boys for coming up with a single product which has eradicated mildew in one fell swoop. Bayleton has been the penicillin of arable farming.

Ah yes, say the plant breeders, but just wait until all the little mildew spores (vive le spore!) find a strain resistant to Bayleton. Then look what a mess you farmers will be in. Far better to go easy on the Bayleton and only use it if you are absolutely certain that the mildew attack in your crop is chronic. Meanwhile, they add, we are working on a variety which is itself resistant to mildew so you won't have to spend all that money on white powder in little paper packets.

There is a bit to be said for this attitude, but not much. The progress in disease control made by the chemists during the past ten years has been so much greater than that of the plant breeders in the past 50 years, that I am now tending to put my faith in chemists. Certainly the Bayletons of this world will be overtaken by events. Nature will continue to find a way round the cleverest inventions of man, but if the history of the twentieth century shows us anything at all, it is that man's ingenuity has managed to keep a few steps in front. Anyway, I've not noticed a plant breeder refusing to take an aspirin in case his headaches develop a resistance. It's all very well for a man who spends his waking hours working on disease resistance in wheat to feel frustrated, but it is another thing for him to take an almost Christian Science attitude to the fungicides which are today available to farmers.

Plant breeders have done well to produce the new varieties of the past few years. But when it comes to disease resistance they have been beaten all ends up – and they know it. It's not surprising that their pride is the first casualty, but they need not expect any Tom, Dicurane or Harry to administer first aid to a battered amour propre. This is not a reason to forget about breeding for disease resistance. Far from it. The day may yet come when the chemists run out of ideas, or the world runs out of materials. Until this nightmare comes true, I shall continue to make full and unrestricted use of all chemicals which are safe to use, in addition to the goodies which flow from Nickerson, NSDO and the others. Long may they flourish.

I am a little less besotted by the joys of agrochemicals than I was then, but the fact remains that although some cereal varieties are today supposed to be resistant to certain diseases (i.e. Rendez- vous wheat and eyespot) it doesn't actually mean that farmers can throw away the spray can.

Prospects for the 1980s

JANUARY 1980

Readers of this paper* probably feel that farmers complain too much. If it isn't the weather it's the price of cattle food or the Green Pound or the lack of subsidies on mustard mills. I cannot honestly blame them for thinking this because there is a strong element of truth in the theory that farmers overlook the good news and concentrate on the bad instead. The same charge could, by the way, be levelled at newspapers too.

The fact is that Cambridgeshire farmers have been doing rather well for the past five years. Ever since the Russians pulled off what has come to be called The Great Grain Robbery in 1973, the prices of wheat and barley have given arable farmers good profits. Mid-Anglia is, of course, the leading arable area in the United Kingdom.

---

* *Cambridge Evening News.*

I realise that there have been some hard times in certain sections of agriculture in the region. Pig men have experienced rather more downs than ups in recent years, and have been fighting an impossible battle against Danish competition caused by the Green Pound. Horticulturists, who play an important role in local farming, have been hit particularly hard by the massive rise in fuel costs. Sugar beet went through a lean period of three extremely bad harvests in succession and, as a result, the acreage has declined somewhat. But overall there can be no doubt that farmers in Cambridgeshire have done better in the past five years than they, their fathers or their grandfathers ever dreamed possible. We should acknowledge this fact and be thankful for it because I fear that after the five good years, we are in for some difficult times ahead.

A spectre is haunting Europe, the spectre of cereal surpluses. Those of you who read the Communist Manifesto in bed each night will recognise the opening lines of this historical relic. But it is true that we are now becoming victims of our own success. It is significant that one of the main causes of the surplus is because the plant breeders of Cambridge at the PBI have been so extraordinarily successful in producing new varieties of wheat which have pushed yields to record levels with each succeeding harvest. Thus this region has played the dual role of both breeding and growing some of the finest cereals in the world.

Such is our success that England today is a net exporter of barley, and is virtually self-sufficient in soft wheat. We do, of course, have to import hard wheat for breadmaking simply because our climate will not enable us to grow this type of wheat which flourishes on the American and Canadian prairies. Consider this achievement of being able to grow enough on this small island to feed a population of 55 million people. It makes a contrast with the gloom and doom surrounding us in the industrial scene.

Thus the future for cereal growers will not be very bright, particularly if one compares it to the recent past. But don't let this make anyone believe that there will be wholesale bankruptcies in the farming community. It will simply mean that we farmers will have to get by on some pretty small profit margins for the next few years. It won't be comfortable, particularly in these inflationary times when you have to make 20% more profit each year just to stay where you are. But we shall manage. There will be fewer new tractors, fewer new buildings and fewer shiny cars. But I do not expect any farmer to experience real hardship unless he is just downright stupid or unlucky.

As far as other crops grown in Mid–Anglia are concerned, the future looks equally gloomy. Sugar beet has just enjoyed its best year for a decade with yields which have given farmers real profits after the equally real losses of the past few years. But this bumper crop has come just at the time when Europe is seeing a sugar molehill being turned into a sugar mountain. Moves are afoot to cut output throughout the EEC, and England will have to endure the biggest reductions of any country. The effect this will have on Cambridgeshire beet growers is hard to predict, but I am certain that whilst the beet acreage will not expand, neither will it contract as the British Sugar Corporation are predicting. The Ely and Felsted factories may well have to close, but this has been on the cards for several years now. The sugar surplus may have accelerated this action; it certainly did not cause it. So the beet growers will definitely have to tighten their belts, and we may even see some people on the light land actually stopping to grow the crop unless their yields show big improvements in the future.

Potatoes make and lose more money than just about any other crop in this area. Four years ago the growers felt as if they had won the football pools, and last year was moderately profitable. But in between the losses were huge. It takes cool nerve and a friendly Bank Manager to stay in the game. Imports from Holland will not make potato growers' lives any easier, but will certainly help to stabilise prices for the housewife. And that can't be a bad thing.

The other crops in this area are all unreliable by their very nature. Oilseed rape seems to be the only exception, and the acreage has been shooting upwards as farmers answer the call to produce more vegetable oil within the Common Market. I suspect that the amount of rape grown will now stabilise, and that the price will certainly not increase in real terms. But in spite of this, rape will remain just about the only break crop which can usually show a profit in all but the worst years. Disease and pigeons will cause more worries to farmers than prices alone.

On the livestock side the future is impossible to predict. The production of all forms of meat, but beef and pork in particular, is always fraught with danger. The profit cycle goes up and down in huge and irregular swings, and this will undoubtedly continue throughout the 1980s. As a general rule, if pig producers are silent it means that they are making lots of money; if they are complaining it means that they are losing lots of money. No livestock man ever enters this field without being well aware of the risks, and I sometimes get the feeling that the better ones actually enjoy the swings and roundabouts as it gives them the chance to outwit their slower colleagues.

As far as milk is concerned, the number of herds in this area continues to decline with each passing year. Those dairy herds which do survive in a region like ours where grass growing is difficult must either be very efficient or very old-fashioned. Either way, the pressure on milk producers will keep growing, so that by the end of the decade I do not expect to see more than two dozen herds in the county of Cambridgeshire.

The 1980s will not be as enjoyable as the 1970s for farmers in the region. There is no doubt that we have all become a bit soft and flabby after the boom times of the recent past. But the farming skills of this area are as high as anywhere in Europe, and I am certain that Cambridgeshire agriculture will not only survive, but it will also flourish in a quiet way during this decade. I would ask the farming community and the public to recognise this fact by making a bargain. If the farmer tries not to complain so much, the latter should show more understanding of our problems. At least we should give it a try.

Written for the Cambridge Evening News. *Hence the bias towards Mid-Anglia.*

Private . . . Come In

JANUARY 1980

Of all man's instincts, the protection of property must run sex a pretty good second. In some cases it is equalled only by the desire for more and bigger property, and I have to confess myself that the pleasures of land ownership are both powerful and indescribable. An Englishman's home may be his castle, but in these days of Capital Transfer Tax and the National Trust, it is not often that his castle is his home. But we'll let that one pass and concentrate instead on how badly we farmers behave. A bit of good old-fashioned masochism never did anyone any harm.

For six days a week we run around putting up notices saying that "Trespassers will be Prosecuted" and on the seventh day we go to church and ask the Lord to "Forgive us our trespasses as we forgive those who trespass against us." Agnostic or atheist farmers manage to avoid this little bit of hypocrisy, but they have a few other problems with which we need not concern ourselves right now, other than to say how hard it must be for them to think that the seasons of the year are all one gigantic accident. Poor chaps.

Only those lucky few who manage to farm the innermost recesses of Caithness and Sutherland can fail to have noticed what has been happening in the past few years. They may not have seen the picknickers, the prampushers, the hikers, the campers and – horror of horrors – the riders. This latter group, which consists of white people on black horses, has given new meaning to the words bte noire. Together they have been taking over the world, or at least my farm. Every year we have more of them as they pour out of the towns and commuter villages to enjoy the things which farmers take for granted.

It may have been all those TV advertisements for margarine and peas which gave our secret away to the urban masses. All those dew-fresh, sun-kissed farmers milking cows by hand in the sunrise and eating Weetabix and instant mashed potatoes didn't just sell food they also brainwashed the British public into thinking that the countryside was fun. And they were right.

Farmers of Britain, the more reactionary of whom still like to call themselves Yeomen, took one look at this trend and began to panic. Taking their cue from King Canute, the patron saint of right-wingers, they first decided that the problem did not really exist at all. As the years passed, they changed their mind (a slow and cumbersome process at the best of times) and that old Dunkirk Spirit came to the fore once again, as it has done so often in our nation's history whenever the Yeomen are threatened by alien hordes.

Up went the signs. PRIVATE. KEEP OUT. NO TRESPAS-SING. Back to their farmhouses they went to load the twelve-bores (the usual quorum for a CLA branch meeting) and put the tractors into a circle. There's nothing quite so good for morale as being in a minority, particularly one which is being persecuted. The problem this minority faced was that, since the persecution did not actually exist, they were forced to imagine it. Fortunately, the Yeomen are an imaginative lot, and they had no trouble convincing themselves that Private Property Was At Risk. This rallying call went out and, from the Test to the Tweed, you could hear the sound of Bentleys starting their engines and shooting sticks being folded with a snap. Back to the Home Farms they went to put up still more signs telling the Great Unwashed to KEEP OUT, KEEP OFF and KEEP AWAY.

Meanwhile a tiny band of entrepreneurial farmers started to let the side down. They actually went so far as to welcome the Great Unwashed, and found that not only were they quite as washed as the farmers themselves, but they were also members of the human race. These renegade farmers started to put up caravan sites, converted cottages into holiday homes, and a few actually created country parks. Their vision was quickly rewarded by the profits which they richly deserved, and the message began to spread throughout the farming world. Of course, the Yeomen would hear

nothing of it. They were too busy polishing their shotguns and replacing the KEEP OUT signs people persisted in pinching to decorate Earls Court bedsitters.

Today the Yeomen show every sign of joining the Giant Pandas and the Chillingham Cattle as an endangered species. Every so often you may catch a glimpse of one at an NFU dinner-dance. If you are lucky enough to meet one face to face, you should go out of your way to humour him. Remarks like "I don't know what the world's coming to" or "Stanley Baldwin knew my father" always go down well. You can tell when his brain is working because he will utter a few grunts before making an Important Pronouncement which usually resembles "I used to think Margaret Thatcher was one of us, but now she seems to be a pinko like that awful Heath."

It is lucky that the Yeomen are disappearing because they were giving the rest of us farmers a very bad name. The 97% of the population who, due to their own sheer carelessness, are not farmers, were beginning to resent us. They were irritated by the fact that the Yeomen felt that the countryside in general and their farms in particular should remain unsullied by outsiders. Each time a farmer had trouble with a footpath or threatened prosecution for trespass, the newspapers printed all the gory details and confirmed the town-dwellers' worst fears.

The time has now come when unless we farmers start behaving sensibly, and allow people free access to our farms, the government will pass laws to force us. The results will be far worse than had we reformed ourselves voluntarily. We should remind the public of their obligations to our animals and our crops, and be prepared to be tough if they refuse to respect these simple conditions. But in the meanwhile we should take down the KEEP OUT signs and put up the WELCOME ones. Time is not on our side.

As relevant today as it was when I wrote it seven years ago. Farmers still regard their own land as being sacred. No outsider should be permitted to set foot on their property without express permission. This is a tragedy.

Fertilise by Computer

FEBRUARY 1980

The merchants of doom and gloom have found a new recruit. Me. The outlook for arable farming today is so dismal that, after five years of optimism, I have now changed my mind. Mind you, my job has not been made any the easier because of old-fashioned Cassandras like Anthony Rosen, and the NFU have been telling the public that things have been terrible for the past few years. I don't suppose that the public believes a single thing we say, and I can't honestly blame them either.

How does this leave a convinced high-input-prophylactic-spraying-go-for-broke-yields-at-all-cost farmer like me? Can I afford to continue farming the way I have for the past three years, or will the cost-price squeeze make intensive cereals obsolete? I don't pretend to know all the answers, but I suspect that other farmers could help me find out. So I started talking to the Organic boys on the off chance that they were on the right track. After all, if disillusioned communists can join the Catholic church, why shouldn't a Schleswig–Holstein nut go organic?

The organic approach has a lot to be said for it. First and foremost, it makes you feel good. Not just ordinarily good, but very good indeed. You are saving energy, saving the ecosystem, saving money as well as promoting health and, in general, doing the Right Thing. If you don't feel some or all of these things, you certainly shouldn't even consider being an organic farmer. We won't go too deeply into the philosophy because it is very easy to get into arguments which are best left to theologians. Questions like whether or not the occasional squirt of MCPA is permissible divide organic farmers like discussing Suez in the Carlton Club.

The fact remains that there are some very good organic farmers, and the system can certainly be made to work successfully. It is all too easy to dismiss them as Muck and Mystery men, but to do so shows one to be ignorant, prejudiced and just plain dumb. However, I have come to the reluctant conclusion that I could not be an organic farmer in 1980, even if experimenting with a small field would be interesting. Our thin land – made worse by our low rainfall – would simply revert to the state it was in before science

– 49 –

entered into agriculture some 50 years ago. Today we can't grow much grass even with the help of Nitram, and without the stuff we would be right back to Dog and Stick farming, with sheep providing the manure which was barely enough for rye, but meant that wheat was never grown at all. No, there's no getting away from the fact that extensive organic farming on infertile soil only makes sense at very low rents indeed. Unfortunately, our landlords appear unwilling to turn the clock back and accept pre-1945 rents with 1980 inflation.

I ruled out organic farming with some sadness and looked for another solution. Far out on the other wing of the farming spectrum, as far from organics as one could possibly get, I came across a very different approach. High in the Cotswolds there exists a firm well known to southern and western farmers, but not to know-it-all East Anglians like myself. A company with the somewhat unimaginative name of Cleanacres has been selling chemicals for many years now from their headquarters at Andoversford. Today they have hit upon a new system which they hope will push the science of cereal growing to new heights. Not for them the rather hit and miss high input approach I have been using so happily (and expensively) but instead a precisely measured technique which leaves only the weather to chance.

The theory is quite simple. Old-fashioned farming is fine for old-fashioned yields, but if you are looking for more than just the occasional crop of 55cwt wheat, then you must pay a lot of attention to small details. It's no good just slapping on 50 units of P and K in the autumn, following this up with 140 units of N in the spring and letting fly with every fungicide in the book. This system may work from time to time, but it will be more luck than judgement. The secret lies in knowing exactly how many nutrients are required, and when they should be applied. Nutrients, of course, include trace elements as well as the aforementioned three Old Faithfuls.

The solution to these problems lies (you've guessed it) with a computer. And the computer itself lives 5000 miles away in Nebraska, USA. Your job, as farmer, is to take elaborate soil samples (one per three acres) and pay Cleanacres £25 per field. You also tell them what varieties you are thinking of growing, what your target yields will be, and various details about your soil types and average rainfall. The sample and the information are sent to Nebraska and, three weeks later, you receive a large sheet of printed paper full of information and precise recommendations. You are told how much fertiliser to put on and when to do it, what trace elements are needed, and how to apply them, and what you should do to build up nutrient reserves for the future. Cleanacres will provide detailed advice and follow-up in the shape of a team of agronomists who will visit the farm and hold your hand (metaphorically, of course). They would clearly love to sell you chemicals, because that's how they make their money, but they won't insist on it as part of the deal. Which is just as well because they are adamant that all chemicals are sold at the full retail price. I have yet to hear of any East Anglian farmer who ever gets less than a 5% discount – and usually a lot more.

My initial reaction was not favourable. Computers are often used these days simply as sales gimmicks to tart up an ordinary job and make it look trendy and modern. I am also unhappy about soil samples – or rather their accuracy – and begin to wonder if we are not all getting just too obsessed with science and having to quantify everything which grows or moves. But, as I reflected in my bath, the mark of a tired farmer is one who refuses to take new ideas seriously and simply dismisses them as being irrelevant. Certainly I had to admit that we had wasted chemicals over the past few years, and I also suspect that our yields have reached a plateau from which they don't want to budge. It is surely stupid to ignore trace elements now that there is something we can do about them. Thus I decided to give the computer a chance, and move on from High Input to Careful Input.

In five years time I may know if this was the right decision, but I somehow doubt it. Nothing in farming is ever that clear. Besides, the older I get the more I realise that we do things because we want to and not simply because the experts tell us to. If you're happy with a system, it's the right one for you. Perhaps the computer will tell me when I'm happy.

The Nebraska system lasted precisely one year at Thriplow before I became bored with the reams of paperwork it generated – not to mention the cost. It was another example of an overly scientific approach to farming which was popular in the early 1980s at the height of the cereal boom.

Microchips on My Shoulder

MARCH 1980

I like to think of myself as a Progressive farmer, but some of you people out there in readerland probably dismiss me as just another trendy. The definition of a Progressive, by the way, is a farmer who is fascinated by new machinery but has not got the courage to admit why. Inside me is a little boy trying – and usually succeeding – to get out. But I don't normally admit this to the salesmen who come round with the glossy brochures illustrating the latest big tractor or combine. Mind you, even the youngest and most inexperienced rep knows all about my type, but we still go through the elaborate ritual of pretending that I am a wholly rational man. I talk about cost-effectiveness, workrates and DIN horsepower while I think about the lovely green paint, the new air-conditioned cab and whether radial tyres are sexier than crossplys.

In common with a few other Progressive farmers, I must confess to having a microchip on my shoulder. I am fascinated by the next generation of farm machinery: computers. Several of us met at Smithfield recently and were treated to an entire day of on-farm computers. Compared to the same meeting a year earlier, when a tiny band of nuts listened to the pioneers of farming computers, this year's event was the big time. Rows of gleaming machines with tiny television screens (VDUs in the jargon) twinkled at us, printers spewed out scrolls of closely typed information and salesmen hovered around answering questions from farmers who were both sceptical and keen at the same time. The software, which had been missing last year, was there with a vengeance. Programmes have now been written with specific agricultural jobs in mind, the most popular of which enables a dairyman to do his own ration formulation on the sort of Least Cost basis which has traditionally been the preserve of the compounders.

As I watched and listened, I could feel the adrenalin starting to work. Optimism flooded through my tiny befuddled brain and I began to believe that, in addition to wanting a computer, I actually needed one. Experts from as far afield as Cornwall and the Highlands told us about the latest developments in agricultural computing. Farmers recounted stirring stories of their own experiences with these machines, and the whole meeting began to take on an almost religious quality, in which the Chosen Few began to spread the Message.

My problem is that, as an arable farmer, it is particularly hard to justify a computer. Where they really score is when you have to keep track of a vast quantity of ever-changing information. Thus the livestock men are natural customers. If you milk a thousand cows and use a complete diet system, it must make sense to have the use of a computer. Likewise, several thousand pigs need a lot of record-keeping and a computer fits the bill admirably. But what about the rest of the world which measures cows in hundreds not thousands? Could the ordinary farmer justify a computer at a cost of £5000?

It is so easy to be carried away thinking about what a computer can do that one forgets what it cannot do. This is, unfortunately, crucial. First and foremost, a computer will not make you a good farmer. It may well make a good farmer better, but it cannot possibly transmogrify a bad farmer into a good one. It will not even save you any labour, and may actually mean that you need more help in the office, not less. It will not make life easier for you if you are the chaotic hit-and-miss type. Indeed, the disciplines imposed by a computer on your office procedures may well drive you mad with fury because it is both plodding and very inflexible. In short, a computer is not the machina ex deo which you have been imagining after reading the newspapers and watching *Tomorrow's World* on the telly.

What fascinates me about these machines is not that they will do the wages, the accounts and the cashflow forecasts, but simply that they will make my life and my farm so much more interesting. Providing that I feed the information into the machine the right way, I can use it to tell me the sort of things I have always wanted to know but have never had the time to work out. I could put in all the field records so that every operation and input was recorded in detail. This is called a Data Base in computerese, and is simply the mass of information which today occupies a thick book in the farm office. But the computer would have a huge advantage over Jane, the Farm Secretary. It will be able to find out, compare and collate information in a second which would otherwise have taken the best part of a morning. Thus I shall be able to compare the yields of fields which have been harrowed once with those which have been harrowed twice – or the ones which had the low rate of Tribunil with the ones which had post-emergent Dicurane. Maybe I shall occasionally come up with information which is actually useful, but I am not counting on it. I certainly will not be a better farmer as a result of the computer, and I would be dishonest to pretend otherwise. But anything which enables me to know more about the farm is both fascinating and fun.

Five years ago I went out and bought a machine which was clearly an unnecessary luxury, because we had been farming perfectly happily without it for years. The machine was called a Sanderson Rough Terrain Truck and life has never been the same. We now have two of them and my mind boggles when I try to remember how we managed without them. Perhaps the same will happen with the computer. I hope so because I shall buy one before long.

> *I did buy one, and then another, and then another and then another. Today we have three computers in the office alone, and we think of them as pieces of furniture. But back in 1980 they were exciting and glamorous gadgets.*

Dear Landlord

JUNE 1980

Dear Pension Fund Manager

I hope you do not think it rude of me writing in this somewhat public way, but I did rather want some of my fellow tenants to have a copy of the letter. The cost of carbon paper and postage is such that I would have had to sell my farm on leaseback to you simply to raise the cash. I am not quite ready for that yet.

Please do not misunderstand my motives. I have come to accept your role in British Agriculture – albeit a bit grudgingly – and realise that before long you and your colleagues in the City will own most of the good arable land in this country. Don't worry about the fact that this makes me sad; it is not the reason I am writing to you. What does worry me very much indeed is a problem which you are causing us farmers. It is a problem which will get a lot worse unless something is done about it very soon.

I am referring to the growing power of the land agents. Before I go any further, I should tell you that I have great respect for some of them as individuals. Those whom I know are almost invariably intelligent, sympathetic and knowledgeable men. They have given me some pretty good lunches over the years and I would not like them to think that I am ungrateful. But the fact remains that land agents are breeding faster than any other animal in farming today, with the possible exception of green aphids. Everywhere I look I see new offices being built and advertisements for staff to fill them. The Senior Partners are (as someone once wrote about Laski at the LSE) ruling empires over which the concrete never sets.

The reason for this expansion is not hard to see. Every time you buy some land you need someone to look after it for you. You also need someone to advise you because there is no way you can know about farming or landowning when you are sitting at your desk somewhere near Liverpool Street. Now I realise all too well that land agents have been around agriculture since long before the first pension fund was a twinkle in the eye of a needle through which a rich man cannot pass.

In the good old days when the Colonel owned the estate, he too used a land agent to look after the place for him. Every three years the rents would go up and the tenants would shout like mad. The gutters were occasionally repaired (those were the days before the land agents had discovered the joys of the Full Repairing and Insuring Lease) and if the Colonel was feeling flush, he might even put up a new barn. The land agent looked after all of this and the tenant rarely, if ever, came into contact with the Colonel (probably because he was seldom sober). But even so, the Colonel did occasionally tell the land agent what to do. He could have lowered a rent to take account of hardship, or let a tenant take over another farm because the son seemed to be a good chap. The tenants all knew that they could get an interview with the old boy if it was ever absolutely necessary.

Today things are rather different. You have lots more tenants than the Colonel and, even with the best will in the world, you cannot keep in touch with all of them. I know that a man from your office visits every farm once a year, and I give you good marks for that. But you take your advice from the land agents because that is what you pay them for. Unfortunately, the advice which they give is rarely, if ever, contradicted by you. Unlike the poor, drunken old Colonel, you simply don't have a clue about your farms or the tenants who rent them. Instead you meet with the Senior Partners to discuss the Big Problems like capital values, vacant possession premiums and other examples of Grand Strategy. As a result, you don't see the hordes of young men who have recently been hired by the companies to whom you pay the large fees and who receive the commissions which keep pace with inflation so very conveniently. These twenty-seven-year-olds, who have just managed to scrape through Agricultural College are now wandering the countryside on your behalf, complete with tweed caps and black labradors. It is not just that experienced middle-aged farmers resent being told what to do by such brainless, chinless and farmless wonders, but they also know that the same chap will be putting the rent up in a year's time.

The power which land agents have over tenant farmers is enormous. No longer does the old Colonel stand in the background as a court of last resort. He is long dead and his executors sold the estate to you. The power that the land agent has over you is just as great and twice as dangerous because you are not even aware of it. You do not see that it is your very ignorance which gives such great power to your knowledgeable advisers. Like a mediaeval king surrounded by courtiers, you sit in your offices and receive the advice for which you pay. Thus the land agent stands between you and your tenants blocking all communication and understanding. One does not have to be clever to see the danger here to both you and the men with mud on their boots.

It is easy for me to complain, but less easy to be constructive; nevertheless I shall try because you have been good enough to read this letter so far. First of all I would like to see a Code of Conduct for land agents which would set out very clearly what they can and cannot do. It should also define their responsibilities towards both landlord and tenant in some detail. Secondly I would like to see you and your colleagues in the Institutions spending more time listening to farmers. This could be done either formally by means of an advisory committee, or informally by having some very frank chats with individual farmers. Unless something is done soon we shall all be aware that while power corrupts, agricultural power corrupts agriculturally.

This infuriated the Land Agents who, it seems, had never been attacked in public before. They were particularly enraged at the description of the young man with his cloth cap and black labrador. Years later elegant land agents from Mayfair still berate me for this. It must have touched a very raw nerve. As a member of a profession which is constantly laughed at, I have little sympathy for the Land Agents who have remained untouched by even the mildest abuse.

The Best Farmer

JULY 1980

Good farmers farm; bad ones become active in the NFU. The others either go broke or write about farming in magazines. You can see which category I come into and I don't suppose you are very surprised. But it came as a bit of a shock to me because for years I had known in my guts that I was an absolutely brilliant farmer.

It all started with the ICI Wheatrace. I knew we were going to win long before we entered the competition. On the team were a local seed merchant with an international reputation, an expert from NSDO who knew more about wheat than most people know about life itself, a female member of ADAS whose beauty and charm was exceeded only by her intelligence, a chemical adviser of quite extraordinary brilliance, the farm foreman and myself. As the Greatest Living Farmer, I knew it was a bit unfair of me even to enter the competition but I managed to stifle my normal under-whelming modesty for a moment and resolved to take first prize with my accustomed effortless superiority.

My confidence grew as the competition progressed. We had clearly done everything right from selecting the perfect moment to apply the correct herbicide to using the right varieties (NSDO ones by some inexplicable coincidence). Timeliness was faultless, our use of labour could not be criticised, weather problems had been anticipated and the costs had been kept right down.

On the evening when we had completed the final form we sat back to enjoy a drink and the certainty that we had won. I began to compose my acceptance speech which would be as witty as it was profound. I could hear the gasps from the audience as our results were announced and tried to practise the world-weary smile which would highlight my natural modesty in front of the world's press.

While I prepared myself, the rest of the team started a sweepstake on the results. In spite of the fact that we all knew we had won, we did at least choose different positions. I was the most pessimistic when I suggested we would come twelfth – but I had to give my colleagues a chance to win something.

We came 235th.

It is impossible to list what makes a good farmer, but certainly energy, attention to detail and a passionate interest in the job must be the main ingredients. Unless I am interested I cannot do a good job. It was for this reason, more than any other, that we gave up dairying to concentrate more fully on cereal seed production. The trouble with this approach is that it encourages specialisation and discourages the good old-fashioned mixed farm. I must admit, however, that I have never been able to understand why mediocre mixed farming is somehow considered to be God-given and Good while acres of beautiful barley condemn one to be described sneeringly as a Barley Baron.

The best farmer I have ever met is a very mixed farmer indeed. He is a German called Hermann Beste and he manages 2000 acres of not very special land in Lower Saxony. A farm of this size is a handful at the best of times, and the more so in Beste's case since it is pretty fragmented, has small fields and some steep banks. But this farmer is only happy when his troubles lie thick on the ground. He relaxes by taking his holiday alone on the lonely and wind-swept island of Heligoland in January each year, when he spends two weeks in the middle of the North Sea recharging his batteries for the work ahead.

The farm's main operation is the growing of seed corn on 1200 acres. He produces five varieties of wheat, six barleys and two oats which means an enormous amount of cleaning and a very strict rotation. But unlike his English counterparts, who simply send their corn off to the merchants, Herr Beste does all the cleaning, dusting and bagging himself in his own grainstore. He looks after all the paperwork involved in the certification of the seed and thus enables the merchant to do nothing more than arrange for a lorry to collect the finished product and take a profit from the eventual customer.

Beste's other arable crops are 240 acres of sugar beet, 240 acres of rape grown for seed, 120 acres of vining peas and a further 25 acres of other vegetables, usually broad beans or spinach.

On the livestock side, the farm carries 65 Friesians which average

6600 litres of milk annually. A pedigree flock of Mutton Merino sheep is exported all over the world, and a pig enterprise produces some 600 hybrid gilts each year and a total of 1500 baconers. All livestock food, with the exception of soya meal, is produced on the farm's very automated mill, and Beste makes good use of sugar beet tops which are fed fresh during the autumn and then ensiled for use during the rest of the winter until grass is available in early May.

Like so may good farmers, Beste enjoys big machinery. His 250hp Schluter pulls an eight-furrow plough with a furrow press. In typical German fashion, he never ploughs less than 12 inches deep and often more. Beste will not even consider direct drilling or minimum cultivations and seems perfectly happy to use masses of power (and fuel) to carry out cultivations which seem extravagant to British eyes. But it is a rash farmer who assumes that his own experience can apply to other farms, and so I just watch with wonderment the procession of giant machines which are needed to prepare a seedbed.

Beste's yields across the farm are good without being spectacular. After last year's below-average harvest his wheat gave 55cwt, barley 47cwt, rape 19cwt and sugar beet 17 tonnes at 17.4% sugar. Thus the farm would not win prizes for yields alone but, compared to the best farmers in Suffolk and Schleswig–Holstein, I have no doubt that Beste's profit margins would more than compensate for the apparent loss of yield. This sort of farm is not really my cup of tea because I know only too well that I would make a terrible mess of trying to run so many different enterprises at a high standard. I am not in the least envious of Herr Beste's life or farm, but if I were to award a cup for the best individual farmer it would go to him. Perhaps I should start looking at a few more British farms and learn a trick or two from them, but nobody ever invites me. I can't imagine why.

Soon after this article appeared, Hermann Beste was awarded the most prestigious prize in German agriculture, the Justus von Liebig Prize. He is today still farming at Rodenberg, near Hanover, but does less work than he used to because the owner's son has taken over much of the management.

Mississippi Rip-off

AUGUST 1980

You all know Mississippi. Happy smiling slaves picking cotton and singing "Ol' Man River" in Paul Robeson voices; riverboats packed with gamblers wagering "the deeds to my plantation" on a single card; Clark Gable telling Vivien Leigh that frankly, he didn't give a damn; very white people lolling round drinking mint juleps or, being farmers, Planter's Punches, magnolias and Spanish moss, old world charm and a certain style. You remember it now, don't you?

Well forget it. The Mississippi Delta is a little different today. The farmers ride round in huge pickup trucks with a couple of rifles in the rear windows. The trucks have four wheel drive to cope with the heavy gumbo clay soil which makes Boxworth EHF look like toytown, and the rifles have telescopic sights to make killing things easier. Forget any ideas of partridges or pheasant you may have. The name of the game is racoon, wolf and other things I take my children to see in Regent's Park. Some of the other things I prefer not to think about; this category includes water moccasins, rattlesnakes and alligators.

The Mississippi Delta is not, as I had imagined, where the river fans out into the Gulf of Mexico. Instead, go upstream from New Orleans for 150 miles and at Natchez there starts a flat valley which stretches out for 50 miles on either side of the river until the hills begin again at Memphis in the state of Tennessee. Until a century ago this region was an undrained swamp inhabited by a few Choctaw Indians and a lot of malaria mosquitoes. Today the former have all disappeared and the latter flourish mightily – but without the disease.

The Delta is to America what the Fens are to England. Flat, fertile, inward-looking and more than a little primitive in social attitudes. King Cotton ruled the area until soyabeans came in after the war to give farmers a break crop which also made money. Within the past five years rice has been introduced and is now far the most profitable crop to grow on the heavy clays, while cotton does better on the free-draining sands further from the river. Together these three crops are what the Delta is all about today.

The farms are magnificent, averaging around 2000 acres each with fields rarely less than 50 acres of level land. The equipment is the sort of thing which draws the crowds at Smithfield. John Deeres, Steigers, Cases and Internationals, all on eight tyres with massive discs of up to 45 feet behind them. The combines often have four-wheel drive to enable them to work in the deep mud which is inevitable in the rice harvest. They are also used for the soyabeans and the tiny amount of winter wheat which is grown.

It is perhaps significant that the farmers I spoke to were unanimous in their praise of the new axial-flow machines, and had either bought one or were planning to do so in the near future. The self-propelled cotton pickers, which bear a superficial resemblance to combines, are everywhere and have been the biggest single cause of the rush from the land to the cities of the north. The change from hand labour to mechanisation in the cotton fields during the 1950s altered the face not only of southern agriculture, but also of northern cities like New York and Detroit.

Yet among these vast machines of the 1980s, I had the uneasy feeling that I was looking at life in the 1880s, because when it comes to their attitudes, the (invariably) white farmers of the Delta are downright primitive. The following facts will give some indication of the problem.

Workers are paid the minimum legal wage of £1.35 per hour and sometimes (albeit unofficially) less than this. No overtime rates are ever paid, even though at busy periods 80-hour weeks are not uncommon. No holidays are given, and even bank holidays are only paid if the employee happened to work that day. Sick pay is non-existent. During the slack winter months, after the cotton has been harvested in December until field work starts again in March, the workers are laid off without pay and are forced onto the inadequate dole, or "welfare" as it is called in the United States.

The farmers I visited were good employers by their own standards. Some managed to employ key workers for the entire year without laying them off. One was actually thinking of contributing to a private health insurance scheme, and yet another had built some of his workers new brick houses. But all the farmers complained bitterly about the low standard of labour, without ever feeling that they themselves might be the cause of the problem, with their archaic ideas and inhuman working conditions.

The factors which have created this extraordinary situation are too complex to go into now. Suffice it to say that even 120 years after slavery was abolished, old attitudes die hard among both blacks and whites.

The paradox of huge and expensive machinery being operated by cheap labour is unparalleled anywhere in the world. Like the Afrikaaners in South Africa, the Mississippi farmer has a blind spot which enables him to overlook the unpleasant side of life. A few of the younger and more progressive farmers are uneasy about the future and admit that they are detecting the first whiff of change coming. But at the same time they are reluctant to improve conditions for fear of what their neighbours would say or do.

It is always difficult when being royally entertained by hospitable hosts to criticise the system, and I must admit I restrained my feelings of indignation – at least in public. But it was a sobering experience and I wondered just how British agriculture would look today if our industry had been untouched by trade unions or government controls for the past century. Thank God for the Tolpuddle Martyrs.

The Mississippi Delta remains unique to this day. There is nowhere in the United States which can be compared to this fertile but primitive backwater. Social attitudes are still as unsophisticated as they were when I first visited Mississippi back in 1979. However, the food, with its Creole influence, is better than anywhere else in North America.

A Subsidy for Cannabis

AUGUST 1980

Marijuana didn't do anything for me on the one occasion when I smoked the stuff. My wife disagrees and insists that I giggled more than usual. But either way I can't say it came anywhere near a stiff whisky. Thus it was not my own personal consumption that made me become interested in growing cannabis on the farm. On the face of it the crop would fit in well with our system; we are always looking for break crops which can go through the combine and nobody at Claas or Massey Ferguson denied that their machines could handle cannabis. Visions of a 50 acre field of lush, green, swaying cannabis turned me on far more than the soggy joint I had coughed over ten years ago.

It was not all that easy ordering the seed. In fact it was well nigh impossible. Hamish Young★, my friendly local seedsman, gulped a bit when I asked him for 50 acres worth of Basic cannabis seed. There was a slight pause before he remembered to ask me what seed rate I intended to use. I replied that I hadn't a clue but was counting on him for advice. Another pause and a cough while he thought about the problem. "I'd like to look into this if I may. Can I ring you back tomorrow please?" he said.

The chap we buy fertiliser from was out of the office but the girl on the switchboard was very helpful. After I had spelt out CANNABIS a couple of times she got the drift of my request. Could her boss recommend a fertiliser application rate for the crop please? Did he feel that I could cut down on the phosphate and was the potash level critical? Leave it with her, she insisted and the boss would be in touch with me as soon as he got back to the office.

The man at ICI felt sure that cannabis could be direct drilled but he hadn't had a great deal of experience with the crop. Could I give him a few hours while he researched the matter further? The crop protection boys were as keen as they were clueless. They had no doubt that MCPA would do a cracking job at weed control but there was just one problem: was cannabis broad-leaved? I admitted that I wasn't too sure about this either and we agreed that I had better hold off with the herbicide until they had done some more homework.

All in all I was getting nowhere fast. There was only one thing left to do. I had to play my trump card. When all else fails and nobody knows the answer to my problems it is a wonderful feeling to realise that help is just a telephone call away. That vast repository of knowledge, that reservoir of talent and know-how, that powerhouse of original yet earthy advice was, as yet, untapped.

ADAS. The very name sent shivers of anticipation down my spine as my fingers quivered on the telephone dial. I could picture our local adviser as he changed into his Superman gear in the phone box outside his office.

"What was that again? Cannabis? Is that anything to do with

★   Hamish Young, a talented Scot, was one of the most interesting members of the British seed trade. He died suddenly (and tragically) last year in his mid-forties.

Hemp? Ah yes, Hemp. Why didn't you say so in the first place?"
Can't help you I'm afraid. But I'll check with Agronomy. Or Soil
Science. No, maybe there's a chap in Pathology who could help. He
was out in India during the war and I have an idea he grew the stuff.
In the meanwhile my advice to you is to do nothing until I have had
a chance to chat with a few of my colleagues. By the way, whatever
happened to that eyespot you had last year? It was eyespot wasn't it?
No, of course, I remember now, it was New Forest Eye. Never
have been one for opticians. Ha-ha. Cold for this time of year isn't
it? I'll be in touch." I don't know what I'd do without ADAS. God
bless them.

There was only one more call to make. I hesitated before dialing
999 and instead called the local police station in Cambridge. After a
short delay I found myself speaking to Detective Inspector Christian of the Drug Squad. "What would you do if I were to grow 50
acres of cannabis on my farm at Thriplow?" I asked him in my most

reasonable voice. "I'd nick you," he said. "Are you serious?" I persisted. "Dead serious" came the reply.

The above saga is not a fairy story and was not written under the influence of cannabis or any other hallucinogenic drug. The fact is that our bureaucratic friends in Brussels are very keen for me (and you) to grow cannabis. They are so keen that they are actually offering a subsidy on the crop. Just like beans, peas, grasses and a whole host of other crops, certified cannabis seed qualifies for a subsidy from Brussels. In this case the amount comes to roughly £3.69 per hundredweight in addition to the market value. The snag is that it is impossible to find out the market value of cannabis because the retailers are either in prison or undercover, and the wholesale trade seems to be handled by some even shadier characters with bulges under their jackets.

There must be a moral here somewhere but I am still looking for it. The only conclusion I have drawn is that I am now reluctantly convinced that the whole tottering edifice of the Common Market will soon come crashing down. As a convinced and passionate European, I am very sad about this, but I am also secretly relieved. To misquote Martin Luther, "The Nearer to Brussels the Further from Europe." It has been an expensive farce from beginning to end –albeit a farce built on noble ideals. But the supreme irony is that nobody has benefited except a tiny group of men called farmers.

A true story which highlights one of the many idiocies of the Common Agricultural Policy. To this day I remain unclear as to why the EEC wants to subsidise cannabis.

The Great Combine Test

OCTOBER 1980

I have always felt that anyone in East Anglia who does not run a Claas combine needs his head examining. It is not that Dr August Claas (whom God preserve at the age of 92) makes better machines than Massey, New Holland or John Deere, it is simply that the service offered by Manns of Saxham is almost perfect. Any single spare part can be bought over the counter, and at harvest time they are open for seven days a week, twenty-four hours a day. But in case any reader feels that I am giving a free plug for the Claas importers, let me redress the balance by saying that they did not exactly cover themselves with glory this year. In fact, as the story will reveal, they showed about as much courage and vigour as an arthritic mouse in an intensive care ward.

It all began, as with most of my good ideas, in the bath. I don't know if cleanliness is really next to godliness, but it is certainly next to thoughtfulness. As I lay there dreaming of harvest, which was still six weeks away, I began to think about combines. The people at International Harvester had promised to let us have their 1460 axial-flow machine to try out on herbage seed. This was one of the crops they had not worked in last year, and they were keen to see if it could handle the pretty unpleasant conditions which this crop sometimes produces. There can be nothing nastier to combine than herbage seed with green regrowth coming through the top, and a brown slime beneath the surface. The critics of axial-flow combines (i.e. everyone who does not actually manufacture them) stated quite categorically that they could not cope with wet conditions. "They're designed for American conditions, old boy," I was told, "they're perfectly all right for maize or wheat on the prairies, but they simply cannot manage in our damp climate, old boy. Have another gin and tonic and we'll talk about out-of-season discounts."

As I thought about how an axial-flow would manage, I began to wonder which combine was the best for herbage seed, or for any other crop if it came to that. The only way to find out would be to have all the different makes of combine working in the same field at the same time. Like Archimedes, who also had his better thoughts in the bath, I realised that the solution was simple; invite all the combine importers to bring a combine along and show what they could do. Politeness dictated that I first contact International Harvester and warn them, because they might not be too keen to have their new and untried machine alongside so many competitors – all of whom had proven track records in herbage seed. My fears were groundless. Michael Bowen of IHC seemed to relish the thought, and cheerfully admitted that if his axial-flow failed to do a good job he would have egg on his face. But he was prepared to take the risk. He even offered to provide one of his conventional combines to keep the 1460 company. Bowen's reaction made me confident that the other combines would be keen to attend what was rapidly becoming the Great Herbage Seed Demo – at least in my own little mind.

I never cease to be amazed by my own naivet and general stupidity. This occasion was to prove yet again how dumb I really am. I made a list of manufacturers to phone, starting with Claas, New Holland, Massey, John Deere and Fahr. A team consisting of Laverda, Dronningborg and Fisher-Humphries was also prepared. It soon became clear that while the small boys were moderately keen to show off their machines, the market leaders were positively appalled at the prospect. In fact it was almost comical watching them run for cover under a smokescreen of excuses, delaying tactics and simply by refusing to reply to phone calls.

This process reached a peak of absurdity when one of the leading importers announced that he could not possibly send a machine because I was clearly organising a "Witch Hunt". When I told him that nothing could be further from my mind, he remained completely unconvinced. I tried to reassure him that there would be no tests made, no measurements taken, and hence no winners or losers, but he did not believe a word I said. It just so happens that this chap's machines are as good as any, and he should thus have had less to worry about than most of the competition. But nothing I said would dissuade him of his neurotic idea that his combines would somehow be ripped to shreds by the opposition and that, as a result, his sales would suffer.

The other Big Boys were somewhat more urbane. "Frightfully sorry old chap, I'd have liked to have helped but unfortunately we just don't have a machine available. You know how things are, and all that". Yes, I was beginning to know precisely how things were. The bigger they were, the harder they feared they would fall. "Business," as my old Jewish grandfather probably didn't say, "is Business."

But combine importers beware. I haven't finished yet and am going to try again next year. So if any of you are reading this, you had better polish up your excuses and make sure that all of your Demonstrators are fully tied up for the month of July. We are lucky to farm early land, and I would be happy to provide 80 acres of winter barley on July 21st next year to stage a demonstration. If any readers can offer an even earlier field I would be happy to hear because it is important that the event is held before most people's harvest gets under way. In the meanwhile I shall be doing some more thinking in my bath and would welcome any suggestions. About combines, not baths.

We bought an IH 1480 in the following year. However, it never really proved satisfactory and, to my great relief, we sold it after three harvests.

Starting Sheep

NOVEMBER 1980

The trouble with this farm is that in the old days it was just too complicated. Now, after five years of simplifying everything and getting rid of a dairy herd and a crop drier, I find that it is all too straightforward. For some years I have preached a very simple doctrine; you should only do what you are interested in, specialise in what you are best at and, contrary to what the old-timers would have us believe, there is no God-given virtue in mixed farming. The extraordinary thing is that I have actually practised what I preached. For a card-carrying hypocrite like me, that is quite an achievement.

But even hypocrites are entitled to change their minds, and I have just changed mine. Not only have I succeeded in contradicting myself, but I have also managed to start an enterprise just at the time when many clever farmers have decided it is time to stop. I am, of course, referring to sheep.

I know less about sheep than I do about horses. You could even say I was pig ignorant and I would not argue. But two things happened to make me feel a bit like St Paul when he was en route for Damascus. I did not, to be fair, see a blinding light. Nor did a voice suggest that I stop kicking against the pricks. Instead, two important events took place in quick succession. The first was the arrival on the farm of a New Zealander who is a sheep man, and the second was the sharp fall in sheep prices as those farmers who know about sheep decided that now was the time to bail out. These two events whetted my appetite somewhat and I spent a bit of time talking to my two neighbours, both of whom are sheep men of credit and renown. They seemed to feel that the world was big enough for the three of us, and were kind enough to give me advice and encouragement. In their case virtue was more than its own reward because I bought ten rams from one and hope to find a good dog from the other.

But before I started buying the animals I drew up some ground rules which the sheep enterprise would have to adhere to if it was going to make any sense on our light land arable farm. They were as follows:–

1. Sheep will eat only home produced fodder, particularly arable by-products.

2. They will graze lucerne in the summer.

3. They will graze herbage seed aftermaths in the autumn and early winter.

4. They will eat beet tops (fresh and ensiled) together with threshed ryegrass stalks in winter and early spring.

5. Beet tops will be carted off the fields to the sheep to enable winter corn to be drilled quickly.

6. No spring corn will be grown to accommodate the sheep feeding.

All this boiled down to the simple premise that the sheep will have to fit in with our existing cropping of winter corn, lucerne, herbage seed and sugar beet. Most of the other sheep men I know make a few concessions to their animals which invariably result in lower cereal yields, or more spring corn – which usually amounts to the same thing.

We decided on a breeding flock so that we could make use of the lucerne during the summer months. The snag about lucerne has always been finding a use for it. In the balmy days of grass-drying this was less of a problem, but today things are not so easy. Silage never seems very satisfactory even with additives, and making good lucerne hay is the fastest way known to man of getting an ulcer or a nervous breakdown (or both). The simplicity of having animals graze the stuff appeals to me hugely, although I am more than a bit worried by the possibility of Bloat. However, I am assured that they graze lucerne very happily in New Zealand, and there are some farmers in this country who have built up a system round the crop. It will demand a higher level of stockmanship than normal, and this is where John, the New Zealander, comes in. I hope that he is as good as I think because the success of the whole operation will depend on him and him alone.

We have started with 300 shearling Mules and are using Suffolk and Hampshire tups so we can lamb early in February in open yards. Beet tops will be the first big hurdle (pun intended) because it will mean having three men spending several weeks collecting and ensiling the stuff. This costs a lot both in time and machinery, and may well be one of the reasons why the whole system fails. But I have no doubt that if we fold the sheep onto the tops we shall be delaying the winter corn drilling – and making the seedbeds worse at the same time.

If all goes well we shall increase the flock in 12 months time to around 800 ewes. This will enable John to become a full-time shepherd, and at this stage we shall try to work out a partnership arrangement so that he is, in effect, his own boss. The details of this sort of setup will be complicated to arrange, but there are farmers who manage this type of system very well and I have recently been picking their brains. The snag seems to be knowing how much to charge the shepherd for rent and keep without either bankrupting him or losing money oneself. This delicate balance will be vital because the eventual objective will be for John to own all the sheep himself and for the farm to get the benefits of the animals without the hassle of looking after them.

Of course, the whole idea may well fail miserably and in a year's time I shall be a sadder, wiser and substantially poorer man. In the meanwhile I am learning a few basic facts about sheep. I know which end the food goes in, and I am already on to the difficult bits like how to tell rams from ewes. All that remains to be seen is whether I get fleeced before the sheep. Watch this space.

Sheep lasted only seven years at Thriplow, during which time the flock grew from 300 to 1000. The original idea of their scavenging arable by-products did not really work out. After a few years we were putting down 60 acres of grass for them to graze. Costs rose as the shepherd needed a Land Rover to get round his far-flung empire, and the arable staff spent more and more time fencing, littering down and lambing the sheep.

John Cherrington

JANUARY 1981

I admire the Brigade of Guards, Motherhood, blackberry and apple pie and John Cherrington. There are some other things I care about but they are not worth mentioning here and, compared to the aforementioned Pantheon, they are rather insignificant. All of these heroic figures have remained pretty secure in my mind for the last few decades until recently, when I began to realise that John Cherrington was wrong. Far be it from me to suggest that he has ceased being to farming journalists what the Grand Canyon is to valleys, but I just happen to think he is wrong about farming. Or, to be more precise, he is wrong about the use of agrochemicals. To sum up a not very technical argument, he's against them and I'm for them. I know he wouldn't put it that simply, and I don't want to make him out to be half as foolish as I am (that would be beyond my powers of persuasion anyway). But it is clear from his recent writings that he does not really like using chemicals at the best of times, and only does so when he feels it is really necessary. Worse still, he seems to have a vague guilty conscience after the awful event.

By now you will undoubtedly be feeling that I am the slappiest-happiest-if-it-grows-spray-it-farmer ever to have crept out of a Tolkan waistcoat. This is not true but, for the purposes of my argument, I shan't waste time denying the charge and, what is more, will further strengthen your prejudices by admitting that I do get huge discounts from my chemical supplier. We all know that it is only the big spenders who get the big discounts.

Five years ago, before I had heard of Laloux and thought that Schleswig-Holstein was a dairying region somewhere between Cambridge and Finland, I was a Cherrington man (boy, actually) through and through. I remember a particularly noisy argument I once had with my father – who survived the ordeal – about whether or not to spray a field of spring barley which was plastered with mildew. The fact that the crop had the disease was beyond question. The leaves had gone past the yellow stage and the whole field looked powdery grey. We really should have been arguing about whether there was any living tissue present, but that would have involved us in the realm of facts, whereas with all really good arguments you should confine yourself solely to prejudice and supposition. I forgot who took what side in the conflict; that was not important. The discussion centred round how much of the crop would be damaged by the sprayer wheelings compared to being left alone to grow (or die). In other words, we were obsessed by details like wheelings rather than the disease itself.

Life was more simple in those days. Chemical bills hardly existed at all, farmworkers' wages were low, tied cottages were securely tied, and nobody even thought of monetarism. Everyone in agriculture was miserable except the farmers and, come to think of it, they weren't too happy either because it was before the Great Grain Robbery and the Arable Boom had still not happened. It was, in short, the heyday of the John Cherrington approach.

Then along came the pocket calculator brigade who counted everything in square metres and tweed caps. These were hotly pursued by those who claimed that Milstem and Calixin had been outdated by other wonder drugs. Finally the two gangs got together, invented the word "prophylactic", and persuaded the trendies like me to spray everything before it even germinated, let alone grew. I became an ardent convert and within a few months could spout figures about spray rates as my literary friends claim they can recite James Joyce's *Ulysses*. The amazing thing was that my yields went up, as they say, in leaps and bounds. The money poured into the bank and my cars became shorter but had more cylinders. Of course, I told the farm workers that this success was entirely due to my own extraordinary skill and that they could take no credit whatsoever. They knew me to be the liar that I am, but I persisted in my belief that pocket calculators and sprays could turn even the poorest farmer into a Rolls-Royce owner overnight. What this technique could do to a good arable farmer was even more stupendous, and this fact was made all the more obscene when they all went out and made potato fortunes in the mid-1970s. So the poor arable farmers became rich, the rich ones very rich, and the very rich ones do not bear thinking about. Farm wages went up a wee bit too.

But after a few harvests the novelty wore off and my pocket calculator rusted away. I ceased to be a true believer and became an agnostic instead. I knew that chemicals were crucial to my way of farming, but they were not the essence of the system. While seed rates were still important and plants per square metre should not be sneezed at, they were not ends in themselves. Other factors entered my tiny prejudiced mind, and they remain there to this day. They can be summarised thus:–

1. Timeliness is the most important thing in farming. Do the right job at the right time. Hours, not days, can be crucial.

2. Chemicals should be used extensively as an insurance policy so long as the value of the crop remains high enough. If the price of cereals falls much more this may not apply.

3. Never hold off using a chemical in case the disease or bug becomes resistant. Just hope that the chemists will stay one jump ahead. They have managed to do so since weeds became a problem in the Garden of Eden.

4. Never feel guilty about polluting the atmosphere. The tests done on these chemicals are excellent and extensive. There are many worthwhile reasons for feeling guilty. Eat your Sunday lunch and then think of Bangladesh.

5. Realise that all the above will be useless without sun and rain, so be suitably humble.

6. Hope that John Cherrington will still be writing when I am proved wrong in one hundred years' time.

I am beginning to sympathise with the Cherrington approach more than I did. Maybe it is middle age, or maybe it is the beginning of the Bad Times for farming. Either way, I am today less aggressively bullish than I was when I wrote this piece. John died early this year and leaves a gap in agriculture that nobody can possibly fill.

Ten Tonnes of Wheat

FEBRUARY 1981

No mucking about, no guessing and no nonsense. We did it. We managed to break the Ten Tonne barrier this harvest and, three months later, I am still thrilled to bits. I shall try and de-smug what follows, but readers who dislike conceit and smugness should stop here because bits and pieces will probably slip through my guard.

The field itself is 16.75 hectares of what we call our best land. By no stretch of the imagination could it be called Man's Land, but it is better than some of the thin chalk which we farm. My friends who farm real wheat land snigger a bit but admit that we need less horsepower to make a seedbed than they do. It was in good heart after two years of lucerne and our first job was to spray Roundup to kill the lucerne and, more important, the couch which manages to get a hold during these two years. The fertiliser was broadcast by a local contractor. We used no nitrogen but 50 units of phosphate and potash.

We ploughed eight inches deep in late September, waited three days before rolling, harrowing and drilling in a single day. The drill was a 30 row MF 30 model with disc coulters, and the seed rate was exactly one hundredweight an acre. The variety was important because it happened to be the latest wheat from NSDO's stable called Norman. We were using pre-basic seed to produce basic this harvest, and at a cost of £35 per bag we could not afford any mistakes.

Immediately after drilling we sprayed the high rate of Tribunil (4.5 kg per hectare) to take care of both broadleaved weeds and blackgrass: In a normal year this would have been all the work needed until the spring, but last year was exceptional in many ways. An attack of slugs, which is rare for us, meant that Draza was broadcast, and in late November we saw mildew in sufficient quantity to justify a dose of Bayleton. This is common in early-drilled barleys, but it was the first time I had seen mildew on wheat before Christmas.

Contrary to ADAS's advice, we put on a large dollop of nitrogen as soon as we could get on the land in mid-February: 70 units of liquid N went on at growth stage 3 with our big sprayer on

February 16th. This did the trick magnificently and the crop put on a noticeable spurt. So did the blackgrass, and it soon became clear that Tribunil had not done a very good job. There was no alternative but to apply a dose of Hytane and so, after checking that we would not damage the crop after its autumnal Tribunil, we went ahead. There could not be many fields which had so much money spent on blackgrass control last year, and I am not exactly proud of what we had to do.

The few broadleaved weeds which survived the winter, and those which germinated in the spring, were taken out with a CMPP which was tank-mixed with chlormequat and Delsene at growth stage 5 in late March. The second top dressing went on at growth stage 7 in mid-April. Once again it was liquid and amounted to another 70 units of liquid nitrogen. By early May another outbreak of mildew caused us to slap on the second Bayleton, and one month later – just after ear emergence which took place on June 4th – we put on a tank mix of Bayleton CF and Metasystox. The former was a prophylactic treatment to guard against septoria and sooty moulds, and the latter was because we had seen a few aphids in the field. One June 9th we shut the gate and waited for harvest. The drought was at its height and the field had received less than one quarter of an inch of rain during the previous six weeks. The plant population amounted to 225 per square metre and the tillers just managed to reach 600 per square metre, so I was not all that optimistic about harvest prospects.

Long before the combine appeared it became clear that something extraordinary was happening. The field seemed to fill out even though the crop had ceased tillering many months ago. Pretty soon we became aware that we were looking at some of the biggest ears of wheat any of us had ever seen. I began to realise that this field was something special, and as July progressed my optimism grew. Random ears of wheat picked throughout the field gave an average of 62 grains, and some contained as many as 100. The flag leaves remained green and healthy and the crop stayed upright even after two massive storms in August, one of which gave us over an inch of rain in four hours. I remembered asking one of my Schleswig-Holstein friends what he did to prevent lodging in August, and he answered simply, "Pray". It seemed a sensible course of action.

On August 23rd NSDO's combine entered the field and for two days (it was a very small combine) I fretted like a father outside a maternity ward. Each load went straight over a weighbridge so there was no possibility of fiddling the figures. The moisture averaged slightly less than 13% and so it would be necessary to adjust the weight to 16% by means of the usual formula. Eventually the last trailer went over the weighbridge and we added up the total. It came to 173 tons 6cwt 54 lbs adjusted to 16% moisture, and even my primitive arithmetic was good enough to see that this was 83 cwt per acre, or 10.35 tonnes per hectare.

Looking back, it is hard to draw any sensible conclusions, except that we had been very lucky. The weather had done the right thing at the right time, and when you farm on light land you cannot ask for anything more. In retrospect, it was probably a mistake relying on Tribunil to take out the blackgrass, but it has done well for us in the past. We could possibly have put on a bit more nitrogen but I felt that 140 units after two years of lucerne was pushing our luck as it was. I have no regrets about using chlormequat, and even John Bingham, the variety's breeder, when he looked at the field before harvest, said that he would have done the same thing himself. So I find myself in the silly position of having achieved my ambition as a cereal grower without actually knowing what I did right. I cannot therefore give readers any advice which will be valuable except to say that all you need to grow a Ten Tonne Crop is rainfall, fertiliser and luck.

This was one of – maybe the most – exciting moments of my farming life. In those days ten tonne crops were not as common as they are now, and the sense of achievement was very real indeed. I shall never forget the enormous size of the ears of Norman, which were as long as small bananas.

The Case Against Burning

FEBRUARY 1981

Somebody once said (I think it was me) that the man who confuses his expectations with his desires is a fool. When it comes to straw burning, there are a lot of fools about. Most of the farmers I know are so keen to ensure that straw burning continues that they simply refuse to accept the reasons for the pressure against it. Now I am as keen as anyone when it comes to burning straw. Indeed, some of the accidents we have had over the years (about which I am not in the least proud) are testimony to my excess of keenness. As a practitioner of minimal cultivations, I reckon a good burn is worth at least ten quid an acre, and I am not so rich that I can afford to throw that sort of money away. But the fact remains that while in the past the opposition to straw burning came from the outer fringes of the conservation lobby, today we are running into trouble from a very different type of person – the ordinary householder.

If only I could go back to the balmy days when all we had to worry about was Marion Shoard* and her band of weirdos. I was – and am – prepared to argue with them until the cows come home because they are inherently so nutty that only a tiny minority of the population shares their opinions. But today it is very different. I find it utterly impossible to argue with a man or woman who tells me that their washing, house and car is covered with a fine coating of ash caused by burning straw. The facts are there for all to see, and I know all too well that if my own house were to be covered with filth from a nearby factory, neither I nor my wife would be terribly convinced if the factory manager (or, worse still, the CBI on his behalf) came round to explain that the reason for all the filth was to reduce his costs. I would, naturally, be deeply sympathetic if he told me that he was manufacturing food or some other vital product. But after listening to his rational and well-argued case for continuing to pollute my house – and those of my neighbours – I would still tell him to go away and damn well stop making everything filthy.

Even if, in stopping the pollution, his costs were to rise massively I would still think that there was no excuse in 1982 for one individual to make everyone elses's lives unpleasant, and their property dirty. If the neighbouring factory manager still refused to stop the pollution, and insisted that he had a perfect right to continue, I would start to put pressure on the politicians at all levels. I know that I would win in the end because more voters live in houses than manage factories and, happily, we live in a democracy in which politicians have to take notice of what the voters want.

* Author of *The Theft of the Countryside*, a strident, exaggerated, totally biased but not wholly unjustified book which accused farmers of wrecking the landscape for selfish reasons.

The moral is clear. There are more people whose houses are covered with our ashes than there are straw-burning farmers. Eventually the politicians will bow to public pressure and we shall be stopped burning straw. What the NFU is doing is no more than a holding operation in the face of overwhelming and invincible odds. By fining farmers for burning hedges, by licensing farmers, by not burning at weekends or on bank holidays, we are trying to fool the public into thinking that the problem will go away. But until someone finds a way of burning a field of straw without making any ashes, I refuse to see why a fire which burns on a Monday makes less mess in the nearby town than a fire which burns on a Sunday.

The NFU is behaving like the generals of the First World War who insisted on using the tactics of the Boer War in the Flanders trenches. They could not believe that the enemy had changed, the conditions had changed and the world had changed. The NFU should stop worrying about the conservationists and instead start thinking about the millions of people who couldn't give a damn about farming or farmers. All they want to do is to live in a world in which the months of August and September do not bring a veil of black dust to cover the ground like malevolent manna from heaven.

My farming friends become very unhappy when I preach this doctrine. They tell me I am being defeatist and, worse still, that I am giving comfort to our enemies. The word "quisling" has even been whispered. Unfortunately, I do not have any easy answers at all because I have been trying hard (but unsuccessfully) to think of what I shall have to do when the burning has to stop. It isn't the straw which worries me; that can easily be chopped behind the combine. It is what to do with the stubble which is giving me – as the Americans say – conniptions.

The debate about straw burning has cooled down a lot since this article appeared. We gave up burning straw that year and now, six years later, (after harvest anyway) I am a happier and more relaxed person as a result.

The New Farm Worker

MARCH 1981

Five years ago I was a worried man. It wasn't just that I felt that the past looked better than the future; all farmers feel that anyway. It was a horrible feeling in my viscera (guts to you) that in 1981 we would be running into serious labour troubles. I wasn't worried about strikes or working to rule or any of the other nightmares which industrialists have to live with. I was scared that there would not be anyone working on the farm at all.

When I started farming ten years ago I inherited a workforce with an average age of over 50. They had all been on the farm since boyhood and, as their mates left to work in factories, they stayed behind and did what their fathers and grandfathers had done before them. The drift from the land had left them stranded high and dry. Their wages were bad, their houses were not good and they knew only too well that everyone else in the pub on a Friday night had more money than they did. What was even worse was that they were being laughed at by the rest of the world for being simple yokels who chewed straw and forked muck. As usual in life, it is not the facts themselves which matter, but what people think the facts are. And there is no doubt that the farm worker was thought to be at the bottom of a very big heap. Thus an inferiority complex had grown up among farm workers so that they tended to be both defensive and resentful.

As if all this were not enough to make farmworkers' lives less fun than the rest of the world's, there were the old prejudices which generation after generation had handed down. Behind the polite – and even respectful – facade which the farmer saw, there lurked some fears which were as strong as they were irrational. Let nobody forget that irrational fears are always the dangerous ones, even if they appear to be patently ridiculous to the rest of the world who do not have to endure them. The spectre of eviction from the tied cottage was probably the nastiest of these ghosts. Nobody I have ever spoken to has actually heard of anyone being evicted, and certainly if this had ever happened in the neighbourhood it would have passed into the folklore. And yet in spite of the fact that it had not actually taken place for generations, the fear still lurked in the minds of men.

My father came across this phenomenon when, in the late 1940s, he decided that the 73 year old foreman should start taking things a bit easier and should not feel the need to put in a six day week. When he broached the subject with the old man, the effect was unmistake-able. The foreman offered to be out of his house by the weekend. He took some convincing that he was being ridiculously sensitive and that he could stay in his house for his lifetime (and his widow after him). But however illogical these fears were, it was a stupid farmer who laughed at them. Hence the legislation which we all felt was unnecessary but which, in hindsight, must have made all farmworkers sleep easier in their beds at night. And that cannot be a bad thing.

It was problems like this which made me certain that no young man would ever voluntarily want to come and work on the farm after the old-timers had retired. I had visions of a transitory army of yob-like school leavers spending a few weeks on the farm before passing on to a better paid job in a local factory, and leaving behind a trail of wrecked machines and badly ploughed fields. I had myself become the victim of the anti-farmworker propaganda which the rest of the world had been putting out so very effectively. I instinctively believed it all and that was why no young, intelligent and energetic young man would ever work here again.

In addition to facing the prospect of having no young workers, I also began to realise that we would be needing a different type of man altogether. Gone were the days when one man was a ploughman, another went on the drill and a third was good on the combine. With a smaller labour force and bigger machines it was going to be necessary for the new generation to be able to turn their hand to every job – and do it well. Instead of specialists, we needed generalists who could plough, drill, spray, run the grain drier overnight or pull a calf from a Charolais cow. They would have to work long hours willingly and keenly at the peak periods yet be content with cutting down trees and repairing roads for months at a time at the slack periods. It seemed an impossible task to find people like this, so I just tucked the worry at the back of my brain (or what passes for one) and waited for the inevitable to happen.

The inevitable became evitable. For no apparent reason, young men started to appear. One was a nurseryman who had almost decided to emigrate with his family to New Zealand (he is today the

Assistant Manager). Another was a Maori on a working holiday from New Zealand (he is today the foreman) and yet another was a regular soldier who became tired of being shot at in Belfast (he is training to become the lorry driver). Since then, the trickle has become a flood and I am constantly turning away boys whom I would have taken like a shot only a few years ago. This is not simply because of today's unemployment because it started long before Mrs Thatcher started to dismantle the country. Admittedly, the wages are a lot better than they were; this may explain why we are able to keep some of the people but it does not convince me that they actually came for the money. The fact is that the old rubbish about the farmworker being an idiotic impoverished bumpkin has now been exposed, and people are no longer so keen to work in mind-numbing jobs for an extra few quid each week.

Jobs on farms are no longer underpaid because, with great respect to Brother Boddy, nobody but a moron pays the basic rate, and most of us pay substantially above the craftsman level. Just at the time that executives have realised that the name of the game is tax-free perks, so also have farmworkers realised that houses free of rent and rates are not the irrelevancy that Sister Maynard would have us believe.

There is still room for improvement. Wages should be still higher for today's new breed of farmworker who can do all the jobs and, even more important, will do them willingly for all hours of the day when the job needs doing. But big pay packets are not enough by themselves perks like BUPA, pensions and long holidays should all be part of a package to attract these men and keep them on the land. The one question which remains to be answered is how to keep them interested and involved now we have paid them well. I don't know the answer. Solve this one and we have, as they say, a whole new ballgame.

Today, seven years later, everybody on the farm (there are only eight of us including the manager, secretary and fitter) is on salary. The money is better, the holidays longer, the perks more extensive and the status slightly more elevated.

Why Grow Sugar Beet?

APRIL 1981

In addition to being a hypocrite, bigot and part-time scribbler, I must admit with no pleasure that I am a pretty bad sugar beet grower. If the size and amount of tackle we own is anything to go by, I should be in the championship class because we have some of the best and biggest machinery money can buy. But the fact of the matter is that, as year succeeds year, our beet yields vary from the dreadful to the dismal. This past year, for example, while all my friends and neighbours (who are usually the same people) were telling me that they had managed to produce 15, 16 or even 17 tons per acre, I found to my horror that we had barely scraped 13.5 tons per acre in what was supposed to be our best year ever. Big deal.

From time to time bright agricultural students or visiting farmers from the Continent turn up at Thriplow and start asking intelligent questions. I can usually manage to parry most of them, but I do have difficulty sounding convincing when some wise guy says to me, "Tell me, Herr Walston, why do you grow sugar beet on your farm?" I clear my throat, look towards the distant horizon and pray that a thunderbolt (or runaway tractor) will knock him to the ground. It never happens so I mutter something about soil structure, disease control and not having all of your eggs in one basket. The questioner never looks totally convinced, however polite he is; the bloody-minded ones are often heard to whisper to their colleagues that if they had yields as low as ours they would not consider growing the crop. Temporary deafness means that I do not hear this remark, and we usually pass on to happier subjects, like whether I believe Avalon is a better wheat than Vuka (Answer: yes, in this country anyway).

The time has come when even I have to ask myself whether what made sense 35 years ago necessarily makes sense today. In the old days (not to be confused with the Good Old Days, which may be defined as being that part of your life when the only problem was whether she would smack your face) we had lots of men on the farm, we grew all spring corn, used very little bagged fertiliser and were unable to control either weeds or diseases with any certainty. Sugar beet was in its element because it made use of labour during the winter, the dung we spread before the crop provided useful fertility for the following cereal, the hand-hoeing controlled weeds which would have flourished in barley, diseases like bunt and take-all were checked, and the soil structure was improved both by the deep ploughing and the action of the tap root itself. All in all, sugar beet made sense.

If one looks at these factors today, everything appears very different indeed. First and foremost we grow nothing but winter corn, and the problems of lifting beet late and trying to make a seedbed out of a field which is wet, smeared and compacted are insuperable. Yields drop by 50% compared to those crops which have been drilled early in good conditions. Our small labour force is at full stretch throughout the autumn, and puddling about lifting beet is the last thing they need at the busiest time of year. Weeds and diseases can now be controlled by our arsenal of chemicals and, as for soil structure, the effect of large machines on wet land more than nullifies any good done by the tap root. Thus if sugar beet is to survive today, it must stand on its own feet as a cash crop rather than as a break crop in the traditional sense. This means that it must average 15 tons per acre year in year out to cover the costs of growing, harvesting and, worst of all, depreciating the machinery.

But for enthusiasts who feel that my pessimism is only a reflection of my own incompetence, there is even worse news. The men in Brussels have long ago decided that there is too much beet in Europe and have put the squeeze on by reducing the price in real terms. The marginal growers like me have had our minds concentrated wonderfully. In the sugar business this is known as sweet reason. It is one of the rare instances in agriculture when, if the price goes down, the crop actually becomes less attractive and the acreage declines. There are alternatives to sugar beet in a way that there are not to dairy cows in Bavaria or cereals in East Anglia. We ourselves have already taken up oilseed rape in a big way and are now looking at peas and beans. None are ideal, but even if they only lose the same amount of money as beet they will at least do it simply and easily without the hassle and problems I have come to dread.

My predicament should bring a smile to the face of Mr Dalsager* because it must be gratifying for him and his minions to see a farmer behaving just as they had intended him to. But they need not get over-confident. I fully intend to be bloody-minded when the

* EEC Agricultural Commissioner.

squeeze comes on cereals. I shall try even harder to increase my yields to maintain my standard of living and, incidentally, to show who's really boss.

This was written at the nadir of my sugar beet confidence. For a brief period I decided to give up the crop altogether. Instead, I reduced the acreage by a third and – as if by magic – yields started to improve. Today I regret that we did not keep our old 300 acres because sugar beet is the most profitable crop we grow.

Hard Cheese

MAY 1981

Lord Chewton came into farming long after he was 30 and so has one big advantage over most of today's farmers; he is not too impressed by many of the industry's sacred cows and does not allow ancient traditions to inevitably blur his eyesight. Chewton makes Cheddar cheese on the edge of the Mendips in Somerset; he milks 325 cows and also buys milk from his father and a few neighbours to turn into high-quality farmhouse Cheddar as well as butter and cream for a flourishing farm shop.

When Chewton took over the family cheesemaking business in 1978 he realised that the existing system was idiotic. The Milk Marketing Board bought the milk from the producer and sold it to the cheesemaker which, in the case of all farmhouse cheesemakers, was one and the same person. This quirk was not very significant, but what did worry Chewton and some of the other cheesemakers was the fact that the Board also sold their cheese. The price they received was bad, and they found that, in some respects, the Board was maddeningly coy; they could never find out to whom and for how much their cheese had been sold. Indeed, some of the more militant cheesemakers even suspected that the Board sold the cheese to itself, stored it for a while and then resold it at a profit which, the cheesemakers felt, should rightfully have been passed to the producers.

Chewton's first job was to build his own cheese store so that he was no longer totally dependent on the Board. A handful of other farmhouse Cheddar makers followed suit and today are able to store and market their own product instead of having the somewhat doubtful privilege of using the Board's services as their Sole Agents. The price paid for good farmhouse Cheddar today is around £2000 per tonne compared to £1500 for the ordinary factory Cheddar.

Long before Detta O'Cathain* made Marketing the trendiest word in agriculture, Lord Chewton was actually doing what the rest of us are being urged to today. The Board were aghast at this breakaway movement but could do little to prevent it and now Chewton has found to his mild surprise that both the price and the demand have risen sharply. He was quite unable to supply all of his orders and thus decided to increase the size of his herd. But there was a snag to this startlingly simple idea. The Milk Marketing Board gives all cheese producers a quota, which they happen to call a Datum, and they were adamant that in spite of the fact Chewton could sell all he produces, they would not allow him to increase his production. Indeed, in October last year they actually cut the quota for all cheese producers by 2%.

The reason the MMB give for reducing the quota is extremely simple. Their objective is to balance the market so cheese is never overproduced. They justify this reduction in the quota by saying that in spite of the fact that most farmhouse cheese producers are, as they claim, able to sell more than they produce, the Board in its guise of far-seeing, wise and omnipotent protector of the cheese industry, knows better. They claim that they have the best interests of the cheesemakers at heart and for this reason the farmhouse producers should abide by the Board's ruling.

There are various wrinkles to this argument, not least of which is the absurdity that whilst the MMB can stop Lord Chewton and his friends from making cheese out of their own milk (and selling at a profit), they are totally impotent to prevent the French Cheddar producers from exporting into this country. And the French, in case you don't know, can make very good Cheddar indeed if it is ever worthwhile for them to do so.

---

* Irish marketing executive who stirred the geriatric (male) farming establishment at its annual ritual known as the Oxford Farming Conference. The ripples she created were more because she was a (gasp) female than because she advocated a serious approach to marketing. Ms O'Cathain has since become an employee of the Milk Marketing Board.

So much for the idea of a balanced market, which is lovely in theory, but results in a bonus for foreign cheesemakers and a forced reduction in output for some English producers. The MMB admit, a bit sheepishly, that imports cannot be stopped. They claim, however, that these are insignificant and result only from the French wishing to "dump" onto the English market for dark political reasons. Either way, it is not surprising that Chewton and the other farmhouse Cheddar makers are less than happy at being held back to make way for the French.

But, as usually with the politics of milk, the situation is far from being clear. Chewton and some of the other cheesemakers are finding that if they keep up their output at its present rate, they may well exceed their quota by May. When this does happen they will have a most unpleasant choice to make; either shut down the cheesemaking and lay off employees, or simply ignore the quota and keep going. Talks between Chewton and the Board have been dragging on for some months with neither side wishing to do anything drastic. But the day may come when the MMB decides to get tough. In this case they would be able to send their tanker lorries onto the farms and remove the milk physically. If this crisis were ever reached, the Board's lorry driver would find an empty bulk tank on Lord Chewton's farm. His own lorry would have got there first.

In the meanwhile there are a lot of tense cheesemakers in the West Country waiting for the spring flush of grass which will bring on the crisis. The bureaucrats of Thames Ditton are even less happy. They realise that if ever they stop a man from using his own milk to make his own cheese, they will be objects of scorn and ridicule for everyone except the French cheesemakers, who will be enjoying the argument immensely. It all gives new poignancy to the old schoolboy expression of "Hard Cheese".

Chewton won and the MMB gave way. The demand for farmhouse cheddar still exceeds supply, and yet the EEC cheese, butter and dried milk mountains continue to rise.

Bloated Sheep?

JUNE 1981

The slurry, as they say on American farms, is about to hit the fan. Within a very few weeks I shall know whether or not once again I have made a total fool of myself. Sadistic readers will be happy to hear that the chances are pretty good. Those with long memories will recall that the idea was to buy a breeding flock of 300 ewes which would eat all our arable by-products without affecting our all-winter-corn-cropping for cereals. One of Wiltshire's leading farmers, who himself has 1300 ewes, wrote to me saying his sheep never made money, and it was impossible for arable sheep to do so if they were costed properly. By the time this bad news reached me we had already made up our minds.

Everything went wonderfully well to start with. We bought 300 handsome mule shearlings, a dog, lots of Flexinet, ten tups and quite a bit of the vet's time. The sheep sat out eating herbage seed aftermaths until Christmas. They looked very picturesque on the hillside, and I soon felt I was a real sheep man. Our shepherd, by then christened Big Bo Peep because of his 6ft 4in New Zealand rugby player's frame (he must be the only jogging shepherd in existence), started training the dog, and the tups did what they were meant to do. By New Year I was convinced that the only mistake I had made was buying too few sheep.

In early January we brought them into the yards and fed them sugar beet top silage and a bit of ryegrass straw. No problems. Towards the end of the month we started them on some concentrates and, sure enough, lambing began smack on schedule with triplets on February 5th. Lambing itself was extraordinarily exciting for an ignorant buffoon like myself. We had rigged up huge floodlights in the yards so that midnight was brighter than midday, and throughout the three weeks or so, the place was full of helpers or onlookers enjoying the novelty.

We were quietly proud of the fact that we managed 1.68 lambs per ewe and about 1.60 per ewe tupped, because everyone had said that with shearlings we could consider 1.30 to be par for the course. The grass started to grow just as the silage began to run out, and so by early March I found it hard to think of a single problem whatsoever to do with the sheep. They were, it is true, eating all the grass which had been earmarked for the cattle, but I was prepared to overlook this slight snag by consigning it to the Pending File which I have in my brain for all those things which I do not wish to think about right now.

It was towards the end of March, however, when the first tiny problem loomed into sight. It was, as they say, no bigger than a man's hand, but it did not go away. The question which kept appearing in my brain was what would happen when the sheep were put out to graze the lucerne. This had always been part of the Master Plan, but it seemed very far away when we were buying the animals back in September. We have grown lucerne on the farm for nearly 40 years but we have never grazed ruminants on the stuff because we had always been able to dry it, ensile it, make hay with it or zero-graze it. Bloat had rarely been a problem except on the odd occasion when the Jerseys did puff up a bit on a wet morning when the zero-grazed lucerne came out of the forage box. But now, as the moment of truth approached, I decided to talk to as many people as possible who had actually folded sheep on lucerne.

The first thing which became clear was that none of them had actually ever grazed a pure stand of lucerne; instead they had all used grass and lucerne mixtures. They cheerfully admitted that pure lucerne would be more bloatworthy than any mixture, and wished me the best of luck. Some of them did have a few helpful hints, but none of them agreed with the others. One man told me that he felt that sheep always blew most when it was windy; "They always seem to eat facing the wind, you know." Another said it would be necessary for me to have a grass paddock nearby onto which I could put the sheep if any trouble started. I did not point out that since our lucerne rotated around the farm, the nearest grass field could be as much as two miles away. The last man warned me that it was not bloat I should be worried about, but the fact that at certain times of year the crop become so bitter and unpalatable that the sheep will jump the netting in search of better grub. I had visions of the sheep wandering amongst the juggernauts and Jaguars on the London-Norwich road. I increased our Third Party insurance.

There was nothing for it. We could hesitate no longer. We decided to send in what the army would call "The Forlorn Hope". Ten barren ewes kindly volunteered to go out onto the lucerne and see if it would ever get into the sheep edition of *The Good Food Guide*. They looked pretty miserable for a day or two as they

daintily picked over the lucerne in an attempt to eat the couch and other weeds. After a few days they were still alive and so we decided that, as far as the rest of the flock was concerned, it was time to put their mouths where our money was. As I write these words, three hours have passed since the last ewe and lamb was put out onto the lucerne. Within a few weeks, or maybe even days, what started as a Noble Venture nine months ago, could well become a fiasco. I'm feeling pretty nervous right now. Perhaps a quick drench would do me good.

Newsflash: At the time of going to press only one ewe had succumbed to bloat on the lucerne. Marketing of lamb was due to start at the end of April.

Another chapter in the Thriplow Sheep Saga. At this time I was still suffused with enthusiasm and – more important – so was the EEC which threw cash at anything which had four legs

*and a fleece. I remembered all too clearly what our vet had told
me when we decided to start a flock. "Remember," he said,
"that a sheep's greatest ambition is to die."*

Memorandum

JULY 1981

To: *Machinery Manufacturers*
From: *Oliver Walston*
Re: *Your survival*

This should really be marked Highly Confidential because the
information it contains is extremely valuable. However, your
competitors have all hired very expensive industrial espionage
agents to find out what you are doing and thus they would be able
to read this document within a few days of your receiving it.
Perhaps you are not aware that they already have the keys to your
filing cabinets and (this may come as a bit of a shock) the deputy
head of your Research and Development is, in fact, a mole.

You have had a pretty rough time recently and therefore you will
undoubtedly be giving a great deal of thought to new products, or
ways by which you can improve your existing machines. Those of
you who are not thinking along these lines do not deserve to
succeed anyway. But the rest of you might at least like to hear what
this particular farmer wants to see in the near future so that he will
be able to start once again buying British machinery and not
imports.

Quality. The secondhand market is dead and the price I am offered
for trade-ins is usually laughable. I have, therefore, given up my old
practice of keeping machines for three or four years before
chopping them in for new models. Instead I shall have to keep them
until they fall to bits and only then start looking for replacements.
This is bad news for those of you who deliberately build in
obsolescence so that the machine will become outdated in a short
time.

The name of the game today must be quality. Build your

machines to last even if it does mean charging more for them. Do not be frightened at the prospect of selling me a tractor every eight years; if you don't want to, the Germans will.

Tractors. By all means keep giving us more and more power, but please make sure that we can use it. Today, the biggest single limiting factor is the lack of comfort. This means that above 5mph the operator is so badly shaken that he is forced to slow down if only to preserve his spinal column in the shape he inherited it at birth. You can get round this problem by designing a suspension system rather like they have on the Mercedes Unimog. Just because the first tractors built did not have springs, there is no reason why you should do the same today.

Combines. Give us a combine monitor which does what it is meant to do. Instead of telling us that we are throwing grain over the back because we went too fast 15 seconds ago, tell us that unless we slow down now, we shall be throwing grain over the back in fifteen seconds time. We need to be told before and not after the problem has arisen. The nearer to the front of the combine the monitor is positioned, the more effective it will be.

Design a self-steering device which means that the whole length of the cutterbar can be used rather than leaving 18 inches empty as is always the case today. No combine driver can keep his knife at the edge of the crop for more than a few minutes at a time and he is so concerned not to leave standing corn that he always keeps a good margin spare on the knife. Solve this problem and you will increase the output of a combine by at least 10% immediately.

Think about incorporating straw so that when the day comes when we are not allowed to burn the stuff, your combines will not be caught unprepared. Give us a straw chopper which chops into smaller bits, and then give us a folding cultivator which, attached to the rear of the combine, will actually go into the stubble and prepare a tilth.

Balers. Keep thinking about straw and, in particular, how it can be used as a source of energy. Today the biggest single problem is that it is so expensive to collect and transport from the field, it is simply not worth the effort. But if you could build a baler which could produce straw bales weighing at least two hundredweight in a conventional shape, things would start to change very rapidly.

Straw burners. The technology of straw burning furnaces is still in its infancy. Even if you give us balers which produce very dense bales, we shall still need furnaces which are more efficient, safer and highly automated before we start buying them in any volume. Concentrate instead on a furnace which will only have to be fed once a week.

Perhaps these are all unrealistic pipe dreams, but I suspect that in some corner of a foreign field men in white coats are already fiddling about with things very similar. Anyway, think about it. You might even come up with some better ideas.

What Can We Do with Straw?

AUGUST 1981

As sure as God made little Conservationists, they're going to stop us burning straw. It may not be next year or the year after, but the day will come when the Bryant and May baler is as obsolete as spats or sock suspenders (apologies to any reader who wears either of these garments). So the sooner we all start thinking about straw the better. You will be appalled to hear that I have been exercising my tiny mind on the problem and have come up with some Good News and some Bad News.

First the Bad News. Forget about buying a straw burning boiler in spite of what the ads or your trendy neighbours may tell you. The boilers themselves are allright but we simply have not solved the problem of getting the straw from the field to the furnace. Today's bales were invented to help stockmen feed and litter down animals. They are made in balers which were a development of the old trussers, and manage to compress straw into light and fluffy bundles which most men can lift easily. What is needed is a bale which resembles me – heavy and dense. By the time you have baled your conventional bales, put them into flat eights, carted them off the field, taken them to the store, stacked them up, unstacked them, taken them to the boiler, loaded them into the boiler and had a quick drink, you have used far more energy than the straw will release when it is burnt. What is more, you have also taken a lot of time.

Mind you, having a straw-burning boiler will win you a lot of

Brownie Points with your local Friends of the Earth and, as a German friend said to me recently, "Every farmer has a small green spot in his heart". Green, in this context, means ecological rather than inexperienced. So unless you want to be elected to the Marion Shoard Canonisation Committee, forget about burning straw in your boiler until someone invents a baler which can produce normal shaped bales weighing at least two hundredweight.

So much for the Bad News, now for the Good News. You may have thought of barley straw as being an adequate filler for grateful ruminants. You were wrong. Break down the lignin and Hay (pun) Presto, you have a deliciously digestible fodder which is quite as good as medium-quality hay. The theory, of course, is far from new and farmers have been messing around with caustic soda, urea and other nasties for ages. But the solution to the problem appears to have been discovered by the clever Danes. Amidst a fanfare of trumpets and background music provided by a heavenly choir, we have just bought a machine which will double the digestibility and food value of our barley straw. If this all sounds like advertiser's guff, and a bit of wishful thinking, I must confess that we have yet to feed the stuff to our animals. However, I have been to Denmark where I visited several farmers who have used these machines (called Am Stra Verters) for three years now. I also chatted to the staff of the Bioteknik Institute who have proved (beyond a shadow of a doubt) that the process does actually double the digestibility of straw as the manufacturers claim.

The Am Stra Verter is like a very large oven, and the bale an equally outsize turkey. Place bale in oven and baste with liquid ammonia (the process is done automatically) for a few hours at 95 degrees centigrade. Allow to cool before removing bale 24 hours later, and serve to stock as you would with hay.

I do not know what this will cost, what with electricity and the ammonia to pay for, but I am assured that it will work out as substantially less than equivalent hay and, what is more, there are none of the problems of haymaking.

The implication for arable farmers is, of course, immense. Suddenly we find that out of the back of the combine is pouring a valuable fodder crop just waiting to be used. Once again the so-called prairies of East Anglia could be littered with sheep and Flexinet, and the yards will be full of bullocks during the winter.

One question remained to be answered. How to get the bales from the combine to the Am Stra Verter? We use large round bales, and transport has always been a bit of a headache. In the past it has been necessary to have one Sanderson in the field, one long trailer doing the moving, and another Sanderson to unload at the other end where the bales are to be used (or stacked). Last year we tried out a French machine made by Benac, but it struck me as being a bit too complicated, too expensive and I was also worried about its strength.

Now, Lo and Behold, this problem appears to have been solved by an English company – which is itself an exciting event. Standens of Ely have been making a big effort to pull themselves together in recent years, and I think they are succeeding. As well as some pretty exciting sugar beet and potato harvesting machinery which they are bringing out this year, they have also produced their Rondo bale carrier. It is a 40 foot long device which, when backed over a row of seven bales, squeezes them and can carry them around very happily until they are dumped by releasing the "bomb doors". It is a machine which appears to be both simple and strong; the only snag is the length which will make it difficult for anyone with a small farmyard.

I have now bought both these two machines and, as a result, we shall abolish both hay and silage this year. Our sheep and cattle will find themselves on a diet which consists solely of treated straw, together with some beet pulp when necessary. There must be a snag or two waiting for us, and I have no doubt that we shall find it soon enough. But in the meantime I am trying to calculate how many animals we need to eat up all our straw and thrashed ryegrass. I hope that the West Country auctioneers take credit cards. That will do very nicely, sir.

I was, as usual, unduly pessimistic about the future of straw burning. Laws have been passed which tighten up on the practice, but nobody has actually stopped farmers burning. Maybe this will still come about – probably as a result of some horrendous straw burning-induced accident. But it hasn't happened yet. The Am Stra Verter was a good idea but lasted only three years at Thriplow. With a large flock of sheep, its throughput was too small. We eventually changed over to having ammonia injected into the bales which were covered by a long plastic "sausage skin".

A New Deal for Tenants?

SEPTEMBER 1981

The Country Landowners Association and the National Farmers Union have agreed to agree about tenancies. How very agreeable of both of them. It is wonderful news for everyone in farming – always assuming, of course, that the present government can be persuaded to introduce the legislation and the opposition can be persuaded not to repeal it. But for the purposes of this discussion we shall conveniently ignore these two minor difficulties and concentrate on what this means to the industry.

The clock will be turned back to the palmy days before the Agriculture (Miscellaneous Provisions) Act became law and gave tenants the right to succeed for up to three generations. Under the new agreement tenancies would once again last for only a single lifetime, and it is also suggested that a few fixed-term tenancies, for up to five years, be introduced to give young men a trial run.

It is not hard to see why everyone is happy. Young men who had long since given up all hope of finding a farm are dusting off their old copies of John Nix★. Small tenants are besieging their bank managers with requests for bigger overdrafts in preparation for the next step up what is invariably called the Farming Ladder. Large tenants are relishing the prospect of the next rent review because the arbitrators have been told they must ignore the scarcity value element when settling a new rent. Landlords in the Great Houses are exultant because once again they will be able to let the estate without losing control of it for up to 100 years. Throughout the length and breadth of the country happy smiling farmers are rejoicing. Except me. I happen to think that everything I have written above is rubbish and will not happen. What is more, the only people who will really benefit are my old friends, the land agents.

Consider the following scenario which is, of course, totally fictitious. Any similarity with living persons is not necessarily accidental. The 500 acre Home Farm has just become vacant

★ The economic guru of Wye College whose annual "Farm Management Pocketbook", is required reading for the entire farming industry.

because the old tenant died without leaving an heir. The retired Wing Commander who owns the land has never wanted to farm himself and so assumes he will re-let to a new tenant. He is keener than ever because his local CLA has told him that the agreement with the NFU has made tenancies safe again. The Wing Commander therefore summons his faithful land agent, who is a junior partner in a national firm. Imagine the Wing Commander's surprise when the land agent clears his throat and begins, "Of course, Wing Commander, we are here to act on your behalf and will therefore do as you wish. However, before putting the Home Farm out to tender as you suggested, I feel it prudent to set a few facts down before you come to any decision. As far as letting is concerned, you must be aware that even though the succession of tenancies has been repealed, you must still assume that the new tenant will stay on for his lifetime and there is a chance, however small, that during this period new legislation will be introduced favouring tenants at the expense of landowners such as yourself. In addition you will, of course, be reducing the value of your land by up to 25% and, even more important, you will be restricting your own freedom of action by letting to an agricultural tenant. Your rents will, of course, be taxed as unearned income. Thus it is the opinion of my firm that, notwithstanding the fact that tenancy succession has been repealed, you should think twice before re-letting."

The Wing Commander is a bit taken aback, but he does not have time to blink before the land agent continues, "We therefore propose the following course of action. Our Farms department should undertake a detailed survey of Home Farm to establish its potential as a farming enterprise. On the basis of this survey we should consider whether or not to set up a partnership between yourself and a neighbouring farmer, or one of the large farming companies who specialise in taking over farms like this. We would also consider whether or not our own farms department should not look after it on your behalf. You will find our fees small and our skill great. At all events we would not propose that you create a tenancy. You will retain the freehold value and great freedom of action. Most important to you, Wing Commander, the income you receive will be that of a working farmer and it will be taxed as earned rather than unearned."

The Wing Commander, none of whose medals were won for mental agility, realises that the agreement between the NFU and the CLA matters not a damn when it comes to his own Home Farm.

The City Institutions are equally unimpressed with the agreement. Even more than the Wing Commander, they are loath to reduce the value of their asset by creating a tenancy, and they also wish to retain maximum flexibility should they ever wish to sell. Thus the men in pinstripes will continue to use their land agents to protect their interests and to run the estates without tenancies whenever possible.

Perhaps I am wrong and once again the landlord-tenant system will flourish in the land. As usual in agriculture today, the land agents hold the key. I wonder how they will use it.

Eventually the Tory government adopted many of the points raised by the CLA-NFU agreement when it repealed the succession of tenancy in its new legislation. There has not so far been a great upsurge in tenancies. On the contrary. While farmers are making a lot of money it makes sense for landlords either to farm themselves, or at least to share the profits by creating partnerships (not tenancies). Now, however, that the industry is no longer making good profits, landlords will gradually see the point to allowing the farmer to farm once again. Tenancies will indeed return, but this will have nothing to do with the artificial agreement reached by the CLA and the NFU.

One Farm – Two Computers

OCTOBER 1981

If there's one thing better than having one computer on the farm it's having two of them. And that is precisely what we have got. In a single fun-filled week in early July we took delivery of both an Apple II and a Rockwell Aim and found ourselves well and truly in the age of the microchip. If you think these are just the demented ravings of a self-confessed gadget freak, you may well be right. Even I would never claim that a computer will make a bad farmer better, but they will certainly make life more interesting and farming more fun.

The Rockwell Aim is a small computer and it came as part of the weighbridge which we installed at the grainstore. In the past we guessed the weights from individual fields by seeing how far up the bins the grain came. It was all rather unsatisfactory as it never took any account of the bushel weight and, as a result, we were often 10% adrift in our estimates. To have an accurate idea, it was necessary to wait until the bins had been emptied and the corn had gone over someone else's weighbridge. For years I dreamed of having our own weighbridge, but whenever I looked into them I found that the big ones were too expensive and the small ones too inaccurate. But Bean Electronics of Ely seem to have solved the problem by building an above-ground bridge (which cuts down the cost of site work) and linking it to the computer. The advantage of the Rockwell Aim is that each morning you feed in the tare weights of the lorries and trailers, and throughout the day it remembers all the information so you receive an instant new weight. The computer will also automatically adjust the weight of the grain to 15.5% moisture and, as a result, we can see how much we shall have to sell after drying.

The computer manages to keep each field separate in its memory and can add up the different totals whenever you want to know what the combines have done that day. It also does all the normal jobs of weighing lorries in and out when they come to collect corn or deliver fertiliser. As with all computers, it devours paper at an alarming rate, but it does provide tickets for the lorry drivers to take with them, and this alone is a feature which makes me sleep better at night. I have often wondered whether we would ever know if a ton or so fell off the back of a lorry between our grainstore and the merchant's yard.

Our other computer is a cleverer machine. After looking round at most of the available farm computers, I finally settled on an Apple provided by Paul Scudamore's Farmplan at Ross-on-Wye. The cost was reasonable at just over £5000 including the software, and there was also the reassuring fact that Farmplan have more computers on farms than any other company. Unlike the Rockwell Aim, which only has a keyboard and a roll of paper, the Apple looks like the real McCoy with its green TV screen, printer and two disc drives. I don't know what its presence in the office does for visiting reps but, to misquote the Duke of Wellington, it certainly impresses me.

It is early days so far and we have not got the accounts onto the computer yet, although this was the main reason for buying it. But in the first couple of months I had a wonderful time. When harvest became too frantic I would retreat to the keyboard and the blinking TV screen and calm myself down with an hour or two of computing. It must be cheaper than sedatives.

I started rather timidly with the Arable Program and for several evenings thought I had made one of my bigger mistakes. Every time I thought I had got the hang of it, the screen would flash ERROR at me and I had to start all over again. The fact that I never even got O Level maths may have had something to do with this, I thought. But within a few days something wonderful started to happen. Instead of having a sulking machine stare blankly back at me, everything began to go right and I realised that I had been trying to be far too clever. I had not bothered to read the instructions to the letter and instead had skipped round merrily relying on my enormous intelligence and intuitive feel. These, by the way, are just the things you should not rely on when trying to work a computer for the first time. After following the instructions to the letter, I began to feel like a man who realises that after hours of practice on a piano he can at last play a tune.

Eureka. It all went right and I found that, having spent days feeding in information about next year's cropping and the price of fertilisers and herbicides, it was now able to answer the questions I was asking. In a euphoric whirl I found that I now craved information as a drug addict needs heroin. I needed it not because it would be useful, but because it was available. Thus I fed in all our monthly rainfall records for the past 53 years and was able to ask the computer to arrange the past 52 Decembers in order of wetness. I put in all the farm vehicles and sorted them in a twinkling in order of age, horsepower or both. I could see how much Dicurane we would need next year, how much it would cost and when we would have to pay for it. The more questions I asked, the better it seemed to work and the more its appetite for raw data increased.

After the initial excitement wore off, I began to be a bit more discriminating. I fed in all our field records for the past year and then gave it the yields which our weighbridge had provided. One day both computers will be able to talk to each other, but until this happens I am still needed to pass information from one to the other. Once the Apple has the necessary data, I was able to ask it all sorts of interesting questions which I could have only found out in the old days if I had been able to set aside an entire afternoon to do the calculations. I asked the computer, for example, to compare the winter barley yields from fields which had received an autumn insecticide against those which had not. The results seemed to suggest that a dose of Metasystox paid excellent dividends, and we shall certainly spray all fields this year. I was able to compare yields with herbicide applications and, as a result, am rather unhappy about Stomp when compared to Chandor.

I must, however, emphasise the point which I made earlier. Computers will not make me a good farmer, nor will they increase profits. Indeed, they will almost certainly not save either time or labour. But what they will do is to provide the sort of information I never had time to dig out in the old days. I know how much it rained the day I was born, and how many horsepower the seventh oldest tractor has. My farming may not be up to much, but my cocktail party conversation has improved enormously.

We now have four computers on the farm. Instead of 48 kilobytes of RAM, they have 1000 kilobytes. Such is progress. The Bean weighbridge never lived up to its promise. It was highly unreliable and needed constant maintenance. After a few years the manufacturers went bankrupt and we spent £25,000 putting in a proper, weights-and-measures-approved Avery bridge which has behaved perfectly ever since.

Importing Chemicals from France

NOVEMBER 1981

"Is it legal?" they all asked me. Farmers in both England and Germany reacted as if I were planning to import heroin. I began to wonder whether I should not first check with the Mafia before bringing herbicides into this country from France. I needn't have worried as I was very far from being the first person in England to do so. Various other clever people had been bringing Avadex and Dicurane by the lorry load for some weeks before I got the urge. The snag was that these people were onto a good thing, and the last thing they needed was to have their techniques and their sources publicised for other farmers to copy. When I tried to find out more about these operations, I soon began to run into a mist of vagueness. Even journalists who had been helpful in telling me what had been happening suddenly became uncertain when I asked for names and phone numbers.

There was nothing for it; I either had to do it myself or shut up. In the most unlikely event that I decided to shut up, I would have to buy from my normal chemical supplier or else try and make contact with one of these slightly secretive importers and pay them a pretty large chunk of the saving they were obtaining for me. Ostensibly I would only be paying for the transport, but in practice I would be asked to cough up half the difference between the French and English price. This was, I reckoned, a bit excessive.

Together with most other farmers, I suspect that we have felt that the Common Market was not directly relevant to us. Of course I exclude the CAP from these thoughts because I spend most of my waking hours thanking Providence (or whoever) for the Intervention system, FHDS and various other odds and ends which put money in my pocket. But when it comes to the Common Market itself, as opposed to the CAP, it seems to have about as much effect on my life as does NATO, the UN or the NFU. Tariff barriers have never meant a lot to me, and import duty only impinges on my pea-sized brain when I buy a bottle of duty-free booze before feeling sick on a Hovercraft. Thus it isn't altogether surprising that during the course of the year I do not give a lot of thought to how I can make use of the Common Market.

In addition to being ignorant about the Common Market, I also happened to think that I was a pretty good businessman. I wouldn't put myself in the Anthony Rosen class but, with my normal retiring modesty, I reckoned that I was well above average. I smugly assumed that when it came to buying there weren't many people keener than me, and when it came to selling I could hold my own with the best of them. We all have our little fantasies, and that was just part of mine.

The trouble is that I am not really a very good businessman and it hurts a bit to realise it. Not only do I lack the sharpness which is necessary but, infinitely more important, I am just downright provincial. My horizons are both narrow and small – much as you would expect to find in a 19th century yeoman, but very far from those you would associate with the sort of self-important agribusiness whizzkid I aspired to be. I am, in short, a country bumpkin with delusions of grandeur.

Just as the 19th century yeoman saw his world as being limited by his own village and the nearest market town, so also did I think that eastern England contained all I would ever need when it came to running the farm. Whenever I needed a quote I would ring a few numbers and act accordingly. There were the odd times when we sold dried lucerne to Cheshire and cattle to Northumberland, and I felt like an international trader. Normally we bought our machines and fertilisers from people in a 20 mile radius, and we sold our corn in only a slightly bigger area.

Thanks to my expedition to France, all this has been placed firmly into perspective. With the minimum of fuss and bother, I have realised that it is now as easy to ask for a quote from a French merchant as it is from one down the road. The old worries about Crossing the Channel, Import Duty and Speaking a Foreign Language (if there's money at stake they'll find someone to speak English) no longer apply. As a result I have resolved to widen my horizons and start thinking like a European and not a South Cambridgeshire version of Dan Archer.

It is now time to get in the car again and head for Dover. Once on the other side, I shall take a leisurely trip through France, Belgium,

Holland and Germany looking for nice friendly agricultural merchants. We'll have a drink or two and exchange phone numbers. Back home again, I shall phone them whenever I need anything just to check that the prices I am quoted by the local merchants are roughly in line with what is available on the Continent. I don't expect to have to take a lorry to Europe very often because it will need a 15% – and preferably a 20% – gap to make the journey worthwhile. Nevertheless, I am convinced that there will be the odd occasion when, for a variety of reasons, one can buy material far cheaper in Europe than one can in this country. I won't only confine my attentions to the other side of the Channel. People like Mole Valley Farmers probably have almost as big a role to play in eastern England as they do in Devon, and I've no doubt that there are some other pretty keen suppliers lurking all over this country.

The results of all this activity can only be good for this farm as I try to contain costs during the next few years. They also add a bit of variety to my life which is no bad thing because, like yours, it is mean, brutish and short.

Our importing Avadex and Dicurane, together with the TV film made of the operation by Anglia Television's Farming Diary, had a profound effect on British agriculture and the agrochemical business. Prices of autumn herbicides dropped by 15% and millions of pounds were wiped off the profits of the multinational agrochemical manufacturers. For many years I was not a popular man among the boardrooms of Ciba-Geigy and the other agrochemical giants.

NFU – *Members and Memos*

DECEMBER 1981

It shows what a naive fool I am to be surprised in the first place. Nevertheless the inflexibility, indifference and sheer inertia of the National Farmers Union never ceases to amaze me. I am being a bit unfair because the same criticism could probably be aimed at most of the large organisations in the world and thus would apply to the Transport and General Workers' Union or the Archdiocese of Chicago, not to mention the Bulgarian Communist Party and Federation of Flying Fish Filleters. The point is, however, that nobody asks me to pay a large annual subscription to these other groups so I don't really care how idiotically they behave. But with the NFU it is another matter.

I can never understand how the NFU succeeds at being so hopeless at national level and yet so good at local level. It's not just my natural sycophancy which makes me say that if Agriculture House went up in a puff of smoke one day and only the County Branches remained, the world would be a lot better place. The local officials of the union are the precise opposite of their colleagues in Knightsbridge; they are practical, down to earth, sympathetic and extremely useful. My own County Secretary (I hope being praised won't jeopardise his career) has on several occasions warned me against some stupid action I was proposing, and has even helped to get me out of some jams which only I got myself into. Likewise the Branch Committee, of which I am an infrequent attender, seems to be valuable, sensible and practical. If only I could say the same about the men who view the world from their offices overlooking Hyde Park, and whose only contact with the world seems to be receiving Resolutions and having a drink with a Headquarters Delegate. Of course, there are some exceptions at Agriculture House who do useful work and even seem to like farmers. I won't embarrass them by using their names, but I'm sure they know who they are and I exclude them from the remarks which follow.

The problem seems to be not simply that these men are cut off both physically and mentally from their members, but that they spend too much time trying to understand the points of view of those people whose interests conflict with NFU members. Some years ago I was very concerned with the problem of cereal seed contracts and, as a result, spent quite a bit of time in Agriculture House speaking to the relevant members of the staff. The reception I received could be summarised as follows:—

1. Only troublemakers come to Agriculture House. You must be a troublemaker.

2. Go through "Normal Channels". Get your Branch to pass a resolution and send it to the County Branch. Get the County

Branch to pass it and send it to headquarters. Then we might think about the problem. Or, then again, we might not.

3. You are imagining the problem. We at Agriculture House are doing a wonderful job and it shows how stupid you are to think otherwise.

4. You don't understand the complexities of the problem because you are only a farmer. We at Agriculture House have to see all sides of the problem and it's far more complicated than you think.

5. UKASTA★ would never accept your ideas. We know because we talk to UKASTA and you don't.

Of all these, it was the last one which distressed me most because it became clear that the staffs of UKASTA and the NFU cared more about keeping each other happy than they did about their members. Maybe I shouldn't have been so surprised because the NFU staff met their UKASTA opposite numbers far more often than they met working farmers. They lunched, drank, chatted and lunched again with UKASTA, and who can really blame them for keeping everything quiet, calm and civilised? To this day the NFU-approved cereal seed contract is a document written by UKASTA for UKASTA's own convenience. I rather suspect that the Grain Contract Notes are not entirely dissimilar, but try asking the chaps at Agriculture House why this is and you will be able to tick off the five points I have listed above.

The other month I once again came into contact with Agriculture House when I was trying to find out about importing Dicurane and Avadex from France. With the exception of a single man at headquarters who was clear, keen and helpful, I was told the following:–

1. The whole subject is very complicated. We are investigating the matter and will let you know.

2. Take the matter up with your Local Branch and thence to your County Branch. We should not really deal with individuals like you.

★ United Kingdom Agricutural Supply Association. The Merchants' organisation.

3. It may or may not be illegal to import/use these chemicals. We don't know yet. Don't do anything for the time being.

4. Speak to your local ADAS man and your local MAFF man and your local BASIS chemical dealer.

5. Stop bothering us. We are busy. Go back to your farm.

Had I taken any of the advice I was offered by Agriculture House, my corn would have been planted, germinated and combined before I would have heard anything. And even then the reply would have been so vague and guarded that it would have been irrelevant. So once again I decided to ignore Agriculture House, and I definitely did not go and speak to my local BASIS dealer, who would certainly have told me not to import the stuff. In common with a lot of other farmers who were bringing in herbicides from across the Channel, I went ahead and bought French Dicurane. I was certainly not the first chap to do so, and I claim no credit, but the facts remain that the prices of herbicides came down for everybody thanks entirely to the actions of many farmers who took the initiative that the NFU refused to face. Indeed, if the people at Agriculture House had their way, they would still be discussing the complex problems with the chemical manufacturers. By now, it is true, they might have issued an Interim Report.

The prices, mind you, would not have come down – but that would not worry the worthies of Agriculture House because it is not part of their job to do anything like this. When in doubt they send a memo, and if it ever comes to a choice between NFU members and NFU memos, the memos seem to win. The members just go on paying their subscriptions.

Harvest 1981

JANUARY 1982

The wisest man I have ever met in agriculture is a German. I once asked him what single piece of advice he would give farmers and he sat and stared at the ceiling as he thought. After a minute or so he said, "I would tell them to forget last year." Ever since then I have been trying to forget last year, but it is a lot more difficult than you might imagine. All farmers tend to do this year what they should have done last year, and they ignore the lessons of the past decade. You only have to look at all the reservoirs which were built in 1977 to see what I mean.

So I don't suppose I should be too depressed about the year which has just finished, but I can't help feeling it was a bit of an anti-climax. Harvest was actually pretty good but, because it was slightly smaller than our record 1979 vintage, I felt disappointed. I had somehow assumed that we would continue from where we had left off the year before. It is, of course, stupid to suppose that one year's record yields will become the next year's average, but it is surprising how often this has actually happened in the recent past.

Our wheats dropped a couple of hundredweight to average 67, and one field of second year Brigand actually fell below the magic three tons per acre mark – which only a few years ago I had considered to be the unattainable target. But to set against that, the Avalons did well at 70cwt. Three fields of Norman, which had looked spectacular throughout the summer, managed to average "only" 74cwt when I had convinced myself (never a difficult task) that they would comfortably exceed 80cwt. Indeed, only our single field of Longbow managed to do just this, and then only after the moisture had been adjusted to 15.5%. This year we shall be pressing ahead with new varieties to keep ahead of the game in the seed-growing business. Out will go Brigand and in will come Fenman and Avocet.

The barleys also dropped by a couple of hundredweight on average, but this fact is a bit misleading because both Igri and Sonja maintained their yields at 53 and 51 hundredweight respectively. Poor Maris Otter, however, let the average down badly as its yield dropped to a five year low of 41cwt. Quite what caused this will always remain a mystery, but I am sure a combination of barley yellow dwarf virus together with mosaic virus did a lot of damage. This last problem is the one which worries me more than all the other arable headaches – with the exception of sterile brome – put together. Nobody seems to know what causes it or how to prevent it. So Otter is definitely on probation this year and instead we are growing a lot of Tipper, which is Nickerson's new creation. They tell us it combines Otter's malting quality with Igri's yield; I hope they are right but I would be satisfied with less. So far I am a bit nervous because Tipper's resistance to Isoproturon appears a bit dodgy. Last autumn we nearly killed two fields of the variety after pre-emergent Tolkan, and so I'm keeping a very close eye on it until we know more details.

The other crops on the farm were pretty mixed. Herbage seed produced some poor results with yields lower than in the past few years. This is, of course, good news for the Trade because of the glut on the market. But low yields, and even lower prices, won't help the crop next year. Nevertheless, herbage seed has always been a crop to stick with and not to get in and out of with the peaks and troughs. Rape, on the other hand, managed to provide the one truly memorable disaster of the season. After the previous harvest's average of 28cwt, I felt that at last we had mastered the crop. I now realise how dumb I am when we scraped 15cwt per acre this year. Storms and snow at flowering did not help matters, but I still cannot understand how we did so badly. Cabbage stem flea beetle hit us hard and, as a result, this year we shall be readier to spray than we have been in the past. We are growing a new variety from the breeders of Jet Neuf called Lingot. Whether it will actually be an improvement remains to be seen. Watch this space.

If rape gave us the bad news, then at least sugar beet restored the balance with the best yields we have had in the past decade. It shows how poor we have been when we start to get excited by an average of 16.5 tons per acre, but for the first time since I started farming the crop has shown a genuine profit. In the light of this fact, I must admit rather sheepishly that I chose this year of all years to reduce our beet acreage by a third. It takes real talent to reduce the acreage on the one year when you make a profit. We grew peas instead, which did unspectacularly but did at least provide a good entry for winter corn. At least they did better than winter beans on some other farms in the area which must qualify as the Disaster of the Year with yields dropping as low as 6 hundredweight per acre even after half a dozen applications of Benlate to control chocolate spot.

So what did I learn? Persist with early drilling in spite of the fact that it did not pay off last year. Spray against barley yellow dwarf virus on all crops drilled before October 12th. Plough headlands against brome. Forget about barley growth regulators as they are simply not worth the money. Keep on with the low-dose high pressure Betanal on sugar beet. Try not to upset agrochemical manufacturers. Keep calm at all times.

Even back in 1982 I was, it appears, worried about sterile brome. Since then it has metamorphosed into our most serious weed problem – apparently resistant to burning, ploughing and all herbicides.

It's Not Much Fun Being a Hypocrite

MARCH 1982

It's not much fun being a hypocrite but, like most farmers, it comes naturally to me. More than any other profession – with the exception of politicians who actually make a living out of it – farmers are better at saying one thing and doing the other without anyone noticing. No wonder the general public gets a bit fed up when we complain that our prices are not high enough or our profits are too low. When I, as an arable farmer, complain that my income has been falling for the past four years (in real terms at least) I expect a sympathetic public to reach for their violins and Kleenex. What is more, I hope that not only will the Brussels bigwigs take note and increase the support prices, but the taxpaying public will dig deeper into their pockets to help me out of what I like to think of as impending poverty. The observation which nobody ever seems to make is that if I can still survive after four years of falling incomes, it only shows how grossly overpaid I must have been four years ago. But was I satisfied four years ago? Looking back – never a difficult task – I suppose I was, but at the time the NFU and the rest of us were undoubtedly bleating that disaster was looming round the corner.

I suppose, however, that if you pay a large organisation to look after your interests, you should not be surprised if they take their job seriously and actually try to convince a sceptical public that if the wolf is not really at the door today, it might be tomorrow. And so on and so on. Imagine how trying it must be for the people at Agriculture House, who are paid to protect farmers' interests, to realise that since no hardship actually exists, they will either have to declare themselves redundant or to invent the hardship. Given that stark choice, it is small wonder that the arable sector has always been presented by the Union as being on the edge of disaster and despair. The snag is that today even the arable sector has serious problems and our representatives should now be telling the world of our hardships. But people who cry "wolf" too often should not be surprised when the rest of the world yawns.

Even ordinary hypocritical farmers like me are only too happy to ignore facts which we find inconvenient. I am, of course, passionately against cereal substitutes being imported into this country and thus forcing down the price of feed grains. I am also against cheap French turkeys coming in at ludicrously low prices which threaten our own turkey producers. I will fight against the cheap imports of Dutch vegetables because I know that they are grossly subsidised by low energy prices. Danish bacon too is something which should be carefully controlled because of the damage it has done to our own bacon producers, and as for French Golden Delicious Apples, the less said the better. I could go on like this for a very long time, but if I did you might think that I too had been contaminated by the NFU infection whereby imports which are a direct threat to British farmers should either be stopped altogether or curtailed at very least.

Imports which farmers themselves wish to buy are a very different matter. The EEC should be used as the Treaty of Rome always intended. It is, after all, a free trade area and so if I can buy Dicurane cheaper in France I should lose no time in doing so. If the producer is so shortsighted or inefficient as to allow a price differential, I can hardly be blamed for this. Indeed, as a businessman it is almost my duty to buy as cheaply as possible. Likewise with tractors and other machinery. If I see a bargain lurking in a Danish showroom who can blame me for whizzing over with a low-loader and saving myself a small fortune? Too bad on the importer or the manufacturer, I tell myself. The name of the game is, and always has been, the Survival of the Fittest. I cannot allow myself to pay more money than necessary simply because some government wants to protect a lame-duck industry. No, when it comes to looking after our own interests, we farmers are in no doubt at all that we should let the cold winds of competition blow as widely as possible. Gone are the protestations of poverty. No longer do we hear about unfair competition. As if by some magic, all our objections evaporate as we realise how wonderful it is for the poacher to dress up like a gamekeeper. To hell with our principles; this is business.

For sheer hypocrisy it is not just hard to beat, it is downright impossible. How we can insist on the one hand that apples and turkeys should be kept out, and at the same time reserve the right to bring in tractors and chemicals, is simply mind-boggling. There is only one word for it and that is the Yiddish expression "chutzpah," which has no adequate English translation other than, possibly, Outrageous Gall. An example of "chutzpah" was when a man who had murdered both his mother and his father asked for clemency from the judge on the grounds that he was an orphan. British farmers take note.

> *Nothing has changed. Farmers still apply a double standard to all their transactions. When they sell milling wheat forward to a merchant and cannot deliver, they feel they should be let off. When the merchant sells them cheap fertiliser and cannot deliver, they reach for their solicitors.*

Red-hot Buyers?

APRIL 1982

There isn't a lot we can do about inflation. Of course, we can push for higher prices. The NFU does that in its sleep. We can try and cut our expenses to the minimum, but that is always easier to talk about than to do. But there is one aspect of farming where our performance has been very bad indeed: buying. Just as everyone thinks that they are above average drivers, so also do all farmers think that they are red hot buyers. But, as usual, we are all kidding ourselves. The fact is that we have two things which conspire against us: the farmer's love of secrecy and an almost total lack of information.

While all farmers love showing their farms to other farmers, they hate talking about the financial nitty-gritties. They may occasionally boast about the price they received for some malting barley, but they only talk about their occasional triumphs. They never ever mention the price they pay for their inputs. Not only are they very secretive, but they also vaguely believe that they have probably done better than their neighbour because of phrases like "This is, of course, a special price for you alone so I'd be grateful if you'd keep it to yourself."

The lack of information is even more striking. When you consider all the market information which is available to farmers when they are selling their produce, you see how little there is for people trying to buy things. You can read it in magazines or listen to the radio to find out how much calves made at Sturminster Newton yesterday or barley fetched at Bury St Edmunds, but when did you last hear about the price of Fubol, Flexinet or a Ford 6610 tractor? True, you can pick up the phone and get a quote from your friendly local dealer, but how will you know whether he is really offering you a keen price? You could always compare notes with your neighbours but, as I have already mentioned, they are not usually very keen to talk about the prices they pay. So all you can do is ring round your normal suppliers and take the lowest price you are offered in the hopes that it is the best you can do. In theory, of course, the answer is a co-operative buying group, but in practice I find that co-ops only pay lip service to the idea of low prices for their customers (sorry, members). What they really care about is high profits (and hence high prices) for themselves.

But if information is hard to come by in this country, just think how much more ignorant we are about prices abroad. We hear vague stories about Grey Imports of tractors or chemicals, and a few of us actually mess about importing the odd load or two for our farms. If only we knew the sort of prices we should be aiming at, we would suddenly realise that what we fondly imagined was a keen price was, in practice, nothing of the sort. Mind you, the trade would not like this at all because they depend on the fact that when the rep calls and offers a price, the farmer will keep it to himself. The rep, in other words, plays upon our desire for secrecy and turns it to his own advantage. Just imagine if all the prices in all the markets were also kept secret so that we only knew what our own animal made, and never knew what the others did. We would be utterly and completely at the mercy of the buyers.

It is time to change all this idiotic secrecy. We should pool all our information and ask the National Farmers Union to provide a service by publishing Guide Prices for different items. The chaps at Agriculture House should speak to their friends at COPA★ so that eventually every European country would provide similar figures

★ The European grouping of all farmers' unions.

at regular intervals. This way we could compare prices across the whole of Europe. No longer would a rep be able to rely on his farmer customers behaving like Trappist monks. Instead, we would break the habit of a lifetime and admit that the price we paid for Dicurane was actually higher than our neighbour's. It might damage our pride to know this, but it would do wonders for our overdrafts. It's up to the NFU to give a lead here. Or will they, as so often before, claim that "It is all too commercial for us"? I hope not, because someone should tell them that farming itself is occasionally commercial. I'm holding my breath.

This remains true today for, as usual, the jealous independence of farmers keeps them from sharing information with each other. Hence they often are the complacent and passive victims of any semi-skilled salesman.

Revolting Farmers

JUNE 1982

I had never before seen 100,000 revolting farmers trying to frighten a government. It was an opportunity I could not afford to miss even if it did mean getting up early in the morning.

The dawn was breaking over the rolling Picardy countryside when we arrived outside the Mairie in the village of Guignicourt. Fifty-five farmers were already there and were standing around in the early morning gloom before getting on board the bus which had been hired to take them to Paris for what was billed as the biggest demonstration of farmers France had ever seen.

The big farmers came in Audis and the peasants in their Deux Chevaux but, as we chatted on the coach, it soon became clear that none of them had ever been on a real live demo before. Neither had I. We were probably a bit nervous, and that might have explained the appearance of small bottles of cognac and calvados which were passed round the very overcrowded bus.

The Place de la Nation in Paris was already half full when we arrived. It was the noise and not the crowd which struck me first. It was as if World War Three was already well under way. Explosions, sirens and bird scarers all combined to make me wish I had stayed in bed that morning. It was never like this, I remembered fondly, with the good old NFU. Plumes of black smoke rose from the crowd and I assumed that some car had been set on fire by an angry mob. Any moment now the riot police would be here with their CS gas, truncheons and rubber bullets.

The banners began to be unfurled as the different groups from all over France manoeuvred into their prearranged positions for the march itself. It was like a geography lesson as the wine growers from Burgundy led sheep farmers from the Massif Central and dairymen from Normandy came behind the arable farmers from Aisne, with whom I had come on the bus that morning.

Most of the banners' slogans referred to the 16% increase in prices which the French farmers were demanding from Brussels. Others, however, attacked Madame Cresson and made rude remarks about her name (which means watercress). But the ones which disturbed me most were the banners which made it clear that the British should get out of the Common Market and stop holding up the price negotiations in Brussels. Mrs Thatcher, it seemed, was as much the object of their ire as Madame Cresson.

Slowly the procession set off down the Rue Voltaire, led by tractors and accompanied by the cacophony of explosions as well as the sound of empty milk churns being dragged along. For the next five hours the procession marched through Paris until it reached the old abattoirs at the Porte de Pantin. There Monsieur Guillaume, the leader of the FNSEA (the French equivalent to the NFU), addressed the crowd.

What effect this demonstration had on Madame Cresson in her offices at the Ministry of Agriculture in the Rue de Varenne is, of course, impossible to assess. When I had spoken to her two weeks earlier she made it clear that she too wanted the extra 16% on farm prices and that it was only the British who were holding things up in order to get their way on the budget problem. Perhaps the demonstration was to frighten the European Commission even more than the French government.

At the end of the day I was left with the abiding impression that the people who had really invented the modern revolution had clearly not lost their talent for mass demonstrations. There had been no violence and not a single policeman was to be seen. So my fears had been unnecessary. I was disappointed in a way because I was looking forward to hearing Madame Cresson say, "If they haven't any bread, let them eat manioc." But I have developed a taste for big demonstrations now and my NFU branch meetings will never be the same again.

Madame Cresson wins my prize for the nicest Minister of Agriculture. Elegant, attractive, and speaking perfect English, she charmed me on the one occasion I met her in her office. Her daughter, who was equally attractive, later spent the summer at Thriplow rogueing wild oats and breaking hearts.

Why Not Simplify Your Farm?

JULY 1982

The question sent shivers down my spine – "How would you manage if you received only the world market price for your wheat?" My immediate reaction was to go red in the face and splutter protests. But the question, which was a serious one, could not – and should not – be laughed off.

I have spent a lot of time this year looking at farms on the other side of the Atlantic, and the more I see, the more uneasy I have become about European farming. One day the tax-paying public is going to wake up with a start and decide that it is fed up with the Common Agricultural Policy. Until this actually happens, of course, I shall continue accepting subsidies with alacrity and gratitude (in that order).

But what steps will I have to take on my farm if ever I have to compete on equal terms with North American wheat producers? The hallmark of American and Canadian farming is simplicity, based on low inputs and very low outputs. The question is whether I can use the same technique on my farm which, for the past six years, has consumed more and more seed, fertiliser, chemicals and money.

The first thing I shall have to do is lower my standard of living drastically. Indeed, my family might in some ways be the better for it. My Canadian counterpart cannot afford fancy cars and holidays but, in his own different ways, he manages to enjoy himself.

Of course, cutting down my own personal expenditure alone will not enable me to survive a wheat price of £70 per tonne. I shall have to do a lot more unpleasant things if I am to stand a chance. After my own creature comforts, the next thing to economise on will be the wages bill. I shall have to reduce our labour force by at least half. I shall have to sack six men, some of whom have worked on the farm all their lives. I myself will have to exchange my office chair for a tractor seat, and there would be no question of a fulltime farm secretary.

But sacking alone will not be enough. The entire cropping system must be changed drastically so that everything can go through the combine. Out will go sugar beet, beef cattle and sheep which are all labour-intensive. Instead we shall grow still more cereals, peas and oilseed rape. Out also will go our picturesque parkland in permanent grass, the areas of the farm we deliberately leave untouched, and probably quite a few hedges too. If we are asked to farm like the North Americans, nobody should be at all surprised if our farms look like North American farms. Conservationists be warned.

The next to feel the pinch will be the sellers of seed, fertiliser and chemicals. There will be no nonsense about paying fancy prices for a new variety of wheat just because it yields 2% more than the old variety. Plant breeders will soon discover that their prosperity is closely linked to mine. Neither will I use chemicals unless aphids threaten to destroy the crop completely. Weed control will be equally primitive, and I shall have to accept that our fields will be full of poppies and grass weeds. My pride in the tidiness of the farm will be a luxury I can no longer afford.

We shall cut our fertiliser by at least half, and possibly more. Twenty-five units of P and K in the seedbed will have to suffice, and no more than 80 units of N for the spring top-dressings. As a direct result, yields will start to fall rapidly. Within three years I would expect wheat to produce no more than 40cwt per acre and barley 30cwt.

The machinery dealer will do no better. I shall start by trying to trade in my smaller machines against a few very large ones, but this will not be easy because the trade-in prices will be so low I shall still have to find large chunks of cash. So I suppose that I shall simply have to make do with the machinery we have today. It is lucky that we are over-equipped.

So much for the variable costs. It won't be easy, but at least there is room for manoeuvre. The fixed costs will be where the trouble really starts. American land is, of course, relatively cheap. The price is around 50% of comparable land in this country, and the rents are equivalently low. Thus my competitor in Kansas or Saskatchewan has one huge advantage about which I can do absolutely nothing. I shall only be able to compete on equal terms if I can reduce my fixed costs to his level, and I don't really see how this is possible.

I shall, of course, expect a lot of sympathy from my Bank Manager when I tell him about my new policy. But at the end of the day he will still expect me to pay interest on my large overdraft. He will not look kindly on my suggestion that he lower the interest rate or postpone repayment. The Agricultural Mortgage Corporation, from whom I have borrowed money to buy expensive land, will be equally stern.

I wonder what my landlord will say, however, when he hears that wheat prices have fallen to £70 per tonne. Today, as I discuss this autumn's rent review with him, he seems pretty tough because he knows that if I give up the farm he can find plenty of other farmers to pay nearly twice what I am paying. But when the price of wheat really does come down, this will be a very different story. He will insist at first that I pay the agreed amount. But gradually, as the first signs of general collapse become clear, he will begin to realise that unless he lowers the rent, he will drive me into bankruptcy.

Whether or not I could actually survive this nightmare will depend on two factors. Will I be able and willing to reduce my own fixed costs by trimming my own lifestyle and sacking half the men on the farm? Will my landlord reduce the rent before I go bankrupt?

So I shall have to continue as I have done for the past decade. Indeed, the more the price of wheat falls, the more I shall have to try to squeeze those extra few hundredweight from the land. This will mean that I shall probably have to increase my inputs, and not reduce them. I shall have to ensure that, regardless of what they do in Kansas, I produce more wheat rather than less. It's a depressing thought because there is something about the simplicity of American system which appeals to me enormously.

Since this was written we have simplified the farm enormously.
The labour force has been reduced by 40% and the livestock has
disappeared completely. It makes me sad, but is inevitable if we
are to survive the new, hostile climate.

Just Figure This Out . . .

JULY 1982

The only time a farmer ever reduces his acreage is when it comes to paying his NFU subscription. Although the Treasurer presumably takes this into account when he sets the annual rate, it always amuses me because for the rest of his life the same farmer acts very differently.

As a rule we seem to round our acreages up very conveniently. I have never heard of a man who farmed 1842 acres, but there seem to be plenty who farm 1900, or even 2000 on an optimistic day. When the Wealth Tax comes it will, of course, be a very different matter, as it is now when you are negotiating a rent with your landlord's agent. At that moment you suddenly remember that what you tell your friends is 2000 acres, and what you know to be 1842, is actually far less. Remove woodlands, waste land, garden tracks, buildings, game strips you put down for pheasants, and concentrate instead on ploughable acres – and as if by magic the figure shrinks to 1531.

Even this is more than you tell the NFU Branch Secretary. He still thinks that you are farming 1265 acres. That was the figure your father told the NFU after the war and you have never got round to altering it.

But if you want to see a farmer at his wildest, you should start talking about yields. Given the slightest encouragement, he will tell you what Huntsman did on Bottom Field the year before last, and how that compared to Brigand which did not have chlormequat on the Twenty Acres. The Triumph which went for malting the year before last (you remember, the one which fetched 123) came off at 52 cwt. It would have been more if it had not been for that wet patch in the field. With an appreciative audience, preferably another farmer – although even a corn merchant will do, he can go on like this for hours. He knows what every field on the farm has yielded for the past ten years.

This would all be very convincing if it were not for two important facts which are often overlooked. The farmer has no means of weighing his corn, he also mixes up different fields, keeping only barley and wheat separate, and stores everything on the floor, not in bins. The truth is that when it comes to the yield of individual fields he does not have a clue. If you press him on this point he may tell you that he counts the trailers as they come from the field ("I can assure you, old chap, that I can estimate the contents of a trailer to within a few hundredweight"). This is nonsense. As the bushel weight alone can increase or decrease yield by up to 20%, not to mention other factors such as the amount in the trailer and the moisture content, it soon becomes clear that the only person the optimistic farmer is fooling is himself.

Then there is the super-scientific farmer. Not for him the crude guesswork of estimating trailer loads. He starts by drilling the required amount of seeds per square metre, or so he claims, and the moment the drill leaves the field he starts counting. His armoury consists of a wooden rectangle which encloses one square metre, a notebook (really trendy farmers have pocket dictating machines) and a pocket calculator.

Long before the thought of harvest is a nightmare in his wife's brain, he can tell you how many plants, tillers and grains a square metre he has on each field. He will adjust his nitrogen accordingly, compensate for winter rainfall, correct everything for the soil moisture deficit and make a complicated calculation of the amount of sunlight which was available for photosynthesis between first and second node.

If you are rash enough to visit him you will see charts on his office wall which graphically display enough garbage to keep the local sanitation department on overtime for a month. It is, in short, extremely impressive.

As usual, I have a nagging doubt. I accept the fact that in the heady days of Laloux and Schleswig-Holstein the super-scientific farmer really did do all this counting – but does he still do it? I believe that he is bored by the rigmarole and keeps up a front only to impress his neighbours. I think he guesses most of the figures and that, as often as not, he does not even put them down in his notebook. In fact he has reverted to type and is merely an old-fashioned, loud-mouthed and slightly dishonest farmer like you and me. No, perhaps not like you. I'm probably the only farmer who fits that description. The rest of you, I am sure, are much nicer.

Most farmers lie about their cereal yields and their lambing percentage. In all other respects they are neither more nor less honest than any other member of the human race.

The Bottom Rung

JULY 1982

There are certain things no farmer can afford to be against. Good husbandry, the NFU, harvest festivals, vintage port and low ground pressure vehicles. Recently another subject has joined the list. The odd thing is that not only do all farmers pay lip service to this new arrival, but so also do the land agents, the City Institutions, the CLA and even the Labour Party. Everyone who matters – except me. I am referring, of course, to what is called "The Bottom Rung on the Farming Ladder", or "New Blood in Agriculture" or "Giving the Young Farmers a Chance".

Before a lynch squad arrives at my door from the local Young Farmers, I had better explain that I am not actually against young men getting a chance to farm (in fact I am in favour of it). Since I myself was born with silver spoons in every available aperture, I can speak with total objectivity about this subject. I just happen to think that it is simply not feasible for young men to rent land today, even if it is desirable. And I certainly do not believe the people who claim, as the crocodile tears splash noisily into their gins and tonics, that if only we could have long-term tenancies everything would be all right. One large and well-known farmer has actually stated that if term tenancies were introduced, the flood of let land which would come onto the market would actually bring rents down. What a wonderful prospect! Lower rents, more let land and young farmers getting the farms they have only dreamed about.

Even if you accept, which I do, that the 1976 Act* has been an unmitigated disaster, I cannot possibly agree that all that is needed is a term tenancy of, say, 10 or 20 years for young farmers to get their chance. I shall (optimistically) forget the fact that it takes £300 per acre to get started, because I shall assume that this will not be a problem for an aspiring young farmer. What I do question, however, is how many landlords would actually grant tenancies to these young farmers.

---

* The Act, passed by the Labour Government, which gave tenants security of occupation for three generations. Welcomed by the somewhat surprised tenant farmers (few of whom ever vote Labour), it effectively stopped all landlords from even considering letting land. An example of legislation damaging precisely those whom it was intended to help.

If one of my neighbours offered some nearby land on a term tenancy, I would be very keen indeed to get hold of it; and so would most of the other farmers in the area. All of us have track records and overdraft facilities which would appeal mightily to the landlord when he came to select a tenant. Most of us would offer very big rents if we could farm the additional land with our existing staff and machinery. It would have to be a pretty odd landlord who would turn down a high rent from an established farmer in favour of a lower rent from a young man who was just starting in farming. But charitable men do exist in the world, and perhaps I am being cynical to suggest otherwise.

I am sceptical (to put it politely) of all these good intentions because term tenancies exist today. The partnership agreements which have so largely supplanted tenancies in recent years are many and varied, but two factors are common to all of them. They are for

limited periods and they all contain a payment which is a rent equivalent. Thus the landlord (sorry, partner) can terminate the tenancy (sorry, agreement) on a specific date and charges rent (sorry, share of the income) to the tenant (sorry, partner). I have yet to hear of a single partnership being given to a new entrant into farming. This leads me to suppose that, while it is convenient for landlords, land agents and City Institutions to claim how keen they are on new blood in farming, they do not actually do anything about it even when they have the chance.

One thing is certain, however, and that is, to ensure that young farmers get their chance in preference to fat cats like myself, legislation will have to be passed which will actually forbid landlords to let land to me, and will stipulate that the land is instead let to new entrants. Will all those who claim to be in favour of "New Blood in Farming" please say whether they would also favour this legislation?

The chances of young men entering agriculture are far better than when this was written. As prosperity and profits decline, people like me are less keen (and even less able) to take on new land. Hence the opportunities open up for those who wish to become farmers. But so does the likelihood of bankruptcy and failure. You can't have it both ways.

Buying a Seed Drill

AUGUST 1982

I am in the market for a new drill and I don't know what to buy. Our Massey Ferguson 30 is now six years old (she's a lovely runner, Sir) and, with over 12,000 acres on the clock it is time we replaced it.

It is a 30 row model which is about the right size for us because it will drill 20 acres at a single fill and can comfortably manage 100 acres a day in good conditions. The snag is that it was built before Massey Ferguson had heard of metrication. The row spacing is 6 7/8 inches which, if you multiply by 30, means that the drill is 206.25

inches wide. We use a tramline based on five of these widths and thus, you can readily understand, we have long since held the record for the oddest and least logical tramline in existence. But, be that as it may, the fact remains that, in spite of the peculiar row widths, the MF 30 is as good a piece of agricultural engineering as money can buy. And, glory of glories, it is British.

I suppose I could buy another MF 30 but this will mean either getting a smaller drill if I insist on the four metre model, or else perpetuating the nonsense of a 27 metre tramline by sticking to the same model. As an iron rule of my farming life, I never replace a machine with a smaller one, so I can rule out the four metre model. And, much as I like our big drill, I am forced to admit that drill technology has moved on apace since the MF 30 went to the drawing board. Today pneumatics have taken over from the traditional system.

In the early days of pneumatic drills, there were only two possibilities in this country: the Accord from Germany and the Tive from Sweden. The first is compact, fully mounted but relatively small. The other is big, strong but a mite cumbersome. I actually visited the Tive factory last year and was struck by two things; the quality of the construction and the price of alcohol in Sweden. The huge Tive hopper holds enough seed for 40 acres, which was most appealing, but I was not keen on the four tyres which would make life difficult in wet conditions. The Accord, even with its twin hoppers, did not have the capacity, but had the advantage of being fully mounted. The problem with both of them – or so I was informed by an ADAS man – was that neither could cope with trashy conditions very well.

If our new drill is to last six years, it will have to spend much of its life working on fields where the stubble lies loose on top because, when they stop us burning, I shall not revert to ploughing unless it becomes absolutely necessary. So, ability to work in trash is crucial.

At the Paris Show there appeared to be a lot more pneumatic drills than I had ever seen before, and I was struck by one called the Roger XT Turbo Grain Drill. Apart from any other feature, it was available as an eight metre drill which would mean that, with three runs, we could have a 24 metre tramline. Other features appeared to be attractive; it is fully mounted and can even be equipped with disc coulters which I happen to like.

Whether it is actually better than its competitors remains to be seen, but I think I shall be taking a close look at it during the summer. There are not many at work in England, so it may even be necessary to pop over to France and visit the factory. Long experience has taught me that Fridays are the best day to go on a business trip to France. The weekend usually delays my return for a couple of days, which is most inconvenient. I also have to endure the bad food and the Duty Free allowance.

> *I was, as it turned out, a bit optimistic about our new machine. The Roger drill only lasted three years. Its main problems were that it was really too heavy to be a mounted drill and that it was not quite strong enough. It was succeeded by a 12 metre Horsch Accord model which can comfortably cover 50 acres. After three seasons it is still giving excellent service.*

Bad News

SEPTEMBER 1982

"The trouble with you," said one of England's biggest flour millers, "is that you only tell us the good news." What he meant, of course, was that I am a loud-mouthed braggart, but he was too polite to put it that way. I knew just what my critic was driving at because I'm getting a bit twitchy these days. You all seem to feel that I spend too much time recounting my triumphs and gloating over the rest of the world. So, for those of you who think this way, there now follows a very abbreviated account of some of the cock-ups I have made in the very recent past. It is not a comprehensive list but it should give you some idea of why good farmers farm and bad ones write for magazines.

Some good news and some bad news. First the good news. Last year we had the best sugar beet year ever; the average yield was over 18 tonnes per acre. Now the bad news. In anticipation of this fact, I saw fit to reduce our beet acreage by one third. We grew peas instead and scraped one tonne per acre (which included a 23% wastage) to show a large loss. It displays a remarkable talent for a farmer to cut back on a crop the year it shows a thumping profit. The sensible people at Thriplow, including my wise and omnipotent father, had told me not to alter the cropping and were far from unhappy that I had made a mess of things.

Worse was yet to come. I signed a pea seed contract with a reputable merchant and assumed that all would be well. Things went very wrong and I finished up being taken to the cleaners. Suffice to say that at the end of the day I received less for the peas – even after the seed subsidy was paid – than I would if I had grown them for feed. The merchant, on the other hand, did magnificently out of the deal and I was left feeling stupid and poor, not to say sadder and (I hope) wiser. The experience has at least taught me that the choice of merchant is important, and I shall not be doing business with that firm again. They stuck to the contract terms and I have only myself to blame. So much for my enormous entrepreneurial flair.

The story of oilseed rape last year makes equally happy reading for all you sadists out there in readerland. In 1980 I realised that I was an expert at growing the crop. The yield of 28cwt per acre was positive proof that I was almost as good as I felt I should be. With my skill as a rape grower, the only problem was knowing how to spend the profits. There was, however, one snag. Last year we managed to scrape 15 cwt per acre and rape showed a huge loss in the accounts. Herbage seed, you may be pleased to know, also did very badly indeed, and certainly played its part in our steadily growing overdraft. As if that were not enough, we came badly unstuck with Maris Otter. The yield fell to a six year low of 39 cwt per acre and I realised that my skill with winter barley existed only in my lurid imagination.

Readers with memories which stretch back over a few months may remember the saga of the ewes which, this spring, started to die in quantities which scared me stiff. It was later diagnosed as grass staggers, an ailment which even the most average stockman might have recognised. I am not, as you will have realised by now, even a half decent stockman. In fact I am hopeless; but I am still interested and like to think I can learn from my mistakes.

This catalogue of catastrophes should, by now, have made you feel a lot more cheerful. If there's one thing a farmer enjoys more than doing well, it's seeing his neighbour do badly. Not too badly, mind you, but just badly enough to be noticed. I myself don't mind having feet of clay, but when it begins to look as if my brain is made of the same material, it is time to start worrying.

Experiences with a Computer

OCTOBER 1982

My first anniversary with the computer passed unnoticed. I should have thrown a party but we were in the middle of harvest and I didn't have the time. My wife, who had grown to loathe the machine, had her hands full with our son aged six weeks. Now I can look back over a year and see if it has all been worthwhile.

I had eventually bought a Farmplan system, which uses an Apple II microcomputer and, during last autumn I settled down to see how it worked. Since I am almost innumerate and could not read (let alone understand) a balance sheet if my life depended on it, I did not want to dive into the accountancy package. Instead I concentrated on the arable field records and spent all my spare time (hence my wife's dislike of the thing) sitting in the office feeding information into the machine and cursing the fact that it kept making mistakes. This, by the way, is the inevitable hallmark of a computer novice; he blames the computer and never himself.

By Christmas the arable program was, in the jargon "up and running". Payroll was still unused because we pay every four weeks and programs were designed for those people who pay every month. Budgeting and Cashflow, which make use of a program called Visicalc, were clearly too complicated for me and I decided to wait until I had more confidence. The accounts package, for which the whole machine had really been bought, was not even up, let alone running. My accountant, who loved the idea of a computerised client, had insisted that he set it all up for us, and this seemed like an excellent idea. The snag is that, like most good accountants, he simply did not have the time – and he also had no idea how slow it was going to be.

By January I had mastered Visicalc and spent hours looking at what would happen to our overdraft if the price of wheat fell by £12.50 per tonne, interest rates rose by 1.5% and the yield per acre rose by an additional 6cwt. Fascinating stuff which gave me a great sense of power but not a lot else. Meanwhile the payroll had staggered onto the computer and made life much easier on paydays.

Easter was notable for the arrival of Programplan, a new set of Farmplan programs written in a brand new language. It meant that we could throw away all the work we had done in the past nine months and enjoy the benefits of this package which, apart from being better, speeded everything up enormously. Instead of staring at a blank screen waiting for numbers to flash in front of me, things happened almost at once.

But still our accounts were far from being computerised. Our accountant had given up the struggle and onto the scene had strode one of Farmplan's quaintly-named Computer Vets in the shape of Brian Tipper from Market Harborough. As spring gave way to summer, Brian paid us visits, the real purpose of which was to help Fiona in the office set everything up. The machine's first anniversary was marked by the fact that our books still consisted of big ledgers rather than small floppy disks. As I write this I wonder whether, by the time you read it, we shall have eventually succeeded in doing the only thing for which a computer really make sense – on an arable farm at least. Without the accounts on the machine, all the other programs are so much fluff.

I've had a wonderful time playing with my Apple and now I know the gross margins for each and every field. Payday is no longer a sweat, and budgeting and cashflow forecasting are suddenly simple. I can also tell you the monthly rainfall figures for the past 50 years with no trouble at all. And yet in spite of all these triumphs, I am still most unhappy that it has taken us this long to get our books onto the machine. I suppose it's really my fault for not pushing harder and sooner. Even when the great day comes and we are up and running, it will still be necessary to keep manual accounts for months longer while Fiona builds up her confidence and skill.

So the moral is that it all takes longer to get going than you might imagine. By all means involve your accountant, but don't let him set it up for you. Use the Computer Vet (or equivalent) and keep up the pressure until the wonderful day dawns when you throw away the ledger and fly solo through the maze of double entry bookkeeping. We haven't got there yet, but I'm an incurable optimist and I keep believing that it can't be long now.

The best thing about the computer for this particular farmer is the word processor. My typewriter is now obsolete and instead I gaze at the little green screen as all these wonderful words appear in print before me. When I am completely happy with what I have written, I just push a button and the printer goes berserk. So if you disagree with anything I say, don't blame me. It's the computer's fault. I just push the buttons.

Open Letter to a Pension Fund Manager

NOVEMBER 1982

Dear Pension Fund Manager

I have recently become a tenant of yours so I shall have to be particularly polite and deferential. But I am a bit worried about the future because I think you are in danger of making a mess of things.

You are still perilously dependent on your land agents. I suppose this is inevitable because you don't really know about land ownership or farming and they do. We all need professional people to help us sometimes, and I admit that there are moments when I need a solicitor. But I would hate to allow my solicitors to have the same total control over my life as your land agent has over your land. I realise that if you pay a man to give you advice, it would be foolish not to take it – at least some of the time. Perhaps when you have owned your estate for a bit longer you will start to have ideas of your own and show a bit of independence.

From this you may deduce that I think land agents are unreliable rogues; you would be wrong. They have an important service to perform and most of them do it exceptionally well. Indeed, many of them are aware of the quite extraordinary power which they wield, and they act with great responsibility. Thus it is no reflection on their profession when I suggest to you that any situation in which so much money (yours) is in the hands of so few men (theirs) may not be altogether healthy.

On a more practical note, it is clear that things are changing fast these days. I have noticed that you are not quite as keen as you once were on farming partnerships. Maybe you have had some bad experiences, or maybe it is simply that there is not as much money in farming as there was. You may have realised that there is a lot to be said for letting farmers do the farming while you sit back and collect the rent. But whatever the reason, I am not sorry to see partnerships fade away. Of course, the demand for tenancies is as strong as ever. You don't seem to be very keen to grant them, and that is probably why you don't buy vacant land. What really interests you is let land. Indeed, I reckon you buy most of the let farms of over 1000 acres which come onto the market these days. It all makes a lot of sense to you today, but I wonder if you have ever thought about the future.

What is going to happen to your 1000 acre farms when today's tenants start dying? Those whose sons can succeed them under the law will not be a problem, but what will you do when suddenly you realise you own vacant possession land? At first glance, of course, it will be wonderful news to your Pension Funds because all of a sudden your asset will rise by about 30%. This will look splendid in the balance sheet, but it won't solve the problem of what to do with the vacant farm. You will have four options:–

You can sell the land, make a capital profit, and reinvest the money.

You can take the farm in hand and farm it yourself.

You can ask one of the giant farming companies to look after it for you.

You can re-let the farm.

If you sell the farm someone else will have to buy it, and I would be surprised if there are many individuals who are able to afford 1000 acres of freehold land. There may be the odd City tycoon looking for a hedge against inflation, but with the taxation system as it is today, there won't be many of these around.

I don't think you will want to take the farm in hand and run it yourself. If you do this too often there will be a terrific outcry by the NFU, who will claim that you are depriving farmers of their living. The one thing you hate above all else is bad publicity, so I doubt that you will do this very often.

You can, of course, engage one of the great farming companies to farm it for you. They will shower you with brochures and figures to prove how wonderful they are. But once again, if you were to do this too often there would be an almighty stink. And do you really want to see England in the hands of those great galumphing companies whose bosses spend more time in helicopters than on the ground? I doubt it.

The obvious solution to you is to re-let the farm. But your financial advisers will be most unhappy unless you charge the incoming tenant the vacant possession premium. Failure to do so, they will tell you, means that you are forsaking a 30% capital gain.

The key money, which at today's prices would amount to £600 an acre, must be paid in addition to the very high rent which has been tendered. I can see a neighbouring farmer able to do this for the odd 100 acres or so on his border, but we are talking about a 1000 acre farm. So maybe you will be forced to break up the 1000 acre farm and either sell or rent it in easily digestible pieces to the neighbours. This is not as simple as it seems because the farm will have only one good house and only one set of buildings. Wouldn't it be odd if you and the other institutions were responsible for turning the clock back in British agriculture so that the economic units which have been built up so laboriously since the beginning of the century are once again divided into fractions?

The answer, of course, is simple. You should behave like the traditional landlords who never minded about vacant possession premiums and key money. They knew that they would be landlords for generations and thus re-let farms as a matter of course. If you fail to do this, you should not be surprised if the pressure to nationalise all tenanted land grows ever stronger.

Perhaps you have thought about what the future holds and how you are going to deal with this problem. perhaps you have a strategy already worked out. I hope you do, because you don't have a lot of time left. It would be interesting to hear from you.

Harvest 1982

NOVEMBER 1982

Harvest was good this year. Contrary to all the traditions which suggest that an early harvest is a bad one, this one was good. We began on July 6th and ended on August 11th. Only the drought of 1976 has ever given us an earlier start or finish, and that was a year I shall be happy to forget. By contrast, this harvest produced the best barleys we have ever had, excellent rape crops, herbage seed which was well above average and peas which I can't complain about. Only the wheats were disappointing and I wondered why.

We invariably use a low seed rate, never more than one hundredweight per acre, and I suspect that the very cold winter thinned out the plant population rather too much. Certainly in the early spring the fields looked rather thinner than I'd like to see them. Some of the crops, particularly those on the chalks, took longer to get going than usual – even after an early top dressing of 80 units, which I had hoped would give them a boost.

The drought in April and May did not help matters, but when the rains came in June the wheats picked up very well indeed. With them rose my spirits and, providing I didn't get out of the car, I could convince myself that we were going to have some reasonable yields. However, once in the fields themselves, it was still clear that the crops were thinner than I'd like them to be, even if the ears were a good size.

A routine application of Bayleton and Captafol went on just after ear emergence and I sat back to wait for harvest with a certain confidence. This optimism was, however, soon drowned by the constant June rains as I watched the ears turn nasty colours. My first reaction was that we had a bad case of septoria, but the experts diagnosed fusarium and botrytis. Surprisingly enough, we had very little take-all, even in the second wheats. There did not seem to be a lot we could do but, in spite of (or perhaps because of) that, I put on a quick splash of Benlate which, some people told me, would at least control the botrytis. I shall never know if this was actually worthwhile. It certainly made me feel better, and that's as good a reason for spending money as I know.

The moment the first field had been cut, we knew that things were not going well. Our weighbridge means that we can no longer afford the luxury of optimism. In the past we would have hoped for a high bushel weight and estimated a yield which erred on the side of generosity; but now we know immediately whether the news is good or not. All our second year wheats, regardless of variety, hovered around 55cwt. Avalon, Longbow and Norman were at least consistent, but it is several years since we were faced with yields as low as this and I felt pretty unhappy.

The first wheats did better, but not spectacularly. One field of Longbow managed to scrape 70cwt, but the others all tipped the scales at between 60 and 65cwt per acre. The Fenman could only produce 63cwt and poor old Avocet, on some thin chalk, produced 56cwt. This variety, incidentally, then ran into certification problems which disappointed the breeders – and didn't make me too happy either because I had booked the field for Avocet next year. I can't complain, however, because one must accept this sort of risk when growing new varieties.

It is not the poor wheat yields which I shall remember about last harvest in years to come. What has struck me is the sheer cynicism of some members of the seed trade. Not all, mind you, because the majority of merchants remain honourable men with whom it is a pleasure to trade. But, as usual in life, it does not take many bad experiences to create a very unpleasant atmosphere.

What conclusions do you draw from the fact that the only two varieties I had no trouble selling for seed were Tipper and Otter? The fact that malting premiums were high and so the varieties were in demand has, perish the thought, nothing to do with it. Certainly there was a serious loose smut problem this year, but why did only Sonja and Igri, the two varieties in surplus, seem to suffer?

A new variety (Lingot) of oilseed rape I was growing for seed never managed to get onto the NIAB recommended list and was obviously going to be difficult for the merchant to sell. Imagine my surprise when I found it had been rejected for cleavers, in spite of the fact that removing cleavers from rape is simplicity itself.

Perhaps this shows how childishly naive I have been in the past. Instead of complaining and feeling hard done-by, perhaps I should have adopted the same tactics. I could have sprinkled wild oats into their Otter and sold it for malting at double the seed premium. I could have had a slight accident in the grainstore which somehow meant that the Tipper had an admixture of wheat and could not be sold for seed. The moisture could have been over 16% in the varieties which were in demand; and so on and so on. Of course, the merchants concerned would have had their suspicions but, as I found out to my cost, they would have had no proof.

I suppose the moral is to look for merchants who do not wriggle and squirm when the market turns against them. They do exist and I'm happy to say I know several of them, so perhaps I should stop complaining and get back to work. But it makes me mad . . .

The Price of Wheat Is Too High

DECEMBER 1982

Any farmer who did not make a profit growing wheat this year has only himself to blame. As Lord Thomson once said about independent television: "It is a licence to print money."

Of course, in the rush to plough up pasture and drill corn, some farmers may have pushed their luck too far. Some are on land which is simply not suitable, others have borrowed too much from the banks and will have, as a result, made a loss this year; but they can hardly blame that on the price of wheat.

The reason wheat growers have done so well is simply that the Intervention system today is cock-eyed beyond belief. Intervention prices are so high that, far from providing a floor to the market, they are, in effect, the ceiling. Instead of being the market of last resort to which the farmer sells as an alternative to bankruptcy, the Intervention Board has actually enriched arable farmers by allowing them to make at least £20 per tonne profit – and usually more.

How can we be surprised that taxpayers and politicians throughout Europe are getting fed up? They are right to be angry, and we farmers should not react like a bunch of agricultural Arthur Scargills. We may laugh at the National Union of Mineworkers for insisting that every pit be kept open at the taxpayers' expense, whether or not we need the coal or can produce it economically, but this is precisely what the NFU is in danger of doing on behalf of cereal growers.

I am an enthusiastic supporter of the Common Market and the whole Intervention System. A totally free market would be clearly unsatisfactory for both farmers and consumers. The siren voices of Richard Body and Enoch Powell may be attractive to the public when they claim that British farming should stand unsupported in the world, and face competition from wherever cheap food may come. Of course, they conveniently forget that every government supports its agriculture and, besides, Messrs Body and Powell share an abiding (even obsessive) hatred of the Common Market. But to dismiss them as "facile and dangerous", which the NFU has done, is to miss the point. These arguments contain more than a grain of truth, and whether we like it or not, they command some support from the British public.

We laugh at our peril when Mr Body points out that we are subsidised to produce food that is unwanted by those who could afford it, and unaffordable to those who need it. How can I, for example, justify the fact that this autumn I sold 800 tonnes of barley to the taxpayers (Intervention) for £110 a tonne ex-farm and made a profit of £20 a tonne in doing so? Now the taxpayer will have to find a further £50 a tonne to store and export this barley – always supposing there is an export market to be found.

I would be a fool not to take advantage of this system while it continues. It is neither illegal nor immoral. It is, however, ridiculous. Many arable farmers will consider me disloyal, and perhaps even a traitor, for even mentioning these facts. I should keep quiet in the hope that nobody will ever notice. And yet any farmer who points out a waste of money which does not involve agriculture would be considered public-spirited. We should beware of double standards.

Intervention prices are too high and should be reduced. For wheat and barley at least, they should be pitched at a level so that if the average farmer sells into Intervention, he will just about manage to break even. Naturally, the above average grower would continue to make a bit of money, and conversely, the below average grower would actually lose money. The latter chap would then be forced either to improve the standard of his farming or get out of cereals altogether. Sad though this might be if it happened to a friend, we should shed no more tears for him than we should for the Coventry motorcycle manufacturer who was unable to face Japanese competition.

At this point politics intrude and make life more complicated. Many governments will be unwilling to see their farmers forced off the land onto the urban dole queues. They might decide, and I would support them strongly, to subsidise these farmers to prevent rural depopulation. This is both fair and wise, but the subsidies which are paid for this reason are purely for social purposes and must not be confused with agricultural support. Taxpayers should be clearly aware that their money is not being used to prop up inefficient farmers but to keep the countryside as it is today. These inducements will also have to be more selective then in the past. A subsidy to keep a man farming in the Auvergne or Argyll should not also be payable to me in Cambridgeshire.

The farmers who will suffer when prices fall are not the small, but the inefficient. There is a common misconception among

farmers today that Big Equals Efficient and Small Equals Inefficient. This is rubbish. We can all think of the agricultural dinosaurs
farming many thousand acres which disprove this theory. Conversely, many small family farms are run at very high levels of
efficiency.

But simply to say that Intervention prices are too high and leave it
at that is irresponsible. We must first find out more about the
average wheat grower; what are his costs, yields and profits? The
table below is based on a survey of 364 farms in East Anglia with an
average of 80 hectares of wheat.

It is clear from the table that since 1971 the wheat grower has had
to produce higher yields every year simply to cover his costs. This
has risen from 2.82 tonnes/hectare in 1971 to 4.45 tonnes/hectare
last year. But even today, this average arable farmer manages pretty
well. His profit, admittedly, is down by a third from the balmy
days of 1978, but his Net Margin shows that even if he took an extra
£15 a tonne for his own living expenses, he would still have made a
healthy profit of £17.30 a tonne last harvest.

Some East Anglian arable farmers will simply not believe these
figures. They also keep management accounts which show that
their costs are higher than these figures would suggest.

Winter Wheat

Net Margins in real terms based on 1981–82 prices

	1982*	1981	1980	1979	1978	1971/2
Price £/tnne	110.4	112.4	117.3	122.8	131.8	125.0
Output £/ha	695.5	706.7	753.2	670.7	745.5	582.5
Yield t/ha	6.3	6.3	6.4	5.5	5.6	4.7
Var costs £/ha	183.5	183.4	175.9	176.4	163.7	112.8
GM £/ha	512.0	523.3	577.3	494.3	581.5	469.7
FIXED COSTS (£/ha)						
Labour	63.9	60.4	59.8	56.7	53.8	64.2
Machinery	121.1	117.1	114.3	113.7	111.8	81.8
Rent/Finance	92.0	91.1	88.5	87.4	80.1	66.6
Sundries	31.5	30.6	31.2	26.3	32.5	29.5
TOTAL	308.5	299.2	293.8	284.1	278.5	241.4
Net Margin (£/ha)	203.5	224.1	283.5	210.2	303.0	228.3
Cost of producing 1 tonne of wheat	78.1	76.7	73.2	84.3	78.3	75.4
Breakeven Yield t/ha	4.5	4.3	4.0	3.8	3.4	2.8

* Estimate

(Figures from the Department of Land Economy, University of Cambridge).

The solution is as simple as it is painful. The Intervention price of wheat should fall to £100 per tonne. If this proves impossible politically, Brussels should ensure that at least it does not rise until, thanks to inflation, this fall has been achieved. The effect would not be catastrophic and the average cereal grower would certainly survive. Admittedly, his profits would not be as large as they have been in the past, and it is possible that if the weather were particularly bad one year he might even make a loss. But if he takes action today by anticipating the future rather than simply reacting to it, there will still be a lot of profitable wheat grown in Britain.

The price of wheat was clearly too high, but I had to screw up my courage to actually say so in print. My fellow farmers must have wished (not for the first time) that I would shut up and stop saying such stupid things.

Commuters Rule, OK?

JANUARY 1983

The phone rang on a Sunday morning last autumn and the voice at the other end told me that he lived in the village but we had not actually met. I assumed this was the prelude to a request for a charitable donation, or perhaps a bale of straw for his daughter's guinea pigs. I was wrong.

"It's the thistles in your meadow next door to us," he said. "The seed is blowing all over our garden and blocking the filter on our swimming pool. Could you please do something about them? You really should have cut them before they got to this stage." I was too flabbergasted to be constructive and muttered something about seeing what I could do after the weekend.

I wish this were simply an isolated incident about which we could all have a good giggle; unfortunately it isn't. There was the man who complained about the smell of bean flowers in the adjoining field (it happens to be my favourite smell and I've often wondered since whether I could not sell bottles of "Essence de Fèves" to a Paris parfumier). Then there is the constant complaint about mud on the road which happens each time it rains during the winter; and so it goes on.

The people who complain about the thistles or the smell of beans are invariably the newcomers to the village. They were attracted by the (relatively) unspoilt nature of this area which, of course, means that farming still predominates over either industry or housing estates.

My assailants are also keen on what they call "preserving the village". This form of preservation needs some explaining because it involves trying to keep everything exactly as it was the day they exchanged contracts for their shiny new bungalow. No more new houses should be built because this destroys what is called "the character of the village". The fact that these people themselves live in new houses is conveniently overlooked. Their houses somehow manage not to destroy "the character of the village". It's only the newer ones which do that. Preservation, therefore, means the maintenance of all that is picturesque – except for the inconvenient thistle down which blocks swimming pool filters – providing someone else pays. Thus the local farmer must preserve the old barn because it looks so pretty, but his cattle should not make a mess on the road because that is both disgusting and dangerous.

The ideal world for these people to inhabit is a Disneyland English Village full of fibreglass cottages and imitation thatch (which is not a fire risk). Plastic poultry cluck noiselessly around a farmyard which produces no smells. Clockwork cows sit among the buttercups mooing every hour on the hour. Tractors and farm machinery live in a picturesque barn polished to a fare-thee-well, but they never venture onto the road bringing mud and muck on their tyres.

Harvest, besides being the prelude to the Harvest Festival, is also the high point in the picturesque year, to be watched from over the hedge while happy workers stook sheaves throughout the night as they drink scrumpy and sing songs – but not too loud. These same farmworkers, besmocked and sounding like Dan Archer, show great deference to the new villagers, whose gardens they tend at weekends and in the evenings. Their wives clean in the house and their children run errands. Most of them live in council houses on the other side of the village, but some of the older ones live in cottages which one day will be sold to yet more newcomers, who will each carry on the Great Tradition of their forebears by placing a carriage lamp outside the door and complaining about the smell of the nearby pigs.

The perfect world, designed by commuters for commuters, is slowly coming to pass. A Hampstead Farming Suburb for people who think they like "living in the country" but cannot actually tolerate the countryside. If there's one thing worse than pollution by straw burning, it is the silent and sinister pollution by commuter. And, by the way, don't forget to cut those thistles before they seed next year.

The Lure of Urea

FEBRUARY 1983

The cost of some of our nitrogen has fallen by 25% this year, which is one reason I'm feeling cheerful these days. The price itself hasn't come down that much but, after two years of dithering, I finally decided to switch to urea this spring. It could, of course, turn out to be a fiasco, and if certain people in the fertiliser world are to be believed, it probably will.

The pessimists, who for some reason all seem to work for companies manufacturing ammonium nitrate, have warned me that I will regret my decision. Our light chalky soil with its high pH will, they claim, reduce the amount of nitrogen available to the plant. It is just this sort of argument which in the past has persuaded me to stay with bagged nitrogen and not to mess about with fads.

But my friendly local ADAS man came up with some good news the other day. His colleagues at Cambridge have been running some pretty extensive trials and they are not at all convinced that urea is any less effective than ammonium nitrate. You can't get much more cautious than ADAS, so I reckon if they are happy it can't be too bad.

Another reason why most people have been so timid about using urea is that it does appear to reduce germination in certain circumstances. However, since we won't be combine drilling I won't be fussed by this. It seems that only if the actual urea prill is right next door to the seed does this particular problem occur. I checked with Brooms Barn experimental station and they are not unduly worried about the effect of urea on sugar beet germination and establishment – always provided it is spread on the surface within two weeks of drilling.

The anti-urea lobby also makes great play out of the fact that at high temperatures, some of the nitrogen in the urea will vaporise and be lost to the atmosphere. Friends in Schleswig-Holstein, who have been using urea for the past five years, take this criticism seriously and ensure that when they apply a final top dressing on to the wheat flag leaf, they always use ammonium nitrate instead. But I've never completely believed that these very late applications really do increase protein. Besides, we grow all of our wheat for seed and so there is no point trying to increase protein.

Urea is 46% nitrogen so, weight for weight, it is one third more concentrated than Nitram. This seemed to be a great advantage as we would have fewer bags to handle. But it wasn't quite as simple as it appeared. Urea is less dense than ammonium nitrate. One normal size bag holds only 40kg instead of the usual 50kg, so at the end of the day what we gained in concentration we lost in density, and we did not save any handling at all. The actual prills themselves seemed more slippery, almost like rape seed, and you have to remember to recalibrate the spreader to take account of the lighter weight of the material.

The price of straight urea is so competitive that I am beginning to regret our decision to go over to liquid nitrogen for all the cereals six years ago. We still use solids on the rape, herbage seed, sugar beet and pasture simply because it allows us to keep two sprayers going as well as the spreader. It is these crops which will therefore be receiving the urea this year.

I don't understand why there is such a big gap in price between liquids and urea because liquid N33 itself usually consists of at least 50% urea. In fact the last load of liquid I received was no less than 60% urea. It is even more mysterious when you remember that ICI, which leads the anti-urea faction, actually owns Chafers, the biggest suppliers of liquid nitrogen. What is yet more confusing is the fact that ICI itself manufacturers urea but seems unwilling to sell it to farmers. There must be some valid commercial reason hidden here, but it seems crazy to me.

However, I really shouldn't complain too much since the price of liquid nitrogen itself is about 5% lower than this time last year. And there's no doubt that liquids still make a great deal of sense to us because we run on a 24 metre tramline. Even with the big new

Accord pneumatic machine, you still can't spread solid fertilisers this wide.

During the past few years there have been some important advances in liquid nitrogen application, particularly the arrival of rainjet nozzles. In the early days we used conventional nozzles. The spray was so fine that we used to scorch the leaves horribly, and there were several occasions when, a few days later, it looked as if we had applied Gramoxone★ rather than nitrogen.

I can't help feeling sorry for the fertiliser business because there's no doubt that today there is a buyer's market. But when ICI and Norsk Hydro put their heads down and charge at each other, the resulting carnage must be good news for the consumer. ICI are determined to maintain their market share at almost any cost and Norsk Hydro, the new owners of Fisons, are equally keen on making up for lost time. The smaller firms are in danger of being squeezed out of existence, which won't do us any good in the long run.

But above and beyond the immediate problems of the fertiliser industry today looms a very unpleasant cloud indeed. The new American payment in kind (PIK) scheme will, so the Department of Agriculture claims, remove 23 million acres from production this year in the United States alone. If you assume that each of these acres would normally have received one hundredweight of compound fertiliser (and it might well be more than this), it means that 1.15 million tonnes of fertiliser will not now be sold. The question on everybody's mind is: what will the effects of this be? Perhaps it will simply not be manufactured, in which case there will be a lot more layoffs in the industry than we have already seen. Perhaps it will flood onto the world market and push prices even lower than they are already. Either way, the damage to the fertiliser industry could be very serious indeed.

So once again I thank heaven that I am a farmer and not a manufacturer. I shall have to be a little more polite when a fertiliser rep next drops into the office. I'll offer him two commodities: tea and sympathy.

★ Paraquat.

New Combines – Old Problems

FEBRUARY 1983

When it comes to new machinery, I'm a pushover. Perhaps this is why we run two different sorts of rotary combines, the IH 1480 axial flow and the Claas 116CS, as well as two conventional machines. Most sensible farmers would hold off before buying a new machine and wait a year or two for the bugs to be sorted out. But I'm not a sensible farmer – which makes my life interesting and hectic.

It is now time to step back and take a cool look at the Claas Dominator 116CS and the International Harvester 1480. My opinions should, of course, be disregarded because I am hopelessly unreliable and biased. I would not for a moment suggest that the problems we have experienced will apply to other farmers with other crops in other parts of the country.

The 1480 started out badly two years ago at Thriplow, simply because the American header was unable to cope with the heavy crops of laid barley. It was partly my fault because, against the advice of the experts, I had been greedy and ordered a 22.5 feet wide header which was simply too big. IH learnt from their mistakes quickly and modified the header in time for last harvest. They did a good job and solved what had been the biggest fault. Even then, our problems were far from being over. No matter how carefully we set up the machine, it seemed sometimes to have a mind of its own. A neighbour, who also owns a 1480, summed it up well when he said that "it is necessary to set it up again each time the sun goes behind a cloud".

Grain losses varied from almost none at all one day to quite intolerable levels the next day. Repeated visits from the after-sales staff did nothing to help. Ted, the fitter, became more and more depressed as he tried every possible combination of rotor speed, forward speed, concave and fan setting. The problem seemed to occur when the straw was ripe. The action of a rotor is a lot harsher than that of a conventional straw-walker and the straw broke up into bits about an inch long. Instead of being carried out of the back of the machine, they dropped onto the sieves and formed an impenetrable layer through which the grain could not fall. An increase in the wind simply sent more grain over the back.

On days like this it was easy to forget all of the 1480's good points. The ease of cleaning, the large tank, the accessible engine and, above all, the cab, which is far better than any other combine. "Cabs don't thresh corn," said Ted. Nevertheless, when the conditions were right, the 1480 did an excellent job.

The Claas 116CS arrived just in time for harvest, and I was full of optimism because we have used Claas combines for 29 years. Compared to the 1480, it is a bigger machine with its 19 feet header and grain tank holding 9000 litres. The Claas header is, after all, the best in the business, so I wasn't surprised to find that it worked well. It also scores over the 1480 because it has a reversible table auger. The cab, however, is really not good at all. It is so small you have to duck as you enter and, once inside, it is dark, cramped and noisy. Not surprising with a 250 horsepower engine only inches behind your head. The working lights are also quite inadequate for night work compared to the 1480's which could happily illuminate Piccadilly Circus.

When it came to performance in the field, the output of the 116CS was enormous. It was at least 30% greater than a Claas Dominator 96 and, with its huge header and grain tank, it fairly ate up the acres. In damp conditions the 116CS really came into its own because it managed to thresh when the conventional machines were leaving half the grains on the ears.

As harvest progressed, we began to discover that it too shared the problem of the 1480. As soon as the straw became ripe, we found that the grain would pour over the sieves. Unlike the 1480, whose loss monitor left a lot to be desired, the Claas at least told you that this was happening. Try as we would, there were days when we were simply unable to control these losses, and I was severely tempted to leave both rotary combines beside the field. This did not happen very often, mind you, but when the conditions were bad, the losses were totally unacceptable. It was an unpleasant feeling to find that the sun is shining and the wheat coming in at 14% moisture, yet the two modern combines are unable to cope.

The conclusion to be drawn, therefore, is that they are both good machines but they have their weak points. Neither liked herbage seed because the damp grass tended to bunch up and come through the machine in great gobs, which did not make for good separation. They were both, however, excellent in rape, and the Claas went well in peas. We didn't try the 1480 because it required spending several hundred pounds on a new set of concaves to handle this crop.

The problem of the straw breaking up and sitting on the sieves is the only serious design fault, and I have no doubt that when it has been solved the technique of rotary combines will really take off. In the meanwhile they are like the little girl with the curl. When they are good, they are very very good and when they are bad they are horrid.

The IH 1480 lasted three years at Thriplow. The Claas 116CS remains to this day (albeit a newer model). Those facts indicate my feelings about the two machines.

To Hell with Co-operatives

FEBRUARY 1983

Charitable farmers have two choices today. They can either make a donation to Oxfam or do business with their local co-operative. I myself would prefer Oxfam, and maybe that is why the local co-operative would not be sorry if I disappeared into a Bombay sewer and never came back.

The recent report which showed that if you want to lose money fast you should sell your corn to a co-operative did not surprise me. What it neglected to tell us, however, was that if you want to lose money even faster, you should not be content simply to sell to your local co-op, you should also buy from them. If you follow this simple advice you will be able to enjoy the exquisite pain on losing on both the roundabouts and the swings all at the same time; and that really takes talent.

A French or German farmer would not have this rather special privilege because co-operatives on the Continent are a very different breed of animal. The difference between a British and a French co-op is the difference between a spaniel and a wolf; both members of the same species, but the similarity ends there. On the other side of the Channel the problem is how to restrain the power of the co-operatives. I keep hearing of private merchants struggling against almost impossible competition. If you travel through Bavaria and see the BayWa signs, you can easily understand how the co-ops have over half the market. Of course, the structure of agriculture is very different and farmers themselves have very different attitudes; but I somehow doubt if these two factors alone can make all that difference.

The trouble with so many British co-operatives is that they so often appear to feel sorry for themselves. They almost feel that their customers – or members as they prefer to call them – owe them a living. The result of this attitude is that they seem to spend so much time talking about the importance of "commitment" and "the ideals of the movement" that they forget why they are here in the first place. "Commitment" is invariably the last desperate cry of an inefficient businessman who finds it impossible to survive without using this rather crude emotional blackmail. The other companies with whom I do business have to manage in this world by giving either a competitive service or a very keen price. They, unfortunately, cannot rely on "commitment" and "co-operation" from farmer customers, who themselves must struggle to keep the overdrafts down. Yet, these private firms seem to have no difficulty in competing with any co-op in the land.

If emotional arm-twisting were the only complaint I had against co-operatives, all would be well. Over the years the dividends we have earned from trading with our co-op have been converted into shares. It seemed a painless way of saving money, and I remained sleepy and happy until I tried to withdraw some of this cash the other day. Only then did I read the small print and discover that our money was actually locked up for 25 years without recall. When I am 65 I can withdraw it, by which time inflation will have rendered it useless. Of course, I cannot sell the shares either because nobody with any brain in their body would want to buy such a worthless piece of paper. So, once again, we are making what amounts to a charitable donation to the local co-op.

The thought has occurred to me that perhaps I am an exceptionally unpleasant sort of person. Maybe my fellow farmers are overjoyed at being allowed the privilege of supporting their friendly local co-ops with interest-free loans. Maybe they are happy about paying higher prices, safe in the knowledge that they are at least showing "commitment". Maybe I'm just a miserable old sod who likes complaining.

For some explicable reason this article annoyed my acquaintances in the co-ops. I suppose they felt I had been just the tiniest bit unfair. It is, however, interesting to note that Eastern Counties Farmers under Peter Purnell, their new Managing Director, has sharpened up enormously since this was written.

Rip-off

MARCH 1983

To put it crudely, agrochemical manufacturers have been taking us for a ride. It started 18 months ago when some shrewd people discovered that prices across the Channel were as much as 40% lower than in Britain. Every sort of vehicle left Dover and returned loaded with Dicurane, Avadex and other goodies.

Faced with this phenomenon, the chemical manufacturers reduced the price of almost every herbicide by 15%. Most of the distributors were caught between being loyal to their supplier (manufacturer) or their customer (farmer). They watched helplessly as some of their best customers sailed over to France and returned with cheap chemicals and duty-free booze.

In order to understand why the agrochemical distributors were in such an impossible position, it is first necessary to know a bit about how the trade is regulated in this country. The important bodies can be summarised as follows:

BAA. The British Agrochemicals Association is the manufacturers' Trade Association.
BASIS. British Agricultural Supply Industry Scheme is the Distributors' Trade Association.
PSPS This stands for Pesticide Safety Precautions Scheme which is run by the Ministry of Agriculture. Its job is to ensure that every chemical sold in Britain is safe to use.

To ensure safety standards are maintained, BASIS promised the Ministry of Agriculture that none of its members would ever sell a chemical which had not been passed by PSPS. And to add teeth to this agreement, it undertook to expel any member who broke this rule. What is more, the BAA (the manufacturers) stated that they would sell their products only to members of BASIS. Thus any chemical distributor who was not a member of BASIS might as well pack up immediately because he would never be able to buy the products from the manufacturers.

It is true that in the autumn of 1981 some counterfeit chemicals were imported into this country by farmers, who found that they had been conned into buying chemicals which were less concentrated than they had thought. The manufacturers lost no time in telling the world that this was precisely the sort of problem which would inevitably appear when PSPS was circumvented. It all looked simple and straightforward.

But soon after the first enterprising farmers had returned from Calais with their Dicurane, PSPS began to take on a very different colour. Gradually, the praiseworthy side of PSPS – acting as protector of the farmer – became a little less clear. Some people dared to suggest that this august body did more than maintain safety standards. It also kept prices high for the farmers and profits high for the manufacturers. This, of course, was a subject which the manufacturers did not want to talk about.

Bayleton was a classic example. Manufactured in a factory at Leverkusen, just north of Cologne, it is packed into a variety of boxes and packages for different markets in different parts of the world. The languages vary and the actual packaging varies. The only thing which remains constant and unchanged is the product itself. Now it just so happens that the English Bayleton has been passed by PSPS, which is why we can go into our distributor's warehouse and buy it off the shelf. Belgian and French and Italian and German and Swiss Bayleton have not been passed by the PSPS.

This is not simply an irrelevant administrative detail. It means that if one day a switched-on distributor finds that he can buy Bayleton cheaper in France than he can in England, he is powerless to take advantage of the price difference. Were he to do so, he would be selling a product which had not been passed by PSPS. He would be kicked out of BASIS and find that no manufacturer would sell him a single product.

Some manufacturers, when faced with these facts, went through the most extraordinary contortions to claim that "the formulations were different". They went on to claim that this was necessary because different countries have different conditions. But they forgot to mention that when it suited them they would happily import, say, Captafol, from the United States and simply cover over the American label. When a manufacturer talked about different formulations, what it usually meant was that one wetter or emulsifier had simply been replaced by another.

Events reached a climax of idiocy when it was explained to me by a leading manufacurer that he had milled his English product particularly fine. If I used the French herbicide I would certainly block the nozzles of my sprayer. I pointed out to him that we actually use French sprayers on the farm so perhaps we should have been using the French herbicide all along!

But the manufacturers had yet another argument which they wheeled on to the stage. It would, they claimed, be very dangerous for an Englishman to use foreign chemicals because he would be unable to read the instructions on the label which were, of course, written in a foreign language.

It is all superficially convincing but, on closer examination, it does not make any sense. The solution has already been discovered by the manufacturers of items as (potentially) hazardous as electrical goods. The instructions are printed in various different languages so that customers in the different countries can understand and use the product in total safety.

The relationship between BAA, BASIS and PSPS, who had for so long been acting as Guardian Angel watching over British farmers, began to look more and more like a cartel. Its original purpose was still valid, but some people began to wonder why, if safety was its only concern, an identical product could not be imported into the United Kingdom. Naturally, the brighter chemical distributors lost no time in getting round the regulations by setting up dummy companies which were not members of BASIS. Any handling of these "grey" or "parallel" imports was done by these companies, which could hardly be expelled by BASIS since they had never been members.

As the months passed, the whole system began to look distinctly creaky. The authorities in Brussels concerned with Fair Trade began to show an active interest in the whole cosy arrangement, and their judgement is expected in the very near future.

One thing is certain. BASIS will never be the same again, and the power of this body to stop a member from trading will be abruptly curtailed. Regardless of how much PSPS has been abused by manufacturers for their own commercial advantage, the fact still remains that British farmers need the protection it offers. What we do not need is the restrictive practice which prevents identical material being imported at a cheaper price.

Kansas Cornucopia

MARCH 1983

The state of Kansas produced more wheat last year than the whole of Australia. This sounds impressive but, after driving 1500 miles through the hard red winter wheat states of Nebraska, Kansas, Oklahoma and Texas, I saw a version of arable farming which left me feeling uneasy.

At first glance the Kansas wheat grower leads a pleasant life. Together with two sons, he can comfortably look after 3000 acres, though the average farm is about one third this size. The land is level, the soil good and the climate – though extreme by our standards – is bearable. He may have to drive 100 miles for some reasonable shopping, but distances like this do not seem to concern him at all.

He is a devout churchman, probably a teetotaller, and is conservative in every sense of the word. In spite of the size of his farm, his attitudes are usually very provincial, with one notable exception. When it comes to the whole subject of exports and foreign trade, he has both strong views and a detailed knowledge. Talk to an English wheat producer about exports and he will give you a blank stare before he admits that he is totally ignorant. Until a few years ago we in Britain did not even worry about Intervention, and we certainly never gave exports even a passing thought. But the Kansas farmer is well aware that at least 60% of his crop is destined for export. It is not surprising that he follows the futures prices on the Kansas City Board of Trade closely.

But it is not only attitudes which make Kansas wheat farmers different from their English counterparts. When it comes actually to growing the crop, their techniques are totally different from ours. The area specialises in hard red winter wheat, which is what the rest of the world likes to use for bread-making. Yields of hard wheat are usually 20% lower than for soft wheat, but in most years the price difference is sufficient to make the crop more attractive.

The straw from the preceding harvest is spread behind the combine and either burnt (there are no effective restrictions) or incorporated. After discing a field twice, they apply a compound, or what they call a "starter" fertiliser. This almost never exceeds 20

– 148 –

units of nitrogen and phosphate. Potash is only used in the rare areas where the soil is deficient. Seed is planted during October at 60lbs per acre with huge drills. Instead of making a headland, they start at the outside of a field and simply go round and round until they finish at the centre. This is faster than our system and, since tramlines are never used, it makes a lot of sense. Pre-emergent herbicides, by the way, are unheard of.

To an English eye the plant populations are low, and I was particularly surprised to see that it was common practice to graze cattle on the wheat throughout the winter. Some of this grazing was so hard that afterwards it was difficult to see any plants remaining, but the farmers were unconcerned. They knew that much of the leaf would probably have been lost to the very hard winter frosts, and that the plant will eventually tiller out (or "stool", as they call it).

Weed control in the spring is usually unnecessary, and on the rare occasions when it is needed, they tend to use 2,4-D simply because it is the cheapest herbicide available. Top dressing never amounts to more than 60 units an acre, and neither fungicides nor growth regulators are ever used. Aphids, or "greenbugs" as they are called, are sometimes a problem and are controlled with an insecticide. But normally between drilling and harvest, a single top dressing is the only fieldwork done.

Any yield of more than one tonne an acre is cause for quiet celebration, but there is not much of that commodity on American farms these days. The price of hard wheat has fallen to £80 per tonne, and that is a delivered price which may mean a trip of up to 50 miles to the elevator. Few farmers have any form of on-farm grain storage, and they therefore make use of the local co-ops and merchants. The larger co-ops are on a scale which makes even the biggest stores in France look puny. The Union Equity co-operative, whose headquarters I visited at Enid, Oklahoma, stores 1.3 million tonnes at a single location. This is the equivalent of 15% of the entire British wheat crop. At harvest time it receives 12,000 trucks a day and can deal with up to 15,000 tonnes an hour. Of the 4.5 million tonnes of grain it handled in 1981, no less than 96% went for export through Union Equity's own dockside terminal at Houston, Texas.

A farmer who grows soft wheat (which is what we produce in the United Kingdom) today has to accept a delivered price of £70 per tonne. It is not surprising that when I told my Kansas counterparts that we receive £120 a tonne – and do not consider 3 tonnes per acre to be exceptional – they wondered if I was a liar or had simply got my decimal point muddled.

In Britain this year it looks as if we shall have a surplus in Intervention of 4 million tonnes of cereals. In America the figure will probably amount to 134 million tonnes, which is more than the total of last year's record harvest in all ten of the EEC countries combined. It is this stark fact which has pushed down prices to a level where bankruptcies among arable farmers are not uncommon. Until this surplus is reduced, there seems little hope that prices will return to a level at which profits are once again possible. Thus both the federal government and the farmers themselves are trying to restrict output.

In the past the government has encouraged farmers to fallow up to 20% of their land by offering deficiency payments and loans. The trouble was that this setaside programme was not very successful. Farmers naturally took their worst land out of production and used the money they had saved to buy more fertiliser for their best land. The result was that output declined only slightly and, in some cases, actually increased.

At Dallas in January, President Reagan announced the Payment In Kind Scheme (PIK) which will supplement, but not replace, the old setaside programme. To participate in PIK, the farmer must start by fallowing 20% of his acreage under the existing scheme. Once he has thus qualified, he can take out up to a further 30% of his land. The inducement is that he will receive not cash but wheat itself. The actual amount is calculated to equal 80% of his average yield in the previous five years.

The wheat itself comes from government reserves and the farmer can do with it what he likes. He can feed it to his own livestock, store it or sell it. But to prevent an avalanche of wheat coming onto the market at the same time, the farmer actually takes delivery at the time he would normally harvest his crop. A Texas farmer will therefore be given his PIK wheat in late May, while a man in North Dakota up on the Canadian border will not receive his wheat until August or September.

The beauty of the PIK scheme is that, as far as the US Treasury is concerned, there will be no need to pay cash to farmers. The Department of Agriculture is also happy because the surplus will actually be reduced. Some farmers, however, are worried that the effect will be to depress the price of wheat still further as farmers may sell their entitlement and, in the short run at least, put more on the market.

But in spite of any reservations they may have, the Farm Bureau (which is the rough equivalent of the NFU) has welcomed PIK enthusiastically. The rest of the world will be looking on to see whether it will work, and I have no doubt that Brussels will be paying particular attention.

After a month in America, I returned to a mild English January. We had just applied a cocktail of fungicides to control mildew, net blotch and rhynchosporium on the winter barleys, and were starting to put the first of three doses of nitrogen on the wheats. Suddenly the simplicity of the American system seemed terribly attractive. But I could not help wondering what would happen if one day my friends in Kansas found that it was worth their while to use the sort of inputs we take for granted in England. Today they are not interested in maximising their yields; their only concern is survival. But if ever they start to look after their wheat as we do, the surplus which the world faces today will look like a molehill. The effect this will have on European arable farming does not bear thinking about.

My first visit to the American Mid-West, just at the end of their arable boom before widespread bankruptcies and hardship became a fact of life. The PIK program was not as successful as Washington had hoped.

Farmers – Unlike TV Producers – Live in the Real World

APRIL 1983

Farmers, unlike television producers, live in the real world. Whether it is mastitis or mildew, septoria or staggers, we have to face unpleasant facts every day. But we survive by dealing with these problems and not by sitting down in a hysterical heap and bewailing our lot. We should do the same when faced with a hostile press.

Like it or not, the media is interested only in sensation, and this will not alter for our benefit. A 4000 acre arable farmer in jail for cutting down trees★ is as much a sensation as a television producer can possibly conjure up. It may annoy us – it does me – but it should not surprise us. The fact is that not many people love us, and they never have. Admittedly, there were brief periods, mainly during wars, when we were heroes, but usually we have not been top of anybody else's pops. So why all the fuss about a stupid, biased, misleading, malicious and unpleasant TV programme?

Instead of crying "foul" we should take a clear look at our industry and see whether there is any justification for the public criticism. There seem to be two main reasons why farmers are attacked these days: economic and environmental.

As far as the economic attack is concerned, it is hard not to sympathise with a public which has suffered as living standards went down and unemployment went up. Not many farmers have experienced either of these problems, let alone both of them. Meanwhile, some sectors of the industry have actually boomed.

We have flourished partly because we have been good at our jobs, but also by collecting subsidies. This is a fact which we must face squarely because unless we understand it we shall never appreciate why so many people in this country look on us with such a mixture of envy and malice.

We can twist and turn, wriggle and wiggle, we can blame the EEC, the politicians, the weather, the Russians or the French but the fact remains that we have been paid to produce what nobody wants.

What is so wrong about admitting this and telling the world that we are grateful? God knows, I am. But instead we try to deny it by making excuses and specious arguments showing how really we are not so well off as it might appear. This approach only makes matters worse because even television producers are not fools (rogues, maybe). They can see through our protestations and realise that we are faintly deceitful and deeply ungrateful.

★ Hughie Batchelor, a Kent farmer who achieved great notoriety when he ignored a Court Order and bulldozed trees to make his fields even bigger. He was gaoled for contempt of court and – with their habitual anti-farmer bias – the media portrayed his actions as being those of a normal greedy, avaricious arable farmer. Batchelor was expelled from the CLA who were, not surprisingly, highly embarrassed by his actions. The NFU, though equally uneasy, took no such drastic action.

The best response to a sceptical public which has been fed a diet of ludicrous television programmes is to admit that our lives are good. We should be proud of the fact that we would not change places with any other profession. Of course, where sectors of the industry, like pigs or poultry, are in trouble, we should make this clear. But we should not be entirely surprised if the public simply does not believe the facts. We farmers have complained for far too long.

The environmental argument is equally clear. The facts are there for everyone to see. Trees and hedges have been pulled out all over the country, and this was done mainly (but not exclusively) by farmers. No matter how many trees we now plant – and we have been planting a lot in recent years – we cannot alter history. Likewise, it is a fact that more and more species of wildlife are becoming endangered due to modern farming methods. These facts alone have made the public very unhappy indeed, and we are deluding ourselves if we do not accept this as a fact.

We should not simply lie down under this avalanche of criticism and surrender without a fight. We should point out that we have only done to our farms what the rest of industry has been criticised for failing to do. We could have remained with the small fields which suited a 19th century dairyman just as the Midlands engineer remained using the tools which suited his great grandfather. And look where the engineering industry is today.

But we should take the environmentalist seriously because many of the things he says are right rather than sitting back and waiting for the next bombardment. Why shouldn't the NFU engage a qualified ecologist who could advise farmers and also speak to the conservationists in their own language?

Of course we shall continue to use chemicals, and only the most lunatic or organic farmers would think otherwise. But this still has to be explained carefully and politely. Sites of Special Scientific Interest (SSSIs) should be welcomed and respected rather than being considered hostile intrusions. All signs telling the public to "Keep Out" should be removed immediately and replaced with signs welcoming the public – but on our clear terms. They must not damage the crops, endanger the livestock or harm game. If they do, we should tell them to go without hesitation.

It is time to stop apologising. It is time to come out from behind the ancient fortifications which the NFU has erected. Instead we must first understand the public's point of view. When we have done this, it is time to go onto the offensive. We must tell them that we are proud to be farmers. We are proud of the fact that our farms are modern and efficient. We are proud of our good labour relations. We are proud to have made the countryside what it is today. We are happy in our job, and we are also grateful for the subsidies which the taxpayers have given us. But, above all, we must be honest and admit our prosperity instead of trying to hide it. Unless we cheerfully talk about the good news, nobody will ever believe us when we tell them about our problems.

After years of timidity, time is not on our side. We must stop being frightened of the rest of the world. Instead we should welcome them onto our farms and show them that, far from being the isolated and complaining old farmers we used to be, we are today happy, confident, and grateful.

> *There had been a spate of television documentaries examining agriculture and the mounting surpluses in the EEC. Each programme was more hostile towards farmers than the last and the whole industry was beginning to feel punch-drunk with this barrage of criticism. The farming press was full of letters from outraged farmers protesting their innocence.*

Weighing Up a Problem

JUNE 1983

If you want to save money you should buy in bulk. This is so obvious that you don't need a fool like me to tell you. Your toilet paper probably comes in huge boxes, you never buy dog food less than 48 tins at a time and the tomato ketchup is decanted from a catering size bottle. It all goes to show that your wife has managed to scrounge an illicit cash and carry card. Congratulations.

The same rules apply to the farm, and that's why a big farmer like me can probably squeeze a good price out of the distributors. Smaller ones join purchasing groups, and some romantic farmers even go so far as to buy from their local co-operatives.

As usual in life, I thought I'd done pretty well until I woke up one day and realised I was being an idiot. It all started with sugar beet pulp which we bought in 50kg bags. They were difficult to handle because after two days they went as hard as tombstones – and about the same size too. One day I noticed that if we bought the pulp in bulk, we would not only save money, we would also avoid the sweat of lifting the hated things. So we did just that and I sat back smugly in the knowledge that with one stroke of pure genius, I had saved both money and effort.

Throughout the first winter I remained in this state of ignorant bliss, and it was only in early March that I began to sense something was seriously amiss. We were running out of beet pulp. We ordered another 20 tonnes and I tried to find out what had gone wrong.

The answer was not hard to find; we were using about 15% more than we had intended because we had no foolproof system of weighing the stuff. Instead of giving a cattle yard three bags a day, we simply gave them a hopper full. Of course, we'd taken the precaution of weighing a hopper at the beginning of the season, but that did not stop us from over-feeding by 15%. So at the end of the winter our feed bill actually went up, even though the cost per tonne had gone down. See what that does for your gross margins.

The other day I heard a story which shows up the problem even more clearly. A friend who has long been keen on liquid fertiliser found to his surprise that he had used at least 10% more liquid nitrogen this spring than planned. At least his supplier charged for this amount extra. He rang me up in a panic to tell me the bad news, and after he'd calmed down a bit, we went over the possible reasons. He reckoned that only three things could have happened to cause the problem. Maybe the supplier made a mistake and simply charged my friend too much. This is unlikely because there are delivery tickets to prove it. Maybe his sprayer was wrongly calibrated and he simply applied too much. This is always possible, but he keeps detailed records of chemicals used and tells me that he is only 2% over target. It is unlikely, to put it mildly, that he would be 2% adrift on chemicals and 10% on nitrogen. Maybe he never actually received what the delivery note stated. He admitted, rather sheepishly, that he did not check the lorry driver for the simple reason that it is rare for anyone to be around the yard when the lorry arrives. Even if anyone is present, they do not look at the sight gauges on the tanks before and after delivery. Perhaps this all goes to show how sloppy he is, but he claims that the sight gauges are often bunged up and it would not necessarily tell him much. I asked him why he didn't keep the gauges clean; he coughed nervously and said he would do so next year.

So the most unpleasant thought lurking round the nether regions of my friend's brain is that perhaps he has been ripped off. I repeat the word perhaps because this is really inconceivable. The supplier is totally reputable and they have been dealing together for ages. Likewise, the supplier's lorry drivers are reliable and prompt. Thus no proof of foul play exists whatsoever. Even in agriculture, a supplier is innocent until proved otherwise.

I tried to calm my friend down, but he remained pretty upset. When he found the bill for nitrogen some £5000 higher than he had budgeted, he suddenly remembered the good old days when fertiliser came on pallets weighing 30cwt each. No nonsense about sight gauges then. All he needed to do was to count the pallets and multiply by 1.5 to find out how many tons had been delivered.

It just goes to show how much farmers have to take on trust these days. Whether it is deliveries to the farm of liquid nitrogen, or loads of wheat going off the farm, we simply have to rely on the honesty of some other man. On the day when a ton of wheat and a thousand litres of liquid nitrogen are both worth well over one hundred pounds, you begin to see why I am worried.

The obvious thing to do is to install a weighbridge on the farm. And this is just what we did two years ago. It does make me feel a lot happier when loads of grain, each weighing up to 22 tonnes each, leave the place. When it comes to the delivery of bulk beet pulp (or even liquid fertiliser, I suppose) we could – and should – weigh each lorry full and empty.

We have got into bad habits over the years by trusting all our suppliers. It is a habit I am reluctant to break because one of the best things about farming is our ability to rely on a handshake. And yet merchants themselves appear to need a weighbridge ticket in addition to our handshakes. Maybe they know something we don't?

> *Our weighbridge was the last expensive toy we bought as the arable boom came slowly to an end and we found we were forced to live in the real world. At £25,000, it cannot possibly be cost-effective, but it certainly is nice knowing all your yields immediately the last trailer returns to the grainstore.*

A Few Seed Merchants Are Honest

JUNE 1983

I once thought that all seed merchants were crooks. Today, I must have mellowed because I reckon that only some of them are. I don't know of any other group of men who, for the past five years, have been so depressed and unhappy. At the drop of a gin and tonic they will tell you how little money they have made, how much overcapacity there is in the trade, how the cowboys are selling seed at less than the cost of production, how premiums and yields are too high, and how terrible the outlook is. And yet they manage to survive. Compared to a seedsman, a farmer is optimism personified.

Mind you, they have arranged things neatly for their own convenience. The cereal seed contract, for example, still remains the most ludicrously lopsided document it has ever been my misfortune to read – let alone sign. It is written by seed merchants for seed merchants, with the pathetic acceptance of the NFU, whose role over the years in negotiations with UKASTA has been laughable. And yet some seed merchants feel that even the standard UKASTA contract is too weak for their own protection. Instead, they have drawn up a contract which gives them unfettered right to reject a crop if it suits them. Now it just so happens that most of these super-tough contracts are used by a group of seed merchants consisting of as-grown wholesalers. The odd thing is that while their role is extremely well known to their colleagues in the seed business, for some odd reason most seed growers ignorantly assume that they are normal merchants.

The typical retail seed merchant is definitely not a crook. He has his own stable of growers with whom he has built up a good relationship over the years. Each spring he estimates which varieties he will be needing for the following year, and decides the acreage accordingly. From time to time, of course, he will guess wrong and find himself with either too much or too little seed. This is less of a problem than it used to be since the advent of the Limited Tonnage clauses whereby he undertakes to move, say, two tonnes per acre and has an option on the balance. When he does find that he has too much of a variety he is in a difficult position, but most seed merchants stick to their promise by paying the premium, even though they will not be able to sell the crop for seed.

Most as-grown wholesalers (not to be confused with wholesalers who sell recleaned seed in bags) are very different animals. Some, of course, are as straight as the best retailers. (The ones who are not will probably reveal themselves by complaining about this article!) They depend on their wits and their luck – which are often hard to distinguish – and do not have a steady retail trade on which to base their business.

The wholesaler lives or dies on shortages. His job is to fill the gaps when the retail trade has guessed wrong. When there is a shortage of a certain variety, the wholesaler will step into the market and sell his crops to the retailer. The greater the shortage, the higher the price he will be able to charge. But if there is actually a surplus of that variety, the wholesaler is in serious trouble. Unlike the retailer, he has no trade with farmers and so can easily find that his whole crop must go for feed.

At this point the wholesaler starts to wriggle. Armed with his contract, which he has had specially written to deal with just such a problem, he begins by rejecting the grower's crop. If he is lucky he will be able to find a straightforward reason, such as the moisture being over 16%. It is hard to argue with this. If he fails, he will begin to look for some sort of contamination, which is usually present in some form or other. Eventually, he will be able to reject the crop "because in his opinion it cannot be cleaned to normal certification standards". Faced with this, the grower can either shut up or go to Arbitration. At the end of the day, whatever he may feel, he will usually shut up – a fact which is well known to the wholesaler.

The trouble is that so few of the as-grown wholesalers ever come clean to the growers about their true purpose. If they ever admitted that they were speculating on shortages, the grower would at least know that his crop's future was uncertain. The wholesaler ought to compensate for this, either by offering high premiums or, better still, participation contracts. But what normally happens is that the grower naively assumes that the wholesaler has a home for his crop when he signs the contract. Many growers do not even notice that the contract is so full of loopholes that the merchant can effectively tear it up whenever it suits him. More fool the grower.

The fact remains that the bulk of the seed trade do not behave like this. Life has been hard, margins have been shrinking, and many of

them have been in serious trouble. The causes are not that the premiums have risen too high; in recent years they have actually fallen in real terms. The problem has been that varieties come and go with such speed that unless they get their sums precisely right, the merchants can be left with large and expensive surpluses. This fact is wonderful news to the wholesaler. He is extremely happy if the retail seed merchants decide to play it safe and only grow 80% of their requirements on contract. He knows that he can fill the gaps very profitably. Eventually, this trend will damage both the retail seed trade and the growers themselves.

It need not necessarily happen like this. The cereal seed trade, like any other trade, needs wholesalers. There is certainly nothing wrong with speculating on new varieties and shortages. We want a new breed of candid as-grown wholesalers who inform growers openly and frankly about their role. These premiums should reflect the greater risks, and they need not be contracts which are, at best, insults to the growers' intelligence.

On the other hand, we seed growers should understand the problems facing the seed trade, even if this means not pressing for ever-increasing premiums. We should be tolerant of mistakes when our seed merchant gets his sums wrong and admits candidly that he cannot sell all of the crop to which he is committed. We should also be very aware of the dangers of growing for wholesalers. We should take a close look at the contract, and if it is full of loopholes, ask ourselves why the merchant has felt it necessary to protect himself like this. But above all, we should make it our business to find out about the man with whom we are signing the contract.

Yet another pathetic whinge about the seed trade. Hardly worth reading.

Farming at Its Frozen Limits

JULY 1983

"If your farm business is going under, what are your best options?" This headline in a Canadian farming paper summed it all up. I wondered when was the last time *Farmers Weekly* had run an article advising British farmers on the best way to go bankrupt. But in Canada you've got to be tough to farm at all.

You've got to be tough to face the temperatures which can drop to minus 70 centigrade. You've got to be tough when the growing season is only 90 days, when the rainfall is only 14 inches a year, and when an August hailstorm can leave you without a crop at all. You've also got to be tough to face a world price of wheat at £70 per tonne. Survival is never taken for granted, whether it is just one crop or your whole farm.

From a lush, wet Cambridgeshire in May I had gone to Canada to watch the spring wheat being planted. I spent ten days driving across the prairies, listening to some exceptional men and seeing how they managed in conditions which made my farm at Thriplow seem like paradise.

The province of Saskatchewan lies at the centre of the Canadian Prairies. It stretches 750 miles from the American border in the south to the sub-arctic wastes of the North West Territories in the north. If the provincial capital, Regina, were situated in London, the north and south borders would be at John O'Groats and Calais.

The climate is so harsh that only the southern third of the province is cultivated at all. The limit of farming lies on a line which is actually south of Lincolnshire, but because of the continental climate, and absence of the Gulf Stream, there is no similarity between the two countries. And yet both the Saskatchewan farmer and I are wheat producers. He grows hard red spring wheat and I grow soft winter varieties, but we both compete on the world market together. The similarities between us begin and end there. We might as well be on different planets.

And in a way we are. As the plane begins its descent over the prairies, it even looks like a different planet. The countryside shows the marks of man far more than anything Marion Shoard complains about in England. And yet it has an awesome beauty with its vast skies across which occasionally sail v-shaped flocks of Canada geese on their way north after the winter.

The landscape, devoid of trees (except those planted round the farmhouses) and dappled with small ponds full of wild duck, is divided every mile by gravel roads running north–south and east–west at right angles to form squares each consisting of 640 acres. These "sections" are the basic unit of land measurement on the prairies. Ask a farmer how much he farms and he will tell you "two and a half sections" rather than 1600 acres. Ask him how to reach his neighbour's farm and he will tell you to "turn north for three miles, west for two miles and then south until you see a pine tree". To an English farmer accustomed to right and left, I found this confusing at first, but later came to see how simple and clear the system is. The irony is that the Federal Government in Ottawa has decreed that Canada must go metric. So, in theory at least, a section now is 259 hectares and my instructions would have been "turn north for 4.8 kilometres, west for 3.2 kilometres". Western Canada, together with much of the American Mid-West, is the only part of the world where the Imperial system is actually part of the countryside and of people's lives. Small wonder that all farmers in Saskatchewan totally refuse to think metric.

The typical Saskatchewan farmer would probably be called a peasant in most other parts of the world. It is true that he lives in a comfortable home with his wife and son, and between them they farm around 1000 acres. But the hard work and small reward make them essentially similar to a farmer with 150 acres in northern Europe. Two thirds of the farm is cropped each year, and the balance is left as "summer fallow". The reason for this apparent waste of land is to retain moisture and fertility in an area where the average precipitation is around 14 inches a year, and almost half this amount comes from melting snow.

After harvest the Saskatchewan farmer will store what grain he can hold on his own farm but, by British standards, the Saskatchewan grain store is a primitive affair consisting of a few metal silos and wooden huts which look more like chicken houses than grain stores. What he cannot store himself he carts to the local grain elevator. These tall buildings, standing in a row beside the inevitable railway line, are the single most notable feature of the Canadian prairies. They tower above the flat landscape like miniature versions of Ely Cathedral overlooking the Fens. Each settlement, however small, has a variety of elevators owned by about six different companies and painted in various colours. Two co-operatives, the Saskatchewan Wheat Pool and the United Grain Growers, handle 80% of the entire crop.

It came as a surprise to me that the price offered by the different grain elevators to the farmer did not vary. They do not compete in price with each other, but act solely as agents for the Canadian Wheat Board which is the monopoly buyer of all the wheat grown in Canada. The actual price the Board pays is fixed before harvest each year. At the end of the season the farmers may also receive an additional payment if the world wheat price is better than anticipated. The only reason a farmer ever has to change the elevator he deals with is if he thinks he will get a better service, or fewer deductions for quality, from another operator.

And yet not a single farmer I spoke to in Canada had any complaints to make against the Wheat Board, so I was forced to admit that the system appeared to be working well. As with so many features of Canadian agriculture, the Wheat Board had started at the time of the depression when prairie farming was on the brink of collapse. A socialist party, now called the New

Democratic Party (NDP), grew up out of the co-operative tradition. Until it was defeated at the last provincial election, it had ruled Saskatchewan for more than 30 years. This tradition of socialist farmers is probably unique in a world where farming and conservatism are usually synonymous.

Today these prairie farmers are less solidly socialist than they were. Perhaps they are reverting to type, but it certainly means that when you visit Saskatchewan farms you hear a wider range of political discussion than anywhere I have ever been before. I had been told in Toronto that it was possible to tell a Saskatchewan farmer's politics by the cap he wears and, sure enough, when I found a man wearing a Sask Wheat Pool cap, the chances were that his views were leftish. If, on the other hand, he was sporting a cap from the Weyburn Inland Terminal, he would certainly be one of the conservative farmers who set up this huge new grain store a few years ago as a direct challenge to the old co-ops.

But in spite of the very strong political divisions in farming, there is not a single farmers' organisation which represents the industry's views. True, the National Farmers' Union* has a few vocal adherents, but most farmers feel that this small and militant organisation is far too extreme to make any sense at all. So the federal government in Ottawa is in the odd position of not having any group to speak to or negotiate with when it wants to find out how farmers are feeling. This must make life pleasant for the Minister of Agriculture.

In Saskatchewan drought is all too common, and water supplies are difficult. Even with wells going down more than 300 feet, the water on farms is often brackish and undrinkable. To solve this problem, many farmers build their own small reservoirs, or "dugouts", as they are called.

After harvest they deliberately leave strips of long stubble which will trap the snow in drifts, and so provide added moisture. But all of these techniques are worthless when drought strikes the prairies. The words "crop failure" are rarely heard in England, but in Saskatchewan they have a chilling reality.

The most important crop is invariably wheat. Saskatchewan produces 60% of Canada's wheat, and the farmers take pride in being their country's breadbasket. The severe climate has, until recently at least, meant that all the wheat – both durum for pasta and

---

* No connection with the British NFU.

hard for bread – is planted in the spring. This remains largely true today, although a few brave men have experimented successfully with winter wheat. Provided there is sufficient snow cover, the crop will usually survive, but without that insulation it is killed immediately by the frosts which regularly drop to minus 40 degrees centigrade.

Spring seeding starts in early May when the snows have melted and the ground dries out. While I was there, the first big 300 horsepower tractors were just beginning to start work pulling up to three 18 feet diskers behind them. Each of these units consists of a simple disc plough with a seed box above which scatters both seed and fertiliser onto the rough tilth. Vast sets of harrows, often 70 feet wide, complete the planting process.

Seed rates at around 60 lbs per acre were low by my standards, and I was surprised to learn that they use no potash with the nitrogen and the phosphate. The reason is that below the fields of Saskatchewan exists the largest potash mine in the world.

A quick squirt of Avadex through a very primitive sprayer before seeding takes care of a serious wild oat problem, and a post-emergence hormone in the spring looks after the broad leaved weeds. From then until harvest, nothing is done to the crop – except to pray that hail will somehow miss the field. This can destroy a field of wheat in less than an hour. One farmer I visited insisted on going to his deep-freeze to show me the hailstones, larger than golf balls, which had destroyed his crop the previous summer. He had deliberately preserved them intact to show sceptical strangers the ferocity of the Saskatchewan climate.

With a growing season which ranges from 120 days in the south, to no more than 100 days in the north, the crops must grow fast. Varieties of cereals have been specially bred for quick maturity, and it is even possible to find a type of oat which needs only 60 days between planting and harvesting. Long days and high temperatures are, of course, essential to this type of farming. But as August draws to an end, the wheat is swathed and left to ripen in the windrow before being harvested with large tractor-drawn combines. Both the IH 1480 axial flows and the New Holland Twin Rotor models are popular in this region.

Saskatchewan farmers may not have rain to worry about during harvest as we do, but a far more serious danger is never far away. If frost strikes before the crop is swathed, the yield falls dramatically as the grains shrivel. In a normal year the farmer will be very happy if his wheat yields one tonne per acre. The average for the province over the last decade amounts to no more than 14cwt.

As you travel north in Saskatchewan, the rainfall increases but the soil gets poorer. Wheat gives way to barley which, I was surprised to learn, usually yields about 60% more. The price, of course, is worse, and farmers grow wheat if they possibly can. But in recent years the crop which has done best in the northern area of the province is oilseed rape. It is called Canola in this part of the world, just to confuse visiting European farmers. But, like so many crops which make money, Canola has recently been overdone; today both disease and insects have become serious problems.

The crop had been grown for several years in succession by some unwise farmers and, even when the experts began to advise at least a four year gap between Canola, the practice was continued. Yields have now, as a result, fallen to around 12cwt per acre and the initial enthusiasm has evaporated a bit. But the crop is still very important in the area where the growing season hovers uncomfortably close to 100 days.

Of all the areas of Saskatchewan which fascinated me most, the northern part promised to be the least like home. The fine weather broke with a vengeance the day I left Regina, and I found myself sliding along deserted roads covered with sheet ice. Driving snow made it difficult to see where the land met the sky, and across the fields deserted tractors and drills were half buried by snowdrifts. It was clear that the spring seeding had come to an abrupt halt.

One day and 250 miles later, I finally achieved what I had set out to do. I had found the man who was literally the last farmer in this part of Canada. Go north from his farm and nothing whatsoever is grown. The next piece of cultivated land would be up past the North Pole and down into Siberia where, I suppose, some clearing in a forest would signal that farming was once again possible on the other side of the world.

The snow was lying deep on the ground when I arrived at the farm north of Carrot River, on the banks of the Saskatchewan River. The farmyard was a collection of rickety buildings, and most of the machinery, except for three vintage Claas Matador combines, stood outside in all weather. The new farmhouse was, however, very comfortable. The fact that it was triple-glazed throughout gave me some clue of how cold it gets in the winter. Minus 72 degrees centigrade is the record here, and minus 40 degrees is perfectly normal.

My welcome could not have been warmer, but when I asked the farmer to show me "the last field" he was a bit puzzled. It seems that nobody had ever asked him this before. I explained that I wanted to see the most northerly field, beyond which all farming ceased, and he soon understood. We went out in his four-wheel-drive pickup truck and stopped at a snow-covered field. A line of scrubby birch and white poplar trees, none more than 30 feet tall, marked the end of the field and the end of agriculture in this part of Canada. It was a bit of an anti-climax. I suppose I had somehow been expecting a dramatic bit of scenery of the sort which would somehow mark a significant point.

The reason was not that the climate had suddenly become impossible, but that here the thin grey soil gives way to what the Canadians call "Muskeg". This is a spongy mass of peat which is very acid, full of large stones and very nearly undrainable. Below it lies permafrost, which makes cultivation even more difficult. But nevertheless the bush is still being pushed back year by year. I was shown a 57 acre field which had been cleared with a bulldozer two years ago. The trees and stumps had been pushed up into windrows where they were drying out. The remaining field had been ploughed with a heavy disc, and this autumn the trees will eventually be burnt before the first crop of wheat is planted next spring.

On our farm back at Thriplow, the fields may have seen two thousand harvests, and certainly fifteen hundred. Here, on the northern edge of the farming world, I was looking at a field which had never produced a single crop during the entire history of this earth. It was an eerie feeling.

The soil is poor, the climate awful (only in the month of July last year did they have no frost at all) and the farmer is 25 miles from the nearest settlement. But the farmer is happy with his lot. His main activity is the raising of leafcutter bees, which he sells throughout Canada and the USA and uses to pollinate the lucerne he grows for seed. He lives among the sort of wildlife we only ever read about in Europe. Bears wander round the farmyard, wolves howl at night and moose, elk, deer, beaver, mink and gophers are common in the bush. I felt as if an Eskimo or a polar bear might suddenly appear round the corner of the barn. But when I looked at the map I realised that I was no further north than Norwich.

The freak May blizzard which had brought the spring seeding to a halt also tried to prevent me leaving Saskatchewan. Conditions were so bad at Regina airport that an incoming plane had crashed the day before and had blocked the main runway. My only escape route was 150 miles away by bus to Saskatoon and thence by air to Toronto. On the plane I had time to collect my thoughts. I realised that by European standards, none of the Saskatchewan farmers I had met should really have been growing cereals at all. To endure those hardships for such puny yields should be sheer lunacy.

Unlike me, they receive only one solitary subsidy from the government; an absurdly low freight rate on the railway. Not for them an Intervention System or export restitutions. No MCAs or target prices. No capital grants or 100% tax allowances on new machinery. No crushing subsidies on oilseed rape or herbage seed subsidies. No incorporation subsidy for peas, no sheepmeat regime, no beef premium. The Common Agricultural Policy seemed a long way away as I looked down on to Lake Superior from 35,000 feet. It was strange that in a country populated by socialistic farmers, agriculture exists in a free market where the efficient survive and the inefficient go bust. Back in Europe, I reflected, the capitalist farmers have discovered how to flourish. When it comes to agriculture, they have abolished the free market altogether. It was all getting too confusing. I was glad to be going home.

This trip whetted my appetite for the Canadian north country. I have since returned twice more, and each time went nearer the North Pole. I ended up at Grise Fjord, Canada's most northerly settlement some 700 miles from the pole where no farming at all is possible.

Bad Debts

AUGUST 1983

I haven't been sleeping very well these last few months. It isn't guilt, or even indigestion. I was worried that a corn merchant might go bust. Like most arable farms, we don't have many customers; probably no more than 20 in the course of a year. The snag is that we sell our grain in big lots to only a handful of merchants. What is worse, because it is all winter corn for seed, it leaves the farm during a hectic eight week period between August and October. You can now begin to see why my nightmares have been outnumbering all my other dreams. If one single merchant goes up the spout, we would be in very serious trouble indeed.

In the good old days this would not have been a problem. Business was leisurely, inflation had not been invented, margins were healthy, and if anyone was likely to go bankrupt, it was the farmer rather than the merchant. Today, we all know the story. Whizz-kid grain buyers operate on margins that usually don't exist at all. They live by volume rather than by profit. One false step and they can lose a fortune on a single telex. Add to this the vagaries of the seed trade with varieties coming and going like women's fashions, and however much I love my merchant customers (and I really do) I can't help feeling very nervous indeed.

My nightmare runs as follows. During August I ship the produce of three fields of winter barley, amounting to 400 tonnes at £120 per tonne, to the merchant. I send him an invoice for £48,000 and ask that he pay in 28 days. But the invoice is only posted after the last load has been collected, by which time it is September 7th. Thus I should (repeat should) get paid 28 days later on October 5th. Meanwhile I begin to load out his two fields of winter wheat totalling 300 tonnes at £130 per tonne. By the time I actually send him an invoice for the wheat amounting to £39,000, I have begun to hear a few rumours about the merchant's financial health. I would, of course, have loved to hold back the wheat until I had been paid for the barley but I cannot do this under the terms of my seed contract. He needs it then if he is to sell it for seed that autumn. What is worse, if I actually do stop the wheat going off the farm to him, I may well be precipitating exactly the disaster I am hoping he will avoid. Rumours will spread, and his impending crash will become a self-fulfilling prophecy.

The cheque for the barley comes due but I hear nothing from the merchant. A casual phone call gets stuck with his secretary, who tells me that he is not available. Days pass and I begin to feel very unhappy indeed. Then it happens. The phone rings and a farmer friend says breathlessly, "Have you heard about Buggins? They've had the Receivers in." I am owed a total of £87,000 without any hope of being paid. Suddenly, what had looked like a promising year now appears very different indeed as I stare a massive loss squarely in the face. At this point I usually wake up and have a cold shower.

This year I can no longer afford these nightmares, even if it does mean spending money to sleep soundly in my bed. I have decided to take out Bad Debt Insurance with a company called Trade Indemnity, which specialises in just this sort of cover. It is not foolproof, and I will only be protected for 80% of the debt, subject, of course, to a lot of conditions in the small print.

But in essence the idea is simple. I first have to make a list of all the people I shall probably be doing business with this year, and I have to estimate the amount I am likely to sell them. Trade Indemnity then looks into the financial health of my customers before agreeing the estimated credit limits I am asking them to insure. In some cases the news is bad and they will only insure me for less than I had wanted. This is a clear signal that all is not well with the merchant in question, and I should tread very carefully. But usually the figures I put forward are accepted without much trouble.

There is, as you would expect, a snag because you have to declare to Trade Indemnity your entire turnover and pay a premium which amounts to .5% of the annual amount. Now there are some firms with whom we deal that I am not in the least worried about. For example, I reckon that British Sugar is pretty safe, and I don't particularly want to insure their debt for next year's beet crop. But Trade Indemnity insists as part of the deal that I must insure both my solid and dodgy customers alike. I suppose it is reasonable of them, but it did rankle a trifle.

From now on I have agreed to inform Trade Indemnity of any account which is more than 60 days overdue. Every three months I tell them what my turnover has been, and I pay a premium which amounts to .5p in the pound. If I want to sell more to a merchant than my original estimate stated, all I have to do is to ring up Trade Indemnity and ask them whether I can exceed my limit. If they refuse to cover me for any more, I can always decide whether I wish to take the risk, or whether I should sell to another customer.

But it is all pretty expensive. This year the cost of the policy will add about £1.50 per acre to our fixed costs, and many farmers may think me crazy at a time when we are trying to reduce costs. But, as with all insurance, it never seems to be worthwhile until the fateful day comes. If it never happens, you're a fool to have paid the premiums. If it does come, you're a wise man. In the meanwhile I shall sleep better. Try putting a price on dreams.

*After three years of paying Trade Indemnity £5000, I decided
to cover this risk myself and gave up this very expensive
insurance. It is all very well sleeping better in bed at night, but
for that amount of money I could have bought a lot of sleeping
pills and still have cash in the bank. All the same, the nightmare
of a bad debt still haunts me as the pressure builds on the seed
trade and farmers alike.*

Buying More Land

NOVEMBER 1983

"Don't you feel guilty?" the young man asked. "You've just
bought some more land and I can't even get a start in farming?" Like
a shower of cold water, the question sobered me up fast. There I
was, a pretty plump fat cat. I had just bought what to me was a
small piece of land on the edge of the farm. But to my questioner, it
was enough to provide him and his family with a living if he was
prepared to work very hard. And judging by his appearance, he was
keen to do just that.

The question contained two of the most crucial issues in
agriculture today. Should farm sizes be limited and how can young
men get their foot on what is known as "the bottom rung of the
ladder"?

Every farmer I know has very strong ideas about the optimum
size of a farm. But for some inexplicable reason it always works out
as being just slightly bigger than the acreage he himself is farming at
the time. I have yet to meet a man who will admit that he is farming
too much land. It's always the other chap who is. Most people, I
suppose, would think that my 3000 acres in a ring fence is certainly
enough land – and probably too much. But such is my conceit that I
reckon I could handle a few hundred acres more without too much
trouble. Of course, I make a clear distinction between land farmed
by an individual like me and land farmed by a Company. That is
why I have no difficulty in saying that Velcourt, Hallsworth,
Gaudery and the others are big enough (too big actually) whilst this
does not apply to me. Hypocritical perhaps, but like so may
farmers, hypocrisy comes naturally to me. I also have an inbuilt

aversion to corporate farms even though I admit that their standards of husbandry are excellent.

Clever agricultural economists who sit in offices with computers think that the economies of scale stop at about 1000 acres, so I suppose if there were to be a limit on lowland farm sizes, it should be there. But I am still not convinced. If you are going to limit the size of farms you should also do the same to supermarket chains, motor car manufacturers, banks and the rest of industry. We all claim that we like things small and yet, given the choice, we go to Sainsburys and not the village shop. So when it comes to the forcible limitation of farm sizes I am totally, unashamedly and irrevocably against the idea. Mind you, if someone took some of my acres away from me I might see things differently. Sour grapes are a crop which many small farmers cultivate only too well.

But when it comes to young men getting a start in farming, the problem is a lot simpler. Amongst all the talk of tenancy reform, one crucial point has been overlooked. It is never easy to break into an industry which is prosperous, and farming since the war has prospered mightily.

There was a time, not so long ago, when "the bottom rung of the ladder" was empty. It was the other rungs of the ladder where the problems lay as farmers went bankrupt with dreadful regularity. Between the wars, in the aptly-named Bad Old Days, landlords were overjoyed to find a tenant at all. Their difficulty was how to keep the tenants they already had. Nobody then complained how hard it was to get into farming. The problem was how to stay in farming. When farmers are doing well there is no space on the bottom rung, but when they are doing badly there is too much space.

Thus I told my young questioner that I did not feel in the slightest bit guilty buying 118 acres. Of course I was sorry that he found it impossible to get into farming, but by holding back from buying this land I would not have helped him in any way at all. In the meanwhile he should decide what sort of agriculture he would like to see today. Would he like a prosperous industry where all rungs of the ladder – not just the bottom one – were occupied by successful farmers? The alternative would be an industry littered with hardship and bankruptcy into which he could enter easily – at his peril. It is a stark choice because he cannot have it both ways. Of course, the soft option is to choose a prosperous agriculture as well as easy entry into the industry. But life does not work like that.

He can forget the NFU/CLA agreement: it is irrelevant. Forget about term tenancies. Forget about fiscal reform for landlords. Forget about partnerships and share farming. Forget the clever schemes of even cleverer land agents. Just remember that only a bankrupt tenant farmer will ever really make space for a young man on the bottom rung. Which would you prefer?

Four years later I am not so sure. The 118 acres I bought was a terrible investment. It was purchased right at the top of the market. Today I would be lucky to receive half of what I paid. At this rate I shall be the bankrupt farmer who will be making room for my questioner. Don't laugh. I'm being serious.

Be Nice to a Conservationist – Plough Up an SSSI

DECEMBER 1983

Nobody – well, almost nobody – loves conservationists as much as I do. Which is just as well because I've been seeing a lot of them recently. We have two Sites of Special Scientific Interest (SSSI) on the farm, and readers of this paper should now be informed that within a few months I shall destroy all of the young trees on one of these sites. I hope I don't end up in gaol. I certainly can't be thrown out of the Country Landowners Association (like Hughie Batchelor) because I am not a member. What is even worse, I am not in the least ashamed of what I propose to do. In fact I have that warm and smug feeling which comes when you know you are doing the right and proper thing. The reason is that the conservationists have asked me to destroy all the young willows growing in Thriplow Meadows and, as you would expect, I bend over backwards to help the Cambridgeshire and Isle of Ely Naturalist Trust.

You see, they have a problem. The SSSI at Thriplow Meadows consists of a few acres of marshy grassland which is rare on the south Cambridgeshire chalks. In addition to being a "wet grassland site", the meadows also grow Marsh Orchids (*Dactylorhiza praetermissa*) which are of great interest to a handful of botanists. In the past we have been quite happy to leave this field untouched, and indeed we let it to the Naturalist Trust for a peppercorn rent. The snag is that the water table is falling little by little each year so the orchids, which need damp conditions, are today struggling to survive.

When I spoke to the Naturalist Trust to find out more about the problem, I was told that "it was the result of farmers draining the land". This knee-jerk reflex of a conservationist to blame farmers should not, I suppose, have surprised me – even if it was baloney. I pointed out, with enormous patience and politeness, that nobody in the area ever drained more than an acre or two because the chalk subsoil makes this unnecessary. When faced with this somewhat blunt fact, the conservationist agreed that it wasn't, after all, the farmers' fault but simply because the Anglian Water Authority was taking more and more water out of the aquifer. In doing so, they have lowered the water table and have threatened this important site. It was pleasant to be able to agree for once that farmers were not to blame.

My first reaction was that if nature had intended willow trees to grow there, then surely that is what should happen on an SSSI. But, of course, I was wrong again. Before long, I was told, the site would be nothing more than willow scrub. I wondered what was wrong with willow scrub, and was told that the orchids would disappear. The meadow should really be grazed – but not overgrazed, the conservationist explained – to keep the vegetation down.

The Naturalist Trust are therefore very worried about the future of our marsh orchids. So worried, indeed, that they have persuaded the Anglian Water Authority to spend no less than £50,000 on an intricate irrigation scheme to maintain the water table at an artificially high level. This work is known as sub-irrigation, and it consists of a network of perforated plastic pipes running below the surface. The water, which is pumped from a borehole which has been specially sunk half a mile away, will ensure the continued prosperity of the marsh orchids. All of which must be a comforting thought to the handful of botanists who once a year come and count these rather pretty flowers. It may be less comforting to those members of the public who pay water rates and are blissfully unaware that £50,000 of their money has been used on this delightful scheme. It certainly places a high cash value on each marsh orchid.

I myself do not cavil about such trifles, because to do so would be ungenerous and petty, but I wonder what the rest of the public feels. The fact is that they do not even know that such a scheme is under way, and still less do they know how much of their money is being spent. One day someone should tell them.

The role of the conservationist in this matter should, perhaps, be questioned. I am all in favour of a museum in which items from the past are preserved, and I have still less objection to places like Laxton, where the mediaeval Three Field System survives today. If the conservationists wish to preserve a meadow as it was 500 years ago, I am only too pleased. But to somehow imply that this is "the natural state of things" is nonsense.

Conservationists have once again taken a brief instant in the history of the world and have decided that this is the moment to preserve for ever. For thousands of years this meadow has existed, but for only a few hundred have men grazed animals on it. This, it seems, is when the conservationists would like to "stop the clock" and preserve it in aspic for the rest of time. I wondered what would have happened if some prehistoric conservationist had decided that dinosaurs and apes must be preserved at all costs. They would have succeeded in stopping evolution dead in its tracks and, as a result, the human race would never have existed. Neither, of course, would conservationists.

P.S. Since writing this piece I am relieved to announce that the foul deed has been done. But not by me. The conservationists decided that they could not wait for the farm staff to find a slack period and so they paid contractors to rip out all the trees. The sub-irrigation system has also been installed. This is good news for Marsh orchid lovers the world over. Not such fun, however, for the willow saplings.

A true story. And if you think this is a bit bizarre, read the article on page 291 which makes this one look tame.

Be Patient – If You Possibly Can

DECEMBER 1983

Patience is a virtue
Virtue is a grace
Grace was a cricketer
Who didn't wash his face

We used to chant this at school, so it is not surprising that I was brainwashed into believing that patience is a Good Thing. I changed my mind when I became a farmer.

Once upon a time, in those misty days when a Smythe Drill was State of The Art, farmers had to be patient. There was no point in hurrying. "There will always be a seedtime" they used to say, "and there will always be a harvest." Sure enough, there was. A horse could only plough so much in a day, a man could only broadcast so much seed. Take-all, bunt and rust were unstoppable, so why worry? No wonder farming was a relaxed profession.

Today I march to a different tune. With one eye watching the weather forecast and the other checking the price of Dicurane in France, I am the stuff that ulcers are made of. No longer do I chew a grain of barley and decide to take a holiday for a week before starting harvest. Armed with a battery of moisture meters (none of which ever agree with each other), I unleash the combines when the moisture gets down to 20%. My neighbours give themselves hernias laughing; and wait a few days. Their drying costs are low, their machinery breakdowns are rare and their nervous breakdowns unheard of.

I would always prefer to do today what the rest of the world does tomorrow. It is not that I am competitive (I am actually, but I am damned if I will admit it),I am just impatient. If there is one thing which can be guaranteed to send me into nervous convulsions, it is seeing a drill or a combine working while ours are still in the shed.

Deep down inside, I know that I am right. For every time I regret my impatience, there are five occasions when I thank heaven that I did not sit on my backside. Of course, there have been moments when I looked foolish. The day when the combines harvested 100 acres at 22% moisture and then the sun came out; if only I had waited, I would have saved a fortune in drying costs. The afternoon the drill went out and almost got stuck in the mud; two more days would have ensured a perfect seedbed but I simply could not wait. I must admit that I have often felt a fool.

In spite of these humiliating fiascos, I will not change my attitude by one iota. I shall still start drilling when it is too wet. The sprayer will still go out even though the wind will carry some of the chemical onto the next-door field. The combine will start even though it cannot thrash properly.

I like to think it makes sense on my size farm. If we start at the right time, we will inevitably finish too late. We are also on very early land, which makes life easier. If pressed, I shall talk boringly about the importance of timeliness. At the end of the day, I know in my guts that I am simply impatient. The longer I farm, the more convinced I am that we farmers do not what we think is right but what we feel is right.

If you think I am crazy, you should look at your own farm for a moment. You probably think that you farm the way you do simply because it "makes sense". If pressed as to why you do things the way you do, you might even cite some trials results which prove conclusively that you are doing the right thing. Any fool can find the trials results which support his own point of view.

You can, for example, find trials which show that drilling in early September does or does not make sense. You can find trials which show that prophylactic spraying is either sensible or stupid. Likewise, there is a body of scientific evidence which shows that 180 units of nitrogen is either the right amount or is far too much. If you read certain German literature, you can even find evidence that straw burning reduces your yields. You have, after all, paid your money and you are entitled to take your choice.

Take care not to fall into the trap of claiming that you farm the way you do because "it makes sense". You do it because you want to do it. I feel happiest being impatient.

Livestock in East Anglia

JANUARY 1984

I'm probably going soft in my old age, but I'm happy to have livestock on the farm. Here in deepest arable south Cambridgeshire we run a suckler herd of 100 Charolais as well as a 500 ewe breeding flock of mules. And for those people out there in readerland who fondly imagine that I am an owner-occupier of 3000 unmortgaged acres, I have some disappointing news. I pay a rent equivalent to 60 per acre. From this you will deduce what you have long suspected. I must be crazy.

It's not necessary to be an ADAS adviser to know that suckler herds only ever make sense where the rents are very low. It's one thing halfway up a mountain in Wales or Scotland with a Hill Cow Subsidy available. Even then, life is far from easy. But it's a very different story in East Anglia. Before you have a suckler herd in this part of the world, you need two possible qualifications: to be rich or stupid. I am fortunate to be both. I am rich compared to the man who runs a suckler herd on a mountainside, and stupid compared to my East Anglian neighbours who all know that livestock in Cambridgeshire is a licence to lose money.

But the fact is I'm still happy with the cattle. We have about 100 acres which were once upon a time parkland. It's not exactly Capability Brown and there are no ornamental lakes or avenues, but the trees look pretty and it would be a shame to plough up the grass. It's too big an area to rent out to pony-owners (besides, I'm not too keen on the pony fraternity) and the cows and calves look lovely there in the summer. So we have cattle. We tell ourselves that they produce muck which is good for the land, and they use straw in the open yards. But we secretly realise that this is nonsense. The herd can only show a profit if we don't charge them any rent for the land they occupy and, instead, load the cost onto the arable department. This is what is called "Creative Bookkeeping" by the trendier accountants, and I'm all in favour of it.

There is another reason why the suckler herd makes more sense than it might first appear. With our all-winter-corn regime, the farm has become ridiculously cyclical. From December, when we finish lifting beet, to mid-July when we start harvest, there isn't a lot to do. But at least with the beef herd there is always littering down, feeding and calving. This provides jobs for several men right through the winter and early spring.

The sheep, however, are a very different matter. We started the flock only four years ago and have built it up from 300 head. I suppose we were fortunate to get into sheep just at the time when the EEC decided to throw money at the industry. Looking back, it was one of my luckier decisions.

The theory was that our sheep would scavenge the arable by-products. They would eat sugar beet tops, thrashed ryegrass straw, pea haulm and other bits and pieces. As far as the fodder is concerned, it has all worked out well. But we are now in danger of becoming victims of our own success. The snag is that a flock of 500 ewes is neither small nor big. It certainly cannot justify a full-time shepherd but yet it needs more than half a man for most of the year. This man also needs an expensive vehicle.

None of this, of course, is a reflection on George, the shepherd, who cheerfully drives a lorry and does lots of other jobs. But he really wants to be a shepherd pure and simple. And I can't blame him either. He's entirely self-taught and, as a result, is keener and more energetic than most of this fellow shepherds. But it certainly makes the foreman's life awkward when he has to find the shepherd jobs to do for the odd hour or two each day. It would be far simpler if he were a full-time shepherd looking after 1200 ewes.

But life is never that easy. We just don't have the forage to feed that number of animals during the summer. To do so would mean altering the cropping and the rotation on the whole farm. This would result in less corn and more grass. It would also mean that the tail was wagging the sheep because we decided from the beginning that the sheep flock would always have to fit in with the arable system and not the other way round.

So we are now caught in a dilemma which suggests that we should either double the size of the flock or reduce it. Of course, we shall almost certainly do nothing at all and just let events take their course. In the meanwhile I look forward to calving and lambing which happen at times of year which would otherwise be boring. There is also the comfy feeling that if the arable bubble ever does burst in a big way, we shall have managed to build up quite a valuable amount of livestock. They might, after all, make the difference between a happy and an unhappy bank manager.

I read this piece with a lump in my throat. We do not have a single animal on the farm any more. It was all very well having livestock while we could afford it. But as soon as the arable boom came to an end in 1987, the sheep were the first casualties. The suckler herd had made room for more sheep three years earlier. Looking backwards, it is clear now that I too was using "Creative Accounting" when I decided that the flock was making money. If today I could still afford to have livestock on land carrying a £53 per acre rent charge, I would love to do so.

Richard Butler for President

FEBRUARY 1984

With friends like you, said the vet one day, who needs enemas? My support is something Sir Richard Butler might prefer to do without. But I'm going to give it to him anyway because he deserves to be re-elected president of the NFU. He's done a good job, and he also happens to be far better than the people who would like to see him defeated.

Of course it's easy to hark back to those wonderful sunlit days when Sir Henry Plumb (of sainted memory) presided over the National Farmers Union. Only those of us now approaching senility can remember that golden age when you could put up a PRIVATE – NO TRESPASSING sign without even a twinge of guilt. Those were the days when FMC was the jewel in the NFU Crown, when only wets and wimps bothered about firebreaks before burning straw, when Richard Body★ and Jack Boddy★★ were nobodies, when rents were low and landlords were friendly. Pigs were making money and poultry was profitable too. Our only problem was that we had to wait twelve months to take delivery of a new tractor, and during that period the price rose four times.

★   Now Sir Richard Body. Tory member of parliament for Holland and Boston. The former Chairman of the Commons Agriculture Select Committee, he is passionately anti Common Market. Body used to (and for all I know still does) contribute to *Private Eye's* "Old Muckspreader" column.
★★   The last General Secretary of the NUAAW before it was swallowed up by the Transport and General Workers Union. Now retired.

Looking backwards is a posture which most farmers seem to find very comfortable. So I don't suppose I should be surprised when I hear how wonderful Sir Henry was and how inadequate Sir Richard is. Nobody seems to bother that Henry Plumb had an easy job to do and Richard Butler has an impossible one. It would be easier (and more rewarding) to teach logic in an insane asylum than run the NFU today.

Here I am sitting in solitary splendour in sunny south Cambridgeshire trying to sell feed barley at the highest possible price. Meanwhile, 200 miles south west of me a depressed Devon dairy farmer is trying to screw a low price for cake out of his not too friendly local merchant. Both of us are dissatisfied without our lot (I'm not really, but for the purpose of this argument I shall pretend to be) so we go along to our local NFU branch to protest. Our complaints wind their way through the labyrinthine complexities of the Union to the County branch and thence to Agriculture House where Headquarters delegates faithfully present our views. These men, the Shock Troops of the NFU (and believe me, some of them are really shocking), make impassioned speeches on behalf of their Cambridgeshire and Devon members. After a drink or two – or three – they go home safe in the knowledge that they at least have done their jobs well. They report back to their County Committees that they delivered the message forcefully and effectively. Bully for them.

The buck, however, stops with the chap who's running the show. Richard Butler, you see, has to keep both me and my Devonian friend happy. Naturally, the dairy farmer is deeply suspicious because he sees Butler as nothing less than another East Anglian Barley Baron. For this reason Butler has to lean over backwards to dispel the impression that he might be biased in my favour. But whatever he does, it is clearly impossible to satisfy both of us.

But the internal problems of the NFU are only the beginnings of Sir Richard's troubles. Many (I almost said most) farmers have so isolated themselves from reality that they live in a never-never world in which unemployment does not really exist and poverty is something which Oxfam should worry about. They spend their time complaining to other farmers about how difficult life is and how few pheasants there will be next year.

But the President of the NFU has to live in the real world and speak to people who, for some inexplicable reason, are not farmers.

He has, for example, to speak to Consumers and explain why we are subsidised to produce food which nobody wants or can afford. He must speak to ratepayers and explain why we don't pay rates on our land. He must address groups of planners and explain why we do not need planning permission for many of our buildings. He must explain to hostile audiences why farmers have remained untouched by the economic winds which have blown throughout the rest of the economy. He must justify – or at least attempt to – straw burning and all the other things we do which annoy the rest of society.

The single most important qualification for someone to run a Union is to be stupid. Those who, unfortunately, have been afflicted with intelligence usually spend most of their time trying to conceal this characteristic from their members. The brighter you are, the more easily you can distinguish the wood from the trees – and the more complicated your life becomes. An Arthur Scargill would have no problem running the NFU. His policy would be simple: highest prices for every commodity, unrestricted straw burning and to hell with the rest of society. I have no doubt that many of the people who wish to see the end of Sir Richard Butler would support this manifesto.

I just happen to be one of those wets who want to see farmers talking and not fighting with the rest of the population. I would like to see the prejudices of farmers giving way to a new understanding of how other people feel about us. To achieve this, a lot of old-fashioned farmers will inevitably be upset unless they are handled with tact and sympathy. Maybe I'm wrong, but I reckon there's a better chance of this happening if Richard Butler stays on at the wheel.

At the time of writing this piece I felt Richard Butler would be a better President than the then Vice President, Simon Gourlay; I was wrong. Gourlay has since shown that he is far better equipped to preside over the NFU at a time when the going is getting rough for farmers.

The Sodbuster

FEBRUARY 1984

"How many acres do you farm?" I asked. John J. Greytak looked up at the ceiling, scratched the back of his head and said in a quiet voice, "I guess I've got around 350,000 acres under the plough, with another half million acres of rough grazing."

In the state of Montana you've got to be large to be noticed at all. It is one and a half times bigger than the United Kingdom, but the population is only the same as Leeds. In the east there are vast, rolling grasslands where once the buffalo kept the Indians company. Seven hundred miles to the west, the Rocky Mountains rise to twelve thousand feet.

John J. Greytak is the most hated man in Montana agriculture today. According to the ranchers, it is because he buys the native grassland, ploughs it up and drills it with wheat. This practice, known as "sodbusting", is – they claim – dangerous, irresponsible and just plain greedy. I was assured that the fragile soils his ploughs expose are not suited to arable farming. Within a few years they will blow away, and he will have wrecked land which took thousands of years to create. But the Montana ranchers also have a problem. Like all American farmers, they believe passionately that a man should be able to do what he likes with his own property. This, after all, is America, the Land of the Free.

Thus, when two or three Montana ranchers are gathered together these days, they don't just talk about the price of beef on the hoof; they agonise over whether or not sodbusting should be made illegal. You can imagine the debate, therefore, when Petroleum County restricted the amount of grassland which could be ploughed by a single farmer to a quarter section (160 acres) per year. Farmers and ranchers were jubilant that the hated Greytak had been stopped. But they also had an uneasy feeling that the principle behind this law might one day curtail their own liberty.

John J. Greytak, on the other hand, is mercifully free of all these doubts. With his 350,000 acres of arable land, and half a million acres of rough grazing, he must be the biggest farmer in the western world. And he has done it all in the last ten years. His formula is simple. Whenever a rancher sells up, Greytak is one of the few buyers of range land. The actual price he pays depends on the quality of the soil and the rainfall in the area, but it varies from £80 to £120 per acre. Had he bought arable land of a similar quality he would have had to pay three times this amount.

In 1982 Greytak ploughed 25,000 acres of range land. Last year his tractors covered 35,000 acres, and this year he is planning to convert no less than 50,000 acres of virgin grassland to wheat production. He will, in other words, be opening an area equivalent to half the size of the Isle of Wight in a single year.

No wonder the other farmers in Montana hate and fear him. Greytak, they insist, isn't a farmer at all. He's a land speculator who is only interested in a quick capital gain. Give him a few years and he will sell the land and get out of farming altogether. That is why he is keen to plough soil which ought never to be ploughed at all. The ranchers are certain that this land will erode so badly that it won't even be able to grow grass for another hundred years. But Greytak, they say, won't be around to worry about the damage he has done.

Behind this vehement denunciation of John J. Greytak, there lingers the unmistakable smell of envy. Greytak is, after all, only doing what most other farmers would love to do, if only they had the cash, the energy and the talent.

It was a grey and windy morning when my plane landed in Billings before breakfast one Saturday. Billings airport is on a high bluff overlooking the town and I could see that the streets were deserted, the shops had not opened, and snow flurries reminded me why not many people ever take holidays during December in Montana. I was in town for one reason only. I had been told to come to the offices of the First Continental Corporation by 10.30 if I wanted to speak to Mr Greytak. Both the name of the Company, and the address, made me head for the financial district with its smart shops and large office buildings. I was wrong. Greytak's operation is on the other side of the tracks. As always in American towns, the world changes abruptly once you cross the railway lines. Walk along a seedy street with garbage blowing in the wind, past derelict petrol stations and working men's clubs without windows, and in the distance you see some grain silos.

Inside the building a computer was working quietly while lorry drivers queued up to get their weighbridge tickets signed after tipping loads of wheat. I was given a paper cup of weak coffee and asked to wait. Half an hour passed while I sat and eavesdropped on a conversation between a man in a check shirt who was lecturing a

young executive on the importance of good machinery maintenance. Finally the conversation broke up and the older man
introduced himself to me. "Hi. I'm John Greytak. You wanted to
see me."

We sat in his small office and he explained how he'd got started.
He never intended to be a farmer, and still didn't really think of
himself as one. "I guess you could call me an entrepreneur really.
I've sold automobiles and real estate. Still do, as a matter of fact. To
me farming is a cold, hard business and I'm in it for the profit." I
began to sympathise with the ranchers. But behind this tough and
very urban exterior, Greytak knew a lot about wheat. He asked me
detailed questions about High Input farming in Europe, and
complained that he had to go to Canada to buy growth regulators
because they weren't available in the United States.

His wheat yields, I learned, depend largely on the rainfall, which
varies enormously in different areas of his holding. "You need four
inches of rain a year to grow an empty ear of wheat. After that we
reckon that for every additional inch of rain we'll get around seven
bushels (3.75cwt) of wheat." The average yield for the whole farm
amounted to just over one tonne per acre for the hard red winter
wheat which is the normal crop in Montana.

On the sensitive matter of prices, he admitted that he was still
able to make money even though he was receiving only £85 per ton
for 14% protein hard breadmaking wheat. His breakeven point was
around £75 per ton. Greytak reckoned that unless something was
done about wheat surpluses in the world, he might find himself
selling at £62 per ton within the near future. "I hate to pray for a
drought," he said, "but that's what we really need for the next two
years. Of course, the best thing would be for the dollar to be
devalued by 25%. It's much too strong and it makes it tough to sell
our wheat when we have to compete with you guys in Europe."

I asked him why he felt the Montana farmers disliked him so
heartily. "I guess there's an element of envy," he mused, "and I
understand why. The cattle business has been a disaster for eight
out of the last ten years. Those guys are hurting badly." But this
lack of affection has not lessened Greytak's drive. "My ambition is
to plough half a million acres and to have 20,000 cattle to scavenge
the by-products from the farming operation."

When it came to running a farm of this size, he admitted that
there were a few problems. "In the United States the large
corporate farms usually fail because of management problems. No

matter how good the boss is, it's tough making sure that the guy on the tractor does things right." It was for this reason that he decided not to own a single combine. Instead he uses contractors at harvest and has as many as 120 machines working on the farm at the same time. "We've got a stronger lever over contractors because they're all profit-oriented. Besides, owning your own machinery creates a blizzard of paperwork," Greytak explained. It is perhaps lucky that he owns the biggest grain silos in Montana, because storing the output from these machines could be a problem. As far as tractors were concerned, he aims to own about half, and to use contractors for the remainder of the work. "There's no point in having small tractors of less than 300 horsepower," he said; "they're only good for running grain augers". Most of Greytak's tractors are either 525 horsepower Big Buds, which pull 70 feet cultivators, or 450 horsepower Steigers which use 60 feet wide machines.

I left Billings as the snow began to fall again and the inhabitants settled in for a hard winter. The outline of the nearby mountains was blurred. So also were my ideas about John J. Greytak. He was clearly not the wicked robber baron I had heard about from the local ranchers, but it was impossible to tell whether his ploughs were destroying the native grassland. You cannot remotely assess a farm without looking at the crops, and one day I shall return to the Big Sky Country to do just that. In the meanwhile I must admit that if I were a Montana farmer, I might be a sodbuster.

I revisited Greytak three years later and found him still in business. As the steam went out of the arable boom, his farming operation had shrunk to a mere 250,000 acres of ploughed land. The controversy over sodbusting had subsided and John J. Greytak, slightly more subdued than when I had first met him, was almost a member of the Montana Establishment.

Boy's Land

MARCH 1984

I don't get many abusive phone calls, but when I do they invariably come from men with clay on their boots. I, of course, farm Boy's Land and, as a result, have succeeded in annoying just about every Man's Land farmer in the country. Or so it seems when the phone rings and a voice says: "If you're half as clever as you think you are, you'd better come over to my farm and tell me what I'm going to do with all my straw." The caller takes a deep breath and continues: "I've farmed this land all my life and I'm telling you straight that there's no way I can possibly incorporate straw."

By now he's really getting into his stride, and he continues: "What's more, you're doing the industry no good at all by saying all those damn fool things. I just wish you'd keep your mouth shut for a bit. We've got enough problems without the likes of you." I know he has finished because there is a faint click as he hangs up without even telling me his name.

My clay-booted friend is, in a way, right. It's all very well for me to announce that I'm not burning straw any more, but what are we going to do with the stuff? It was to answer this question that I attended a couple of conferences recently. One was at the National Agricultural Centre, Stoneleigh, along with 250 worried farmers.

The other was a slightly more select occasion organised by the Claas combine people at their factory in Germany. There, a handful of us sat and listened to German advisers, and a heavy land farmer, tell us of their experiences during the past decade. If all had gone according to plan, I would now be one of the best-informed men in British agriculture. But it didn't work out like that, which is why I am far more muddled than I was before.

There are, happily, a few things about which there is no argument. You should definitely have a chopper on your combine, and you should make sure that the knives are kept sharp during harvest so that the length of the chopped straw stays as close to 2 inches as possible. So hurry and order your combine chopper today. They'll all be sold out soon.

The confusion begins even before the combine has left the field. Do you need to put on nitrogen to help the straw break down? Most people reckon it is a good idea for the first few years, but others think this is a waste of money.

When it comes to straw incorporation, the experts themselves disagree about how to mix the straw into the top eight inches of the soil. There is even one school of thought which maintains that incorporation itself is a waste of time; just plough the stuff straight under, they say. I myself will not do this, except on a single field just to see what happens.

Instead I'll play it safe and put a set of heavy discs into the field the moment the combine leaves. After that I shall wait for as long as I dare before using a cultivator at about eight inches. I won't buy one of those fancy and very expensive Soil-Saver gadgets because I think they are unnecessary gimmicks. But it is important to get a fast forward speed, and to do this we shall take the wings off our big cultivators and use a 150 hp tractor to try and travel at around 6mph.

With a lot of luck, these two operations should have mixed the chopped straw into the top layer of the soil. But, of course, in real life it is never that easy. The soil may well be too puffy, and it might be necessary to roll before ploughing.

The Germans, who are the acknowledged experts in the whole business of straw incorporation, feel that the deeper you plough, the more virile you are. I, on the other hand, like ploughing to no more than ten inches. I've never claimed to be particularly virile either. On some of our land the chalk is only eight inches deep, and we shall certainly have difficulties on those fields.

Our existing ploughs are English, and so have relatively small underbeam clearances. Their inter-body clearance is also much less than on a normal German plough. I have already decided to dispense with the skims and use trashboards instead, but I can't make up my mind whether or not to buy longer legs and increase the underbeam clearance to around 30 inches.

Once you have ploughed properly your problems should, repeat should, have disappeared. But, naturally, they won't. The Germans go to endless lengths – and use lots of power – to produce seedbeds for winter corn which would be better suited for onions. After a furrow press comes a combination of spring tines, rolls, crumbler bars and the job is finished off with a power harrow. I won't waste my time with this sort of procession. Instead we'll use a Dutch harrow and drill straight behind.

And here we get back to my abusive telephone friend again. He is angry because he needs more horsepower to incorporate straw than I do. He insists that unless he is allowed to burn straw, he won't be able to grow winter wheat at all. I am afraid I am not entirely sympathetic to his plight. Why should he be surprised? It has always been more difficult to farm strong land, and nothing will ever change that.

I just don't believe him when he says that he can't grow winter wheat at all without burning straw. But he should face the fact that nobody has a God-given right to grow whatever crop he wishes. If it just so happens that in future heavy land cannot grow winter wheat, he will have to alter his cropping. I cannot grow vegetables on my chalk, nor can I grow pineapples if it comes to that. I just have to find the crops which suit my land and do the best job I can. But I promise to be more polite the next time you ring.

We are still using straw choppers and mouldboard ploughs to deal with our straw. However, since those early days of experimentation, we have given up straw incorporation as recommended by the Germans. The problem of ungerminated seeds turning up in the next year's crop as volunteers became too acute. After a quick discing, we plough and furrow press the land. ADAS have decided that the best method is simply to chop the straw and plough it straight in. Once again it looks as if the German farmer is using more power than he needs to.

Walston's First Law of Gastronomy

APRIL 1984

The farms in Lincolnshire are the best in Europe, but the restaurants in that county are worse than in East Germany. My own Cambridgeshire – where the farming isn't bad either – is only tolerable if you have acquired a taste for rancid chips, overcooked vegetables, microwaved meat and semi-thawed Black Forest Gateau. Rupert Brooke may have called Cambridgeshire "The shire for men who understand", but in a Cambridgeshire restaurant today you understand only one thing: the true meaning of despair.

I feel a bit sheepish, not to say cowed, admitting such piggish tendencies in this country. Britain's gifts to gastronomy have, after all, included such delicacies as spaghetti ring, Mother's Pride and motorway cafs with their smell of stale malt vinegar and greasy tables on which uncomplaining natives eat cold fried eggs with enjoyment and HP sauce.

Happily, it is still possible to have excellent meals in private houses, and I'm delighted to know some farmers who display alarmingly gluttonous tendencies. But the fact remains that I have never yet eaten a really – repeat really – good meal in an East Anglian restaurant. This is a profoundly worrying problem which I often think about as I lie in the bath planning my next trip to France.

And then one day it happened. As the water turned tepid and a ring formed round the edge, I made the Great Discovery.

I am now in a position to reveal what will undoubtedly become known to generations as yet unborn as Walston's First Law of Gastronomy. It goes thus: "The quality of restaurants in a given area is in direct inverse proportion to the prosperity of agriculture in the same area." In other words, the better the farming the worse the cooking.

If you doubt this proposition for a second, I suggest you get hold of the following three volumes, *The Good Food Guide*, the *Michelin Guide To France* and the *Michelin Guide To Germany*. Turn to the map sections and look at the arable areas of these countries. Examine, for instance, Lincolnshire and see how many good restaurants appear. Open the red *Michelin Guide To France* and look at the Beauce, the region around Chartres which grows the best wheat in the country. You will be hard pushed to find a single restaurant with a rosette. If you are still unconvinced, open the German Michelin and look at Schleswig-Holstein where the biggest and best German farms are located. You will find a gastronomic desert.

As I drive west from Cambridgeshire, I find that something odd happens the moment I leave Bedfordshire. It's not just that I am leaving the brickworks and the Brussels sprouts behind me (although it helps). Gradually, good restaurants start appearing. As the prosperity of the local agriculture declines, the standard of cooking improves. Thus, by the time I reach Gloucestershire, choosing a place to eat becomes difficult because there are so many possibilities. The same is true in France when I move south from the Paris basin. The starred restaurants grow ever more frequent until I

reach the Lyonnais where almost every village has food of the sort I only dream about in England.

In Germany, the nearer to the Bavarian border I get, the happier my stomach becomes. There is that magical moment when I actually cross what the Germans call "The White Sausage Equator". This imaginary line, which runs along the River Main, marks the northerly limits of that masterpiece of Bavarian butchers – the Weisswurst. This sublime sausage, which has to be eaten fresh before midday, is one of the very rare examples of German food which is superior to its French counterpart – the boring boudin blanc.

Across the Atlantic Walston's First Law of Gastronomy is equally valid. Eat a meal in the wheatlands of Kansas or Saskatchewan and you can guarantee that it sprang fully-clothed from the freezer by way of the microwave. But go south to the poor farms of the Mississippi Delta and the food becomes ever more interesting until it reaches a peak of excellence in the Creole cooking of deepest Louisiana.

But as with all immutable Laws, some mutations do occur. I have to admit that there are a few exceptions for which I have no convincing explanations. Why, for example, is the food so uniformly awful in Scotland when the farming isn't that hot either? I am, of course, still researching this particular problem.

By the time this humble treatise appears I shall once again be conducting my research on the far side of the Atlantic. This time the trail will lead me to the Appalachian Mountains of West Virginia where the farming is certainly poor but the Bourbon whiskey is sublime. I shall be there, however, not to sample the alcohol but to look for a vegetable. It is called "ramps" and is said to taste and smell stronger than any garlic or onion known to man. It grows only on the northern slopes of the Appalachians. Every spring the town of Richwood holds a Ramps Festival, and this year I shall make the arduous pilgrimage from south Cambridgeshire to see what all the fuss is about.

I am, of course, optimistic because I know that however bad the food is in West Virginia, it will certainly be better than Lincolnshire.

Walston's First Law of Gastronomy has since been joined by the Second Law: "The longer the cork, the better the wine".

Open Up Your Farms to the Public

MAY 1984

Farmer-bashing is the latest national sport and, as a result, I'm beginning to sympathise with foxes, partridges and electric hares at greyhound stadiums. Like those bald, blue-chinned flabby wrestlers on television, we are fast becoming The Men They Love To

Hate. In public I pretend I don't care. In fact I make jokes at my own expense and hope the rest of the world will leave me alone.

But when faced with a continual barrage from every newspaper and television station in the land, I remember the words of my American political hero, Adlai Stevenson, "I'm too old to cry, but it hurts too much to laugh." This is the dilemma of today's thinking farmer.

The temptation is to sulk. As Brussels tightens the screws on horn and corn alike, it is all too easy to adopt a siege mentality. I can just hear the John Waynes of the NFU ordering that the wagons be put in a circle. I hope I'm wrong, because this would be fatal.

Now is the time to go on to the offensive. Now is the time that farmers should put their mouths where the money is. Now is the time when we should open our doors, our barns, our dairies and our farms. Now is the time to have an Open Day.

It doesn't matter what you do or how you do it, just get the people onto your farm. Use gimmicks, bribery, sex, violence or even just good old-fashioned charm. "The end," as Lenin said, "justifies the means." Try a little Leninism on your farm. But not too much.

So you won't be entirely surprised to learn that we are having an Open Day at Thriplow on Sunday, June 10th. Unlike many farmers, we've never done this before, so we are navigating blind. We may make some pretty spectacular mistakes, but in the hope that other farms can profit from our cock-ups, this is what we are proposing to do.

The one group of people we are not trying to attract is farmers. We won't be looking for sharp eyespot in the wheat, mildew in the barley or phoma in the rape. Instead, we shall be lining up all our machinery: 20 tractors, four combines, three lorries and a sugar beet harvester. A neighbour will be bringing a 1941 Fordson Major and a binder which will contrast with the Claas 116CS combine. We shall attach as many implements as possible and will put them in chronological order to demonstrate the sequence of events in the farming year. The drivers of these machines will be there to answer questions and (where possible) demonstrate.

Our local paper, one of the most vehemently anti-farmer organs between Tipperary and Tomsk, is actually being very helpful indeed. It is organising a scarecrow competition, and the actual judging will take place during the Open Day. This will, we hope, attract a lot of people who might not normally have come, and certainly the publicity provided by the paper will do a lot of good.

We already have a farm museum in a disused barn, and although it is a primitive affair compared to many, we shall be moving most of the contents down to the grainstore where the Open Day is being held. In addition to the above attractions, we have persuaded the local thatcher to turn up, and there will be a lady making corn dollies. Never underestimate the power of nostalgia. We ourselves will, however, resist the temptation to dress up in smocks and chew straw.

On the livestock side, we shall be showing off the sheep and beef cattle. George, the shepherd, will be shearing and a lady from the village will be spinning and weaving. Our dairy herd now consists of two cows, but we might be able to do some hand milking for fun. The odd goat, rabbit and chicken will make up the rest of the menagerie. I have no doubt that the majority of the public will head straight for the livestock. They inevitably prefer furry animals to fungicides, and I can't say I blame them either.

We shall be selling various souvenirs, including mugs, caps and badges with the farm's name on them. This should at least enable us to cover our costs. Any profit is being given to the local spastics' school, and they will be bringing ponies to give children rides.

So much for the display itself. On the practical side we are still feeling our way. Who does the catering? How many toilets do we need? What about car parks? What happens if it rains? But there is another problem which is more important than all the others put together. If our Open Day is to make any sense at all, we must ensure that the visitors go away understanding farming better than when they came. They should realise that we are not avaricious destroyers of the countryside who plaster the fields with chemicals, put sows in farrowing crates and rip out hedges when we are short of amusement.

It won't be an easy task, but by inviting the public to come and see for themselves, we will at least have made a start.

The Open Day was a success. About 500 people turned up to look at the animals and the machinery. However, we have not repeated the excercise. It took a lot of work, cost a lot of money, and now that we employ only seven people on 3000 acres, we simply do not have the time or the staff to organise another Open Day. A pity.

Send a Tonne to Africa

JUNE 1984

Thank goodness my television has a remote control. I can tolerate wars, murder, riots, road accidents and drug addiction if I have to, but I absolutely refuse to watch pictures of starving human beings. At the first sign of a swollen belly, I switch my mind off – and the television too.

I have a vague idea that most farmers share this feeling, and so by now you will be thinking of turning to the classified ads to see what second-hand machinery is available this week, or who is looking for a working farm manager in Suffolk. But stop. Stay tuned to this column for as long as your stomach allows.

I suppose the reason I turn off my TV set is because I feel uneasy. I almost said guilty. My farm produces more food than anyone in Europe seems to want, and yet at the same time there are people dying of starvation. This paradox is so unpleasant to think about that I simply cop out altogether and don't even start.

Of course, I reassure myself, it's not my fault. We farmers are only doing what governments have asked us. The problem of starvation is one for the politicians to face. My job is to produce food; theirs is to see it reaches the people who need it. But with harvest now only a few weeks away, it is time to face reality even if it stinks. And I suppose starvation does stink if ever you are near enough to smell anything. But back home in comfy Cambridgeshire it looks as if once again our wheat and barley will yield reasonably well. Our oilseed rape would have done better if the pigeons had left it alone. The peas won't break any records and the sugar beet was all re-drilled. But one thing is certain; we shall have a harvest at Thriplow this year. Which is more than can be said for lots of African farmers. Some of them have not had a harvest for four years. Four years without a harvest.

Like so many complacent, fat Englishmen, I was brought up on the old adage that "there'll always be a seed time and there'll always be a harvest". And so there is. Harvest is what comes after haytime, just as lunch comes after breakfast and supper comes after tea. With great difficulty I can just imagine what it would be like if one of our fields did not produce a crop this year. But the idea of not having a harvest at all is impossible to visualise. And to miss four consecutive harvests is so ludicrous that it would be laughable if it weren't so horrible. The solution is to dismiss these thoughts from my head and get on with the serious business of preparing the combine. And wondering what's for supper.

But this harvest there is no excuse any longer. This summer we can make sure that at least a tiny amount of our crop goes to feed starving people. The Send a Tonne to Africa campaign means that no longer can I just sit back and think it is someone elses's problem. Now it is my problem.

Of course, there will be lots of excuses. There is the prosperous farmer who buys you a drink and begins: "It deserves to succeed, old chap, but frankly I've given quite a bit away already this year and so won't be able to cough up." Nudge nudge, wink wink. Know what I mean?

Then there is the businessman who isn't fooled by anybody. "It's a great idea in theory but, believe me, I know what goes on in Africa. The wheat will never reach the people who need it. It'll be either eaten by rats or sold on the black market. Of course, I'd love to help you but I'd just be throwing my money away."

This excuse is patently ridiculous because it neglects the crucial fact that the wheat will be given to War on Want, which is made up of professionals in the business of food aid, just as we farmers are professionals in the business of growing food. It is true that there will be more wastage in Africa than we would tolerate in this country, but to use this as an excuse for not contributing is a shameful manoeuvre which deserves to be exposed.

There is the cynical television producer who, after completing yet another film showing how greedy and unpleasant farmers really are, has no doubt at all. "It's a typically empty gesture to salve your own consciences," he says. "The worst thing you can possibly do is to dump wheat into the Third World. You'll do far more harm than good by making them dependent on direct food aid from rich countries."

This man is perfectly correct. He is right to remind us that what the poor countries need is not food as much as technology and cash. But he has failed to understand that Send a Tonne to Africa is simply a short-term measure to help a specific problem – famine. When human beings are starving, there is no point talking about economic infrastructure when all they need is food.

Lastly, there's the small farmer who's got it all worked out. "It's all very well for you big boys," he begins, "but I've only got a hundred acres and I can't afford to throw money around like you can." He's right, of course. I am a spendthrift. But he could still manage half a tonne of barley without feeling the pinch.

So this summer when you are on the combine, in the barn or just dropping off to sleep, force yourself to think about the unthinkable. Before you switch your brain off and the television on, wonder what it would be like if you were facing your fifth harvest without a crop. Send a Tonne to Africa. Or half a tonne. It might just make a difference.

The Send a Tonne campaign, which had a shipload of wheat in Africa before Bob Geldof even thought of the idea of Band-Aid, raised £2.2 million in 12 months. We were fortunate that the appeal coincided with the biggest harvest in the history of British agriculture. It would be difficult (probably impossible) to repeat the success in today's economic climate.

Welcome to the Real World

JULY 1984

British growers are now producing wheat at the world market price. This may surprise you if, like me, you have been brainwashed into believing that we are all flabby, feather-bedded, highcost producers. It isn't true any longer.

This all became clear in the middle of a transatlantic phone call to my friend, Loren Wehrenberg, an American wheat grower. Loren, who farms in northern Oklahoma, finished his harvest by the end of June. Yields were down by a couple of hundredweight from last year to one tonne per acre, but he was reasonably happy with a price of £96 ex farm. He had just been offered £104 per tonne delivered to the inland dock at Tulsa some 100 miles away, and had agreed to sell some of his crop at this price.

Of course, Loren Wehrenberg grows hard red winter wheat with a protein content of around 14% so it can't be compared too closely with British feed wheat. But nevertheless, his price is probably only

£7 a tonne less than we shall receive in England this summer. By the time Loren's Oklahoma wheat has been shipped to Rotterdam, there won't be much of a price difference between my Avalon and his hard red winter.

After speaking to Loren, I realised that farming by phone was fun. So I had a quick check round some of my other friends. I rang Bob Linnell, a Canadian wheat farmer who has 800 acres of Saskatchewan prairie. Bob only grows spring corn because the winters are so fierce. Unlike Loren, he was not a happy man. Since seeding the wheat in May, there had been only 1.5 inches of rain and crops looked poor. Harvest won't be until late August but Bob reckoned that his yields would be around 14cwt an acre, instead of the 18cwt he got last year. The price is going to be £87 a tonne, which is also slightly less than last year. But all was not gloom in Saskatchewan, Bob said. The oilseed rape growers were having a wonderful time, with the price reaching £355 a tonne, compared to £235 last year.

By now my dialling finger was twitching uncontrollably. As with all addicts, the only solution was to indulge the craving. I turned my attention to Europe and rang Francis Cappelle, who farms just outside Laon in northern France. His sugar beet looked excellent, he said, which was particularly galling because we've re-drilled all ours. He was less happy with the rape because the pigeons had given him hell last winter, but he was confident that he would get at least a tonne an acre – and probably more. The cereals looked well, and he would be disappointed if any of them did less than 3 tonnes per acre. But the price was a different matter altogether. There was almost no premium for milling wheat, and it looked as if £100 a tonne would be par for the course at harvest time. The gap between Picardy and Oklahoma prices is almost too narrow to measure.

The news from Germany was very different. Christof Schwab, who farms near Regensburg in Bavaria, has had the coldest summer he can remember. Some of his wheats have only just started flowering, and harvest will be at least two weeks later than usual. The crop itself looks good, and he's optimistic about yields. The price will be at least 10% down on last year and he thinks he will be lucky if he can make £110 per tonne. But his real worry is the maize which, after all this cold weather, is very bad indeed. Sugar beet, on the other hand, is reasonable. In this part of Europe, where yields of 30 tonnes per acre are normal and you can sell your beet contract to another grower for £2500 an acre, it looks as if there will be a lot of sugar in Bavaria once again.

Further north in Germany, the Schleswig-Holstein farmers have also had a cold, wet June. Dr Haberland, who advises a group of 30 farmers in the Kiel area, thinks that cereal yields will only be average this year – certainly less than last year's good harvest. Beet looks better than he's known it for some time, but rape is disappointing. Few large Holstein farmers sell grain at harvest time, so Haberland did not want to predict a price other than to say it would be down by at least 8% on last year. Ear diseases on wheat which are now showing in the region would, he felt, certainly affect the quality, and this would also have the effect of pushing prices down.

So the picture across northern Europe appears to be consistent. Prices coming down while yields (with the possible exception of Britain) remaining static. Maybe the CAP will be able to stagger on for another year or so without major surgery. Hooray.

But before we all start becoming too optimistic, it's worth remembering that the main reason why the price gap between Loren Wehrenberg's wheat and mine has narrowed so much is simply because the dollar is strong today. At $1.31 to the pound, a lot of people reckon it is overvalued by 25% and will, as a result, come down. As someone who is sending his wife and children to the States this summer, I certainly hope it does.

And for all those charming and refined men in Brussels, I have some bad news for you, too. Just in case you were beginning to think that you were going to save a fortune on export restitutions, forget it. I reckon that for every ten tonnes of corn which goes through a combine in Britain this harvest, nearly three tonnes will be surplus to our needs. It looks as if there will be around five million tonnes to export this year. The trouble is that I couldn't bring myself to tell Loren Wehrenberg the news. I want to remain his friend.

The Common Ground

AUGUST 1984

The loudest noise around the countryside these days is the sound of farmers changing their minds. Opinions about straw burning, conservationists, and even the CAP are beginning to shift. It is reminiscent of the crew of the Titanic when they realised that their unsinkable ship was actually filling with water.

Since the last war, we farmers have insulated ourselves from the real, snug and smug in the belief that we are somehow different. But now we have been well and truly rumbled. Of course, this makes no difference to the good old-fashioned diehards, most of whom are so reactionary that they like to call themselves Yeomen. These men have a sneaking sympathy with Hughie Batchelor. For all his faults, they say, at least he's standing up for the right of a farmer to do anything he wants with his own land. Unlike Mr Batchelor, however, they prefer growling over a gin and tonic at home rather than over a tree stump outside. But we can forget this tired bunch of tattered Yeomen because their numbers and influence are very small indeed.

A more significant type of farmer is represented by Monty Keen*, who is reluctantly coming to terms with the fact that history is passing us by. He accepts that the conservation lobby is here to stay, and even pays them the compliment that it is admirable in concept and belated in action. But, having made that slight genuflection, he goes on to ridicule the more crazy excesses of the movement. This is like shooting fish in a barrel. We can all think of outrageously stupid things which conservationists have said or done. Marion Shoard is the classic example of one who destroyed her own case with twisted facts and exaggerated accusations. It is no more sensible for us to concentrate on these excesses than it is for conservationists to pretend that Mr Batchelor is a typical arable farmer.

Monty's keenness to cite examples of conservationists' madness may go down well at his local NFU branch meetings, but in the wider world it does neither his nor my case any good at all.

* Former editor of *British Farmer & Stockbreeder*.

But Monty Keen's position is today very fashionable. In the same magazine, David Richardson★★ (whom Heaven preserve) blames the Ministry of Agriculture for some of our problems. He cites the House of Lords Select Committee as saying that Ministry has been too keen on output and not keen enough on conservation. This is, of course, perfectly true, but coming from a farmer – let alone one as thoughtful as David – it is an extraordinary case of both missing the point and passing the buck. You might just as well blame prostitutes for causing lust, or roast beef for causing gluttony.

We all know that MAFF would never have been able to do this without the active and enthusiastic support of every farmer who ever accepted a grant or a subsidy, If you insist on blaming MAFF, you should also accept that we farmers must bear more of the blame than any ADAS man or civil servant.

The solution to our problem is as simple as it is painful. Farmers should rejoin society once again and become normal members of the population. We should stop hiding behind any excuse which comes to hand, whether it be MAFF or Marion Shoard. We should realise that the rules which apply to every other industry should also apply to us, whether these be rates, planning permission or pollution control. We should welcome people onto our land and tear down the stupid, selfish and self-defeating signs which say PRIVATE – KEEP OUT. We should start talking to the Ramblers' Association, the Friends of the Earth and the Animal Rights people. Each of these groups contains not just extremist loonies, but also balanced and serious individuals who have never actually spoken to a real farmer in their lives. It is to these people we should now talk.

Above all, we should realise that we have not, and have never had, a God-given right to be set apart from the rest of the world. So stop sneering at the people who criticise us, and begin to understand that we have some things in common. It is up to us to start the dialogue, but it cannot be done if we persist in mocking their motives and dismissing them all as nuts. It is already late, so we must start today.

★★ Journalist, TV megastar and part-time Norfolk farmer.

Stubble Digesters –
and Other Quack Remedies

AUGUST 1984

Damaroids – the Great Rejuvenator. This advertisement high above the Charing Cross Road used to tickle my schoolboy curiosity whenever I visited London. I didn't know what a rejuvenator was (in fact I'm not too clear today, either) and I didn't care much. But I longed to know what they looked and tasted like. I shall never know.

Today, many decades later, I am a deeply suspicious and cynical person – particularly when it comes to patent medicines and quack remedies. So you can imagine my feelings when Dave Gould, the farm manager, told me he had bought three little bottles of something called Cytozyme Stubble Digester Extra. Dave, who is not normally the sort of chap salesmen dream about, had pounced on this product because, as some of you may remember, we have decided to stop burning straw this harvest.

I'm prepared to try anything if it makes straw incorporation easier. That includes Stubble Digester Extra. If the leaflet is to be believed, it "facilitates seedbed preparations", "prevents the formation of toxins", and makes "available the nutrients contained within the straw residues to the following crop". It was just too good to be true. I was a bit surprised that there were no recommendations on how it should be mixed with Pimms No. 3, reduce wear in my tractor gearbox, restore the hair on my receding temples or cure warts. But at £5.50 an acre, what can you expect?

This miracle material is not home-brewed. It is imported from gay, swinging, sun-drenched Salt Lake City where it is carefully formulated by Cytozyme Laboratories to the most exact specification, consisting of Enzymatic protein...2.5%, Organics...11.9%, and (the one I thought I'd got rid of when I stopped burning straw) Ash...4.2%. It doesn't mention any other active ingredients; I assume the remainder is just water or air. So hurry, hurry, hurry while stocks – and my credibility – last.

Alert readers may just have detected the slightest hint of scepticism in my description of Cytozyme Stubble Digester Extra. This is grossly unfair because, such is my faith in the product that I have actually used 20 acres' worth, and am now waiting to see how well the stubble has actually been digested.

The act of using this stuff provided the most exciting moment of harvest this year. We had our four combines in the field of winter barley. Alongside them were two 20 tonne lorries, and behind this convoy were two pigtale cultivators which we had sent in to start the straw incorporation process. But best of all was the sight of the sprayer running alongside the combine as it applied the Stubble Digester Extra. The overall effect was a cross between Billy Smart's and Piccadilly Circus.

Apart from the thrills provided by Stubble Digesters, harvest has at least been different this year. Yields of winter barley have been excellent. Panda is the obvious replacement for Igri, even though it is full of loose smut and different varietal impurities which the French breeder has been unable to remove. It may give seedsmen nightmares, but it yields magnificently.

Tipper also did well, and it is a pity that the maltsters have decided to give it the thumbs down. But at last, in Halcyon, it looks as if we have a real replacement for Maris Otter. Ours yielded more than 65cwt per acre over the weighbridge, and I can understand why the seed is completely sold out for the autumn.

The one very serious problem so far has been the very large number of green berries in the sample. This has made drying very difficult. We decided to take the moisture down to 14% to be on the safe side, but two days after going through the drier, it had climbed back up to 17%. Likewise, some barley which came in off the field at 15%, somehow crept up to over 16% the following morning. I am just glad we have a continuous flow drier which can cope with the problem, and don't have to rely on ambient air.

In a few days we shall start the rape which, thanks to the pigeons, looks pretty ordinary. For the second year running we have let the crop ripen without either swathing or dessicating. This not only saves money, but also conveniently ripens between the barley and the wheat.

The durum wheat looks worse and worse at it nears harvest. It is plastered with disease, but this is our own fault as we drilled it much earlier than the experts recommended. The French breeder told me the other day that Capdur was really a spring variety. That will teach me not to plant durum on September 9th. The winter wheats look reasonable, but I've given up trying to predict yields as I find that I am often out by as much as 20%. I am, as football managers say, quietly confident. The snag is that I find it almost impossible to be quiet.

Meanwhile, the strain of harvest is beginning to catch up with me. If any of you readers out there happen to have any spare Damaroids, why not pop them into a plain, brown envelope and send them to me? In return I might even let you have a quick swig of my Stubble Digester Extra.

A load of rubbish. The stubble digester, that is.

Hybrid Wheat

SEPTEMBER 1984

It was the sort of landscape which would give a conservationist kittens. Wheat as far as the eye could see and – better still – not a single hedge for hundreds of miles. There I was, smack in the middle of Kansas, on a cold, bright January morning. And, as if the landscape wasn't enough, the architecture was pretty mind-blowing too. I had just driven past a single grainstore which was almost one mile long. It made my smallholding back in Cambridgeshire seem a bit trivial.

But it wasn't just the scenery which was different. Inside the barn on Hal Judy's farm I was examining his Allis Chalmers Gleaner combine when my eye caught a sign he had pinned to the wall. It said, in big letters: "We grow Rohm and Haas HYBREX hybrid wheat." This simple poster made my juices flow faster than any bit of farm machinery. That afternoon I went to the local research station run by Rohm & Haas. Two days later I was at the headquarters in Philadelphia speaking to Chuck Baker, who is in charge of the hybrid wheat programme.

It seemed too good to be true, so when I got back to England, I asked my plant breeding friends whether the Hybrex programme was a gimmick. They all agreed it was not. What's more, they told me, Rohm & Haas was not alone in the field. Nickersons were also working along similar lines. My curiosity grew. Later that summer I visited Rohm & Haas at Toulouse, in southern France, as well as Nickersons at Rothwell in Lincolnshire.

Before we go any further in this everyday story of plant breeding folk, I'd better explain a bit about hybrid wheat for those who, like me, are more ignorant than they care to admit. Wheat is self-fertile. It pollinates itself, which makes life convenient for farmers, but very difficult for a plant breeder who wants to cross one variety with another. So, while maize breeders have been creating hybrids for decades simply by cutting off the tassles (and effectively castrating the plant), wheat breeders have been stuck in their laboratories trying to solve the problem of how to stop the plant pollinating itself. Eventually they came up with a method called the cytoplasmic technique. The snag was that it wasn't really practicable to do this on a field scale.

And then came the breakthrough. Heavenly choirs probably sang, and the sky must have turned vermillion when a scientist somewhere came up with a chemical which, if sprayed on wheat, effectively sterilises the male organs of the plant. All of a sudden, hybrid wheat became more than just a dream.

As you read this timeless prose, wheat breeders the world over are lying in beds dreaming of hybrids. They are doing so not simply because they are incurable romantics, but for hard commercial reasons which will make them lots of money. It's not just that a hybrid should (repeat should) yield more, have better quality and more disease resistance than conventional varieties, though, heaven knows, this is exciting enough. There is another, far more seductive, reason.

If you have ever tried planting the seeds from an F1 hybrid tomato in your greenhouse, you will have realised that you cannot reproduce hybrids. You have to go back to the breeder every year to obtain your seeds. Just imagine what this will do for the average plant breeder. No longer does he have to worry about farm-saved seed, or about whether the merchants are paying their royalties.

Of course, the cost of producing hybrids is very high indeed, and it is estimated that the price to the farmer will be around three times as high as today's C2 seed. So the economics will only make sense if hybrid wheats actually yield at least 15% more than the best – not the average – conventional wheat. That's not an easy target to attain, particularly when men like John Bingham at the Plant Breeding Institute keep pushing yields up each year with their new conventional varieties.

But in spite of the difficulties ahead, both Rohm & Haas and Nickersons are optimistic. They have already spent millions of pounds, and are now getting near to the day when hybrid wheat is commercially available. I found their enthusiasm contagious and, as a seed grower, wanted to get involved as soon as possible.

This spring we ploughed up part of a field of winter barley and drilled spring wheat in a pattern which, from the air, looked like the Union Jack. The reason for this apparent eccentricity was a trial which Nickerson carried out to look into the movement of pollen. The results are still on the Secret List, but at least we managed to grow some hybrid wheat at Thriplow this harvest. It was a fascinating experience and only whetted my appetite.

The next stage begins this autumn when we shall actually be drilling a 10 acre plot to produce hybrid wheat seed on a field scale. If all goes according to schedule, Nickersons hope to have hybrid wheat seed on the market in the autumn of 1988.

I haven't been so excited since I first visited Schleswig-Holstein and Professor Laloux back in 1977. Once again we may be on the edge of another cereal revolution, and I'm glad to be in at the beginning. Of course, it all may fail. But whatever happens, I shall always remember those few minutes in Hal Judy's barn.

For three years after I wrote this, it looked as if hybrid wheat was the wave of the future. At Thriplow we worked closely with Rothwell Plant Breeders (part of the Shell empire) and became very optimistic about the prospects of huge increases of yield and quality. But then in 1987 everything ground to a halt as the chemical ran into toxicity problems in the United States and the entire programme was halted. Today the outlook for the Shell programme is very unclear. Meanwhile ICI bought the Rohm & Haas hybrid programme and are pressing ahead with great energy.

The New Villager

SEPTEMBER 1984

*Any similarity between the fictional characters described below
and people living today is entirely deliberate. If you think you
recognise your neighbour, you are probably correct.*

Near the bottom of my list of favourite things, far below the
Neanderthal farmer and hysterical conservationist, lurks a species
we all know very well: the New Villager. He must not be confused
with normal inhabitants of the village, who are pleasant and
sympathetic people.

In spite of only being a tiny minority in each village, the New
Villager is easy to spot because of various distinguishing marks
which set him apart from the crowd. The first and most obvious of
these is the fact that within days of moving into the village he
announces how important it is for everything to be preserved just as
he found it. He talks about the "essential character of the village"
which, for some strange reason, has not been affected by the arrival
of his own mock Georgian maisonette, complete with anodised
aluminium carriage lamp.

You can, by the way, always tell what sort of trees were cut
down to make space for his house because, with rare good taste, he
names his house after them. Thus the inhabitant of "The Beeches"
almost certainly caused a fine stand of beeches to be bulldozed to
make room for his bijou residence. It may be the residual guilt
brought about by this slight readjustment of the landscape which
makes him describe anyone else who cuts down a tree as a "vandal".
He is, for similar reasons, extremely keen to have a Tree Preservation Order slapped on every tree which managed to escape his (or
his builder's) attentions.

The New Villager is attracted to the village because it is
"frightfully rural" and "jolly peaceful". And so it was before he and
his friends arrived and started to convert it into a replica of every
suburb man has ever perpetrated. Streets must now all have names
on little plaques. Pavements must have nice little kerbs. Street lights
(preferably the orange sort) must be placed at regular intervals. But
farming, the industry which made the village peaceful and rural in

the first place, receives no thanks from the New Villager. On the contrary.

The Parish Council, to which so many New Villagers are drawn like flies to a dung heap, sends out a steady stream of complaints to local farmers. In winter they are told that they must keep mud off the road because it is both messy and dangerous. Mud, of course, has no place in the village of today, except as a medium in which to grow bedding plants by the patio.

Hedges, the Parish Council states, are cut down much too hard. They should be left as they were "in the old days" and not trimmed with a flail. The fact that the New Villager spends hours each summer primping his own little hedge into obsessive shapes is carefully forgotten. There is always one rule for the farmer and another for the New Villager.

The sound of the grain drier during harvest is an outrageous bit of noise pollution, or so the New Villager announces to a respectful audience in the pub. He bought his house in March, so how was he to know that harvest involved noisy and dusty machinery? It was never like that in Constable's painting, "The Haywain", which many New Villagers hang above the fireplace to show what the countryside could still look like if it weren't for those damned farmers.

But even when the local farmer behaves like a yokel, and drives cattle or sheep down the street, the New Villager is still outraged. These animals make the most disgusting messes which really should be cleared up before they become a health risk. What is even worse, the animals sometimes even stray off the road and eat the roses in the New Villager's garden. He loses no time in demanding compensation. He did not know – nor did he care – that in law it is the householder's responsibility to fence his garden against live-stock. But instead of finding out facts, he does what every New Villager does best. He blames the farmer.

At harvest time smuts from the burning straw only serve to increase his resentment towards farmers. He writes hysterical letters to the local newspaper condemning farmers, not simply for straw-burning, but also "for being interested only in profits". The New Villager's employer is a company which also tries to maximise its profits, but to him this seems perfectly legitimate. After all, his job depends on it.

But of all the things which make the New Villager most angry about farmers, it is what he calls "The Rape of the Countryside" which exasperates him most. He points to the big fields of East Anglia and fulminates about how "Prairie Farming" has ruined the landscape. It is, of course, all the fault of the greedy farmers.

But each morning as he leaves his house, built on land which had been agricultural until a few years ago, he sees no contradiction. As he drives to work along a dual carriageway which has chopped

whole farms in half, he feels no regret. When he arrives at his office which was erected on a green-field site where cows used to graze, it never occurs to him that he himself is to blame. No, the New Villager knows that he, and he alone, really understands the countryside. What's more, he has a little Flymo and a few plastic gnomes to prove it.

The New Villager today is even more widespread and even more virulent than he was in 1984. Waves of them are engulfing even the more remote villages in Britain as they seek peace and tranquility (on their terms). They have coined their own battle-cry: NIMBY, which, being translated, means "Not In My Back Yard". Let farmers beware.

Harvest 1984

NOVEMBER 1984

If there's one thing a farmer enjoys more than growing a good crop of wheat, it's seeing his neighbour grow a bad one. So I shall be spreading happiness throughout the country by telling you about our field of Longbow which yielded 37cwt an acre last harvest. It was the sort of crop that nightmares are made of.

Everything looked good until May, when we began to notice that the plant was very thin. Soon after ear-emergence, it became clear that the crop was simply dying. In spite of our usual fungicide programme, we could do nothing to halt the decline. When the combine entered the field the ears were black and mouldy, standing straight up in the air. An ADAS post-mortem failed to find a single clue, so I must put it down to bad husbandry and blame myself. Secretly, I reckon it was take-all. In future I shall be less keen to grow third wheats.

Otherwise our harvest was good. Had it not been for the fact that last year we did even better, I would now be very happy indeed. I have now come to expect that every harvest is bigger than the last. The wheats – including the aforementioned Longbow – averaged 68cwt, which was 3cwt down on the year before. Individual fields did pretty well, notably Brock which managed over 85cwt. The other new varieties, like Brimstone and Moulin, also looked impressive. I just hope that their milling quality is as good as the breeder claims. Mission managed 70cwt and may have a future, but I am not too optimistic that it will compete with the newcomers for much more than a year.

So much for the soft wheat. The story of our two fields of durum wheat makes less happy reading. The crop looked good throughout the growing season, and it was only just before harvest that we realised many of the ears contained no grain at all. We managed 31cwt an acre which was, I suppose, better than some. So much for my optimism. Looking back, I now realise that we drilled one field much too early – on September 9th. It obviously was not a durum year. Never one to let a few facts get in the way of my opinions, I shall persist with the crop for another year and see what happens.

The barleys also did reasonably well, averaging 63cwt, which was again a bit down on last year. Maris Otter, which we should have dropped three years ago, soldiers on, and even survived a bad attack of barley yellow mosaic virus to give 55cwt. Tipper, which I had hoped would be with us for many years, never quite made the grade. It yielded well enough, but the maltsters didn't seem to be as keen as Nickersons had predicted. It reminded me of their Ark Royal which was always meant to take over from Proctor, but never quite managed to because it lacked the quality.

Halcyon, on the other hand, looks very good indeed. In spite of its weak straw, I have little doubt that it will succeed Otter as the best winter malting barley. Panda did well and, at Thriplow at least, out-performs Igri easily. But however good it is as a feed barley, it is a nightmare for seed growers because of its apparently fatal attraction for loose smut. Unless the breeders can solve this problem, they will have killed an otherwise excellent variety. That would be a pity.

But it was after harvest that the fun really began. In my own typically modest way, I had decided to give up straw-burning completely. Straw incorporation would be the name of the game. We had bought two lovely new six-furrow mounted Dowdes-wells, complete with high clearance, trashboards and furrow presses. The combines, including the IH 1480, had all been fitted with straw choppers and were ready to go. I pretended that I hadn't a care in the world, but underneath my flinty exterior there was a very nervous little farmer trying to stay in.

It was a piece of cake. One pass with the cultivator as fast as possible, another with the set of discs and most of the chopped straw was mixed into the top four inches of the soil. No nonsense with fancy – and horribly expensive – machines like the Soil Saver. We just used what was already lying round the farm. The fields were left for as long as possible before ploughing which, for some of the early barleys, meant as much as six weeks. The ploughs did well, but the furrow presses were almost miraculous. I cannot begin to understand why we have never used them before. In most conditions you can drill straight into the tilth they leave, although we prefer to put a Dutch harrow over first to level the ground.

So when drilling began in early September, I was a happy little chap. I was also much poorer because the cost of fuel, wages and plough iron was a lot more than if we had simply burned the straw and disced the land twice. But overall, the operation had been very successful. And even the seedbeds were better.

Of course, it had been an easy year. The weather had been on our side, and things could have been very different in a dry autumn. We are also – I am continuously reminded – on "Boy's Land". Yet in spite of all these ifs and buts, I was feeling pretty pleased.

But the euphoria didn't last long. A few weeks later life stopped being so simple. On a windy fen outside Peterborough I met one of the great ADAS gurus. He told me that straw incorporation was a complete waste of time. Just chop the stuff and plough it straight in, he said. For once in my life, I was speechless.

No Burning – Post Mortem

NOVEMBER 1984

I was feeling pretty smug when I arrived at the Tractors at Work Demonstration in early September. Back at Thriplow, in spite of my worst fears, straw incorporation had been going well.

Then it happened. An ADAS man in the shape of their leading East Anglian soil scientist told me that I had got it all wrong. Incorporation, said Brian Davies, was not necessary. Just plough the straw straight in after chopping behind the combine. The shock of realising that (if he was right) I had been wasting time and money, was only slightly greater than that of finding an ADAS man with a clear opinion. It was an offgoing back-to-the-drawing-board situation.

The story really began a year before. It was late August 1983 and harvest was drawing to an end. We were burning a field of barley straw and had taken all the necessary precautions, when I noticed that the heat from the flames had singed all the leaves on the trees beside the field. Within hours they would turn brown, so every passing motorist would see that, yet again, farmers had damaged the countryside. This was not the first time it had happened, and my nerves were beginning to fray. Straw burning, which had once been one of my favourite jobs, had now become a tense and frightening experience.

Then and there I decided we would stop burning completely. As harvest approached this year, however, I began to realise that it is one thing having a big mouth – telling the world we would not burn – but it was quite another putting the principle into practice. During the winter and spring I had attended umpteen conferences on straw incorporation. Each time I had come away feeling more confused than before. On several visits to Germany, I grilled my friends on how deep to plough, what machines to use, how often to change the chopper knives and other little details which obsess farmers like me. They were unanimous in one thing only; the need to incorporate straw before ploughing. Resist the temptation, they said, to plough the chopped straw straight in. You may think you are saving time and money, but you will live to regret it. The straw will form a solid layer at the bottom of the furrow, where it will remain until you plough it out the following year. When it came to applying nitrogen on the straw, opinion was divided, with the majority thinking that this was necessary – at least for the first few years.

I ordered choppers for the combines and two new Dowdeswell six-furrow mounted ploughs, complete with furrow presses. Just to be on the safe side, the ploughs had the maximum clearance under the beam of 30 inches and had trashboards instead of skims. We already had two sets of heavy discs and lexitine cultivators, so I hoped to be able to get away without buying fancy expensive gadgets.

The first thing we discovered was that the discs did not do a good job straight after the combines. The straw was so thick that they were hardly able to penetrate the dry soil. So we put on the cultivators and tried again. The 16 feet Cousins flexitine on our 150 hp tractor was just too wide. It went into the soil all right, but the forward speed was far too slow to create the turbulence which is vital to mix the straw into the top four inches. We either had to buy a bigger tractor or use a smaller cultivator.

The latter course was the simplest to achieve. We folded up the wings and found that, with a width of only 7 feet, we could travel at 7 mph. The effect was magic. The soil boiled and swirled around the 3 inch tines – and our fuel bill doubled overnight. The discs were much happier in the tilth which the cultivators created. In a perfect world we should have crossed the cultivators, but the drivers found this too bumpy and they reduced speed. So we took the easy option and disced in the same direction. The results were good.

After wasting money on twenty acres worth of so-called Stubble Digester Extra, I resisted the temptation to spend anything on extra nitrogen. Five weeks after we combined our first field of barley, the ploughs went in to complete the job. We had never used furrow presses before, as I had assumed that they were either gimmicks or only suited to the very light blowing soils of the Breckland. How wrong I was. They made a magnificent job of breaking the clods, compressing the soil and keeping in the small amount of moisture which was left after nearly a month without rain. My fears about blockages under the plough beam were unfounded and, looking back, I think we could have managed with our old ploughs. The trashboards, however, were clearly essential. I was also relieved to see that, even though were only ploughing eight or nine inches deep, we were able to bury all the straw.

The eventual seedbeds we made this autumn have been good to excellent. There are the odd pieces of straw on the surface, but this is certainly no worse than after an average burn. Of course, it has all cost a lot of extra money. It is impossible to estimate exactly how much extra fuel, wages, time, plough iron and wear and tear we have used. It is clearly far more than had we just burnt the straw and then disced the land a couple of times before drilling. On top of this there may even be a yield penalty next year. I am still a mite nervous about the toxins being given off by the decomposing straw.

So, even on our light land, straw incorporation is an expensive operation. On heavy land the problems will be much more difficult, so I well understand why farmers with clay on their boots want to go on burning. I wonder if the general public will be equally understanding.

Send a Tonne to Africa –
Looking Back

JANUARY 1985

In May last year, two things were already clear. The European grain harvest was going to be massive and the famine in Africa would be the worst for many years. It was to link these two events that the Send A Tonne to Africa appeal was launched. Its objective was to raise 10,000 tonnes of wheat from British farmers.

I began by telephoning Oxfam. If British farmers raised 10,000 tonnes of wheat and shipped it to Africa, could Oxfam make use of it? The reply was polite and firm. They did not deal in food aid, nor did they think it was helpful because it damaged the local economy. However, if the British farmers were able to give cash instead of wheat, Oxfam would accept this gratefully.

Somewhat disappointed, I rang Christian Aid and asked the same question. The response was identical. Thank you but no thank you. By now I was beginning to realise that my idea may have sounded good in theory, but in practice the aid agencies were very unenthusiastic.

As a last attempt, I rang War on Want and found myself speaking to James Firebrace, Project Officer for the Horn of Africa. He too stressed that they would much prefer money, but when he realised that it was either wheat or nothing, he agreed to co-operate. We would, however, have to ship the grain out to Port Sudan from where it would be trucked into Eritrea and Tigre. These two rebellious provinces of Ethiopia are largely ignored by western governments. They therefore receive pitifully small amounts of food aid.

Throughout July the appeal gathered speed very slowly. Farmers were too busy with their harvest to worry about selling wheat. But life was anything but quiet. In August the BBC made a television documentary about food aid. The crew came down to the farm to interview me about Send a Tonne to Africa. They brought with them one of Oxfam's experts who was interviewed in the harvest field with combines roaring up and down behind him. Although he admitted that in very rare emergencies food aid was desirable, he was adamant that money rather than wheat was preferable. The whole tenor of his argument was that he was implacably against food aid.

This man was, unfortunately, typical of aid experts, both private and governmental. During the 1970s they had come to feel that food aid was destructive and dangerous while development aid was desirable. In Orwell's *Animal Farm* the animals' slogan was "Four legs good. Two legs bad." The aid experts had modified this and instead were chanting "Food aid bad. Development aid good."

Like so many clichs, it contained a lot of truth. To dump food on a country destroys the agriculture as well as doing a great deal of damage in other ways. But the ritual repeating of this slogan by the aid charities had long since become purely mechanical. Throughout the world they had forgotten that when starvation threatens a continent, it is too late for development aid. Food – and lots of it – is needed urgently.

Like so many people who allow slogans to replace thought, the agencies discovered their mistake late in the day. In the meanwhile people were dying for lack of food. Four months after it had turned down the offer of 10,000 tonnes of wheat, and eight weeks after it's expert had pooh-poohed food aid on television, Oxfam changed its mind. It decided to buy 10,000 tonnes of wheat for immediate shipment to Ethiopia.

A few weeks later, after the BBC had aroused Bob Geldof and the entire world with pictures from Korem, all criticisms of food aid were hastily forgotten. Some aid agencies even forgot their own immediate past and put out press statements criticising the government for not reacting faster to the famine. These bodies claimed that they had been warning of impending starvation for the past 18 months. For reasons which are not hard to understand, they somehow forgot to mention that they themselves had refused the offer of wheat only four months earlier. Such are the politics of the aid industry.

The first load of wheat from Send a Tonne to Africa left Hull on October 11th. It was on the Greek freighter, *Elpis*, which also contained 10,000 tonnes of wheat from Oxfam and 4,000 tonnes given by the ODA*. The cargo was destined for the port of Assab, from where it would be distributed throughout Ethiopia. Our wheat almost never made it because on two occasions after they had agreed to take it, Oxfam attempted to tear up the agreement – the

* Overseas Development Administration (i.e. the Ministry for Overseas Aid).

last time only 12 hours before the ship was due to load.

This chaotic way of doing business is, I discovered, not untypical of the way aid agencies manage their affairs. But if the actual organisation left a bit to be desired, the way in which the wheat was bought was even more ludicrous. At no time did either OXFAM or ODA see fit to speak to either a farmer or a merchant to find out about wheat. OXFAM instead relied upon the advice of a multinational grain trader to buy and ship the wheat. It neither knew, nor probably cared, that the wheat which was being bought by its agent was a minimum of 76 kg hectolitre weight at no more than 15% moisture. It was therefore buying expensive Intervention Standard wheat instead of the ordinary DNQ feed wheat. The difference in price, so a merchant told me, was at least £5 per tonne. In other words, for the same amount of money they could have bought 400 tonnes more wheat. That would have fed an extra 400 families for a year.

The ODA was even less businesslike when, in November, it set out to buy 6500 tonnes of wheat for Ethiopia. Rather than use a multinational grain trader, it asked the World Food Programme★ (WFP) in Rome to buy the wheat. The WFP asked for tenders, but the wheat it was specifying was far from being ordinary feed wheat. It was insisting on the following standards: moisture below 13.5%, Hagberg 300, protein 11.5% and a hectolitre weight of 76. A leading Lincolnshire grain merchant assured me that wheat of this standard did not even exist within the United Kingdom, yet it was being bought by the British Government with taxpayers' money.

The wheat which the WFP was ordering was of such superb baking quality that even the most expensive Paris pâtisseries making croissants would not need such material. When told that the wheat was going to feed starving Ethiopians and would be used within weeks to make unleavened bread, the WFP official in Rome simply shrugged and repeated that this was "standard practice".

Eventually the ODA in London woke up. It insisted that a new specification be drawn up only a few hours before the original tender closed. After this episode, the ODA eventually purchased feed wheat which was, of course, far cheaper. In doing so it saved the taxpayer about £20 per tonne – and ensured that the wheat did at least come from British farms.

These events surprised me. I had naively assumed that both the

★   The United Nations body which handles food aid to the Third World.

governmental and non-governmental aid agencies would at least be experienced at buying wheat and shipping it around the globe. But it was clear that the commercial disciplines which keep private companies efficient do not apply to aid agencies. Perhaps they need a farmer or two to help them.

> *The Send a Tonne Appeal was an exciting yet sobering experience. The generosity of the farming community was far greater than I had dared hope, but the general incompetence of some aid agencies was equally surprising. Send a Tonne to Africa was wound up 12 months after it was founded, having raised £2.2 million and shipped 12,000 tonnes of wheat. Its successor, the Send a Tonne Development Fund, has a new objective: to raise money for development (NB not food) aid. Response from farmers, now that the economic squeeze is on, is less than it was in 1984, but is still better than nothing at all.*
>
> *Now, at the time of writing, the rains have failed in Ethiopia and once again famine threatens millions. Send a Tonne to Africa has been re-launched and it remains to see whether the farming world will respond as it did last time.*

Eritrea – Diary from a Starving Land

JANUARY 1985

November 8th, Port Sudan
Here at the Palace Hotel there are more aid workers than hotel staff. UNICEF, WHO, MVI, Euro Action, and a few I've never heard of. We have contributed to the surplus by bringing John Cunnington from War on Want. Sudan is traditionally a wheat-exporting country. Until the drought this year. Now they must import the stuff.

Two men came round to see us this evening. Mustafa, tall and bearded in a Sudanese white robe and turban, runs the Eritrean People's Liberation Front (EPLF) in town. he speaks little English. His colleague, Negusse Berhe, is with the Eritrean Relief Association (ERA). Small, wiry like so many Eritreans, he speaks excellent

English. Started by saying that they need food more than anything else. Medicines were the second priority, and trucks etc. the third. They had received 5000 tonnes of wheat from the Americans two months ago, and about a year earlier 2000 tonnes from the Danish churches. But he was clearly very happy that he was getting 1000 tonnes from Send a Tonne to Africa tomorrow when the *Elpis* docks.

November 10th, Port Sudan
Elpis arrives, but Sudanese Security (i.e. Secret Police) won't let us film the wheat being unloaded. It seems that the Sudan is happy to help Eritrea but doesn't want any publicity.

I had the afternoon to spare so hitched a lift with a UNICEF jeep out to a refugee camp 200 km west on the main Khartoum road. A grey, almost lunar, landscape. Three neat lines of matting shelters. A sound of distant coughing as we approached. They all have TB. Apart from the coughing there's almost complete silence. People walk as if in a trance. They seem very dignified. No begging mothers tugged at my clothes as I had half expected. But no kids playing either. The children are thin and listless, but in better shape than the very old and very young. The babies are the worst of all. Their skin hangs in wrinkles off their matchstick bones.

I stayed for two hours in the late afternoon as the sun began to go down. A woman dies in front of me. They wrapped her up tightly in a shroud and carried her off on a stretcher with a man and a mattock (the gravedigger) going in front. Nobody else in the camp seemed to notice or care. But suddenly two dozen other women gathered round the corpse and began to wail. As the stretcher moved off they followed, picking up handfuls of dust which they threw over themselves. The dead woman's shelter was then dismantled by her neighbours. She lived alone. The Chilean doctor I was with said simply, "The cause of death was marasmus. You would call it starvation".

November 11th. Port Sudan
The journey from Port Sudan to the EPLF base camp at Erota normally takes nine hours in a jeep. We took nearly 24. The roughest track I have ever known. Bouncing around in the back of the Toyota, a fractured skull seemed a real possibility. Tropical storms light up the desert with flashes of lightning. Streams appear from nowhere. Our driver veers off the track trying to cross a flooded wadi. We are stuck up to our axles.

Three hours sleep in some nameless shelter before pressing on as dawn breaks over the desert. Although we are still officially in the Sudan, it is clear that the EPLF are in control. We stop for breakfast and eat sorghum bread (sour and nasty) with bean paste. Our driver collects a Kalashnikov rifle and we start climbing up into the mountains and across the border.

November 12th. Erota, Eritrea
Arrived at midday in a deserted dried-up valley. Where is everyone? Is this some form of ruse? Hidden in the hillside is a comfortable guest house with electric lights and primitive plumbing. Tomato salad for lunch, a quick shower and sleep for four hours. Can we wash clothes? "Yes," says our guide, "but don't hang any bright colours outside." "Quite right," said I knowingly, "they'll only fade in the bright sun." "No," comes the reply, "they'll be spotted by Ethiopian MiGs." I shall never make a guerrilla.

November 13th. Erota
To the hospital. Like everything in this country, you don't know it's there until you stumble into it. Perfectly camouflaged along both sides of a valley stretching for three and a half miles, it consists of 1200 beds and has its own operating theatres, pill manufacturing plant and all the normal departments (cardio-vascular, orthopaedic etc.) you would expect to find in a hospital of this size.

Doctor Nerayo, deputy head, is clearly a politician as much as a doctor. I haven't seen charisma before, only read about it. But this man has it in large measure. Coffee after lunch served in Eritrean manner; coffee beans roasted over charcoal, then ground with pestle and mortar. Amazingly seductive smells. Ginger added to the coffee which is served in small cups. I think it's the best I've ever drunk. Or is it just the location and the people and the atmosphere? No, it's the best coffee ever. Definitely.

When Eritreans greet each other they rub shoulders. Like a rugby collision in slow motion. Very attractive. When I try it I realise how bony all Eritreans are. And how fat I am.

Spent all afternoon watching wheat being distributed. Extraordinary organisation. ERA knows the names, ages and numbers of every family, even though most are nomads and have walked eleven hours to the site. Rations of 500 grammes per person per day. Each head of family is summoned by name to collect his allocation. Women and men sit separately, talking quietly. No fuss, no panic. People look thin, but far better than in the Sudan refugee camps. No evident starvation here. Dusk falls and men start praying to Mecca in the light of their bonfires.

November 15th. Himbol

Woken at 7am by the sound of jet engines. Panic. Two MiG 23s on armed reconnaissance. It was all over in 15 seconds. They were looking for any EPLF truck which got stranded last night and is now in the open. No wonder everything is so well camouflaged. I went out this morning for the normal al fresco defecation and realised I was lost. Our tent was so well hidden I couldn't find it. The jeep is hidden under a thorn tree with its windscreen covered to stop any stray reflections.

We are joined by the local ERA man, Jonas Debessai. He looks like Lenin and has an encyclopaedic knowledge of matters British because he is addicted to the BBC World Service. Our other guide, Geb, is from the EPLF; he's the one with the Kalashnikov rifle. The driver, Gemayel, speaks no English but handles the Toyota magnificently. Especially when chasing antelopes across the desert at night with the rest of us being thrown around in the back.

November 16th. Zara

Arrived at midnight after a five hour drive. Travel in this country is only at night because of air raids. The discomfort of bumping along the tracks is something which I find very difficult indeed. Our sleeping accommodation consisted of a hut with two beds. On stripping the blanket we found a scorpion, a mouse and some of the biggest ants I have ever seen. But I'm too tired to care.

Woken by flies at 7am. More MiGs came over this morning. I now feel a bit differently about planes. Hitherto they were just machines I read about. Now they are frightening things. On the rare occasions when we do travel in daylight, I find myself looking for cover in case of attack. It will all sound ludicrously melodramatic when I get back to England, but it seems commonsense here.

Went to another food distribution. Most impressive. The EPLF is in complete control of 2100 people, some of whom have walked nine hours to get here. No sign of marasmus here. People look hungry and thin, but none as bad as in the Sudan camps. I suppose the really hungry ones are too weak to walk.

Met a barefoot doctor, an attractive woman in fatigues, doing a surgery nearby. She claims that 80% of the population suffer from malnutrition. Eritrean women are – for black Africa – extraordinarily liberated. They are active as fighters, and in all other jobs. Both they and the men are extremely good looking with their aquiline features and high cheekbones.

Still no firm news of our British wheat, though ERA assures me it has been unloaded and is on its way up country by a different route.

November 17th. Girmaica
An awful ten hour journey last night. Hot, bumpy beyond any nightmare. But at last we arrived as the sun was coming up. Girmaica must be unique in Eritrea. You can actually see it. Instead of everything being hidden in hillsides, it is a village spread out on the plain. There is a well nearby which is opened twice a day for the locals to get water. But its real importance is as a trading centre on the route from Asmara to Kassala in the Sudan. There are even shops, which is strange since Eritrea is a cashless society. Nobody gets paid. The EPLF provides food, clothing and housing. Here in Girmaica there is even a pub. We drank warm beer at $1 a bottle. And brandy too, distilled in Asmara. After two weeks without alcohol I'm prepared to forget that the beer was warm and the cognac diluted. It was wonderful.

The EPLF has brought us here to show the American Food Aid which, they claim, has been sold by Ethiopian army officers for their own private profit. Sure enough, we saw bags of sorghum grits and milk powder "Furnished by the people of the United States". They are en route to Sudanese markets by camel. Not very smart of the Eritreans to show our TV camera. The British public won't differentiate between the Ethiopian (bad) and the Eritrean (good). They will just remember that food aid gets flogged off by Africans and will draw their own conclusions.

November 18th. Tessenei
Once one of Eritrea's biggest towns, Tessenei is now deserted. The EPLF captured it in January. Burnt-out Russian bomber at the airport. On to Ali Ghidir where the Italians had a 6000 acre estate until 1977. Superb land, flat and fertile, irrigated by the nearby Gash River. Now deserted. Farm machinery rusting away. The land, which could grow magnificent crops, hardly used at all. Saw some sorghum being harvested, the only food production I have seen in Eritrea so far. And none of this has anything to do with the drought. What would happen if hungry Ethiopia and hungry Eritrea stopped fighting each other?

November 19th. Sawa
A sight I hope I shall never see again. Human beings eating wheat. Not bread or porridge, but simply wheat soaked in water. Kids ate quietly but the adults fought to get the food and – worse still – to keep it from the others. Afterwards the kids picked spilt grains of wheat out of the sand. "The farmers plant seeds but harvest dust," said Jonas. At Sawa even the chicken coop is camouflaged against air raids.

November 20th. Zara
The hospital here has a kerosene-powered fridge. We drank iced water which, to my surprise, is less thirst-quenching than warm water. The patients were mostly civilians with shrapnel wounds from air raids, but some cases of malnutrition. One child was so thin that as he lay under the sheet the slight dip in the mattress made his bed appear completely flat. Some TB cases too.

The military hospital looked like '*MASH*' but with dirt, squalor, pain and smell. And no humour at all. The surgeon and the anaesthetist were washing up after an operation which they performed by torchlight.

November 21st. Hombul
A five hour journey last night. I'm getting very blas about travelling over bumpy tracks with a Kalashnikov between my legs. News came through that the Ethiopians have bombed the school at Erota. Three kids killed and thirteen wounded. Hang around all day keeping the flies off as we wait for darkness. It's the right country in which to be reading *Scoop*.

November 22nd. Hishkub
Another hidden town. This is obviously the Kremlin of Eritrea. It is the centre of what they call the Mass organisation but anyone else would call the Government. The EPLF is organised on classic Marxist-Leninist lines with its Politburo at the top of the heap, its Central Committee below that and its "Cells" in each town. The paradox is that the EPLF is fighting not some reactionary white colonialist capitalist power, but the Marxist regime of Colonel Menghistu in Addis Abbaba, behind whom stands the USSR itself.

I shared my bed with a mouse. In the afternoon I was taken to see the prize prisoners of war. An Ethiopian MiG pilot and two colonels were paraded for us. The pilot, who spoke good English, seemed healthy enough but was obviously dispirited. I felt sorry for him, but then remembered the kids who had been killed by his colleagues the day before.

November 23rd. Nakfa

A bad night. This is the war zone proper. As we approached the town at midnight the driver switched off all our lights because the road can be seen from the Ethiopian positions. We arrived at the dugout guest house to find a Danish journalist asleep on the only bed. He awoke to tell us they had just endured a bombardment by Ethiopian 130mm guns which had been very frightening. Nakfa once had a population of 7000 but today is a ruin. Only the minaret remains, like St Paul's after the Blitz.

We had been warned to remain still if a MiG came over, and only to run for cover after it had passed. But when we heard the jet engines, I panicked in a genteel manner and bolted for the shade of a ruined building. Felt very foolish because the plane was miles away and very high.

A sweaty walk over the hills to see a captured T55 tank. The Eritreans have liberated a lot of artillery from the Ethiopians and now point them south towards the front lines which are only a mile away. On the way to the tank we had a slight detour to what looked like a hole in the hillside under some cactus. On closer inspection it turned out to be a theatre, complete with stage and curtain. We were given a concert by the Ethiopian Prisoners' Culture Group. All a bit like *It Ain't 'Arf Hot Mum*, but good clean fun.

November 24th. Erota

Back at base camp, complete with a mattress on the floor and a shower of sorts. Great consternation as a snake crawled out of the lavatory this morning. At the hospital I saw the kids who had been wounded in the air raid. Also a man whose leg and hand had been blown off by a land mine. His dressings were being changed, which was a horrible sight. No painkillers – only aspirins.

November 25th. Erota

The Director of Education showed us where the bombs had fallen on the school. They were, he claimed, American fragmentation bombs. It could have been far worse because the kids were eating lunch under the trees at the time.

On our way to Solomuna Camp we finally found the first convoy of Send a Tonne to Africa wheat. Instantly recognisable in white plastic sacks. A strangely moving moment – for me at least –

to see the wheat given by the British farmers in Eritrea at last. A girl with the inevitable Kalashnikov sat atop the first load. On our way through the mountains we met a second convoy with our wheat on board.

November 26th. Solomuna
This is the Eritrean Relief Association's biggest camp for displaced persons. Like everything else in this country, it's invisible. After a short walk up a dried river bed, we came across 200 orphans getting their weekly bath. So many tiny black bodies covered with white soap looked lovely. Squeals of happiness as they all messed about. All boys circumcised. Maybe girls too because the local Beja people go in for it.

November 28th. Khartoum
Our plane left at 4am. For the past three weeks I had been promising myself a drink. Ordered a bourbon on the rocks. It tasted foul. Maybe the water from an Eritrean well is better after all. I must be suffering from premature nostalgia.

The object of this trip – apart from making a film for Anglia Television – was to satisfy myself that the food which was contributed by generous British farmers actually reached the people who needed it. It did.

We Got Ourselves into This Mess

FEBRUARY 1985

Velocette, Royal Enfield, Triumph, BSA, Sunbeam, Ariel, Match-less, AJS, Vincent, Francis Barnett, James, Greeves, Ambassador, Norton, DMW, Douglas, Wooler, Scott. The names from my boyhood only 30 years ago. They would all be alive and well today if only the motorcycle industry had enjoyed the same privileges which we farmers do today. In those days there were no vast Intervention stores stuffed full with unsold motorbikes.

No benign Brussels bureaucrat fixed minimum prices and kept the Japanese models out. No angry demonstrations took place on the streets of Coventry and West Bromwich. Instead, the companies just went bust in a sad and gradual procession because, as the Americans say, "they couldn't cut the mustard."

As the motorcycle industry disappeared, not a single voice of protest was raised by the NFU. The reason was simple: farmers were in favour of free enterprise. They still are today – except when they look in the mirror. This hypocrisy (the NFU would probably call it a "paradox") is part of our daily lives. When a local grain merchant or machinery dealer calls in the Receivers, we may be sad but we don't start writing letters of protest to our MP. We blame the company for being too extravagant, too sleepy, too greedy or just too inefficient. Life goes on normally.

But just wait until old farmer Buggins goes broke. All hell will be let loose. We shall be told that this is the beginning of the end of British Agriculture, that the basic fabric of society is threatened and that "the Government should do something". We shall say this even though we know that Buggins was a bad farmer. His fields were full of wild oats, his yields (even the ones he admitted to in the pub) were dreadful, his potatoes rotted in the ground and his sheep lambed late and infrequently.

The trouble is that men like Buggins may actually be the ones who survive the coming squeeze. He inherited his land ages ago and pays neither rent nor mortgage. His machinery is ancient, he saves his own seed and doesn't believe in fungicides. So his costs are low and his overdraft is non-existent.

The people who will feel the strain first are those energetic types who went out and borrowed money to buy land and machinery. What had seemed such a good idea only a few years ago could well appear foolish greed today. But these people (and I include myself in this category) must resist the temptation to pass the buck. Farmers love blaming others for their misfortunes and they will undoubtedly try to say that it was the Bank Manager's fault for lending the money or the land agent's for talking them into a fancy price. This sort of whingeing will fool nobody except ourselves. We are all grown-up now. We got ourselves into this mess and we'll have to get ourselves out. But how?

The short answer is that we shall have to produce less, and preferably at a lower cost. There are two ways this can be achieved: either by bureaucratic controls (quotas etc.) or by the working of the free market. The first course of action will preserve the inefficient and create jobs for a new army of bureaucrats. The second will lead to a lot of farmers going broke. If it were the motorbike industry, farmers would have no doubts. But the man who stares back at you from the mirror when you shave in the morning finds the arguments rather less than convincing,

Of course, the choice will not be quite as stark as I have painted. No government, whatever its political hue, will allow the agricultural industry to disappear. But what they will allow – and maybe even encourage – is for the most inefficient to go bust and for marginal land to come out of production. So I cheer myself up with the belief that so long as I can remain just better than the average, I should survive.

Readers who have become accustomed to my normal delightful optimism may be perplexed by this onrush of gloom. The reason is that I have just returned from Hawaii where 8000 members of the American Farm Bureau were meeting for their annual convention. The new Reagan government has decided to reduce all agricultural subsidies drastically. The free market and not Washington civil servants will fix prices. Down will come all commodities, and with them world prices will also fall.

The pressure on Brussels will become intolerable, and the effects in Britain will be felt before long. But if all this sounds a bit airy-fairy to you, then try the following piece of information and see how you feel. Senator Thomas Harkin from Iowa expects that 10 percent of the farmers in his state will go bankrupt this year. Iowa is roughly the equivalent of Norfolk. And 10% is 10%.

Survival Plan

MARCH 1985

It's time for loudmouths like me to stop prattling on about the problems facing agriculture today. Any fool can write a page or two about the end of the Common Agricultural Policy, why American farmers are going bust and what will happen to cereal prices over the next year. But it takes real talent to do something about it – and that's what separates good farmers from puffed-up pundits.

During the winter, as the storm clouds gathered in Brussels and

Washington DC, I have been trying to figure out what I can do on the farm to survive. To better farmers than me, my plans will appear obvious and banal, but that is never a reason for doing nothing.

The most important objective is to keep costs down which, as we all know, is easy to talk about but almost impossible to achieve. I start with an advantage over the good farmers because during the past decade my fixed costs – unlike theirs – have crept up year by year as I become ever flabbier (in every sense of the word).

We shall not replace men when they retire. Thus when Don, the combine driver, retires this harvest, no full-time young man will take his place. Instead a student may help out for a month or two. We may even make more use of contractors but (see below) even this is unlikely.

We shall make equipment last longer. I have been threatening to do this for the past few years, but my iron will inevitably breaks down after a good harvest when I see new and shiny machines in the local dealer's yard. This time I mean business. Or, in the case of the local dealer, lack of business. It is, of course, the single easiest way to save money, and that is why I am grateful that I do not sell tractors or combines for a living. Life would be very rough indeed.

We shall completely alter our fertiliser policy. In the distant past we combine drilled all the corn but, as the autumn workload grew tighter, we broadcast the fertiliser to increase our work rate. But this too became too tight, so five years ago we started using a delivered-and-spread service. The contractor was excellent and the price very keen so I have been entirely happy for many years.

But a simple thought struck me forcibly the other day. Why pay a contractor to apply phosphate and potash in the autumn when we could do it ourselves in the early spring? Then we have the men, the time and the machinery. What is more, we could buy straights in bulk and save money too. As if that were not enough, by putting it on later, we would be financing the fertiliser for less time. So our overdraft would come down too.

Thus in future we shall be applying our own phosphate and potash in February each year. We shall buy in bulk and use men and machinery at our slackest time of year. We might also be helping the fertiliser manufacturers who complain so bitterly about the seasonal nature of the job.

We shall spend a lot of money installing a large grain dresser. This will not only be used as a pre-cleaner for all the corn as it goes into the grainstore but, far more important, be used to clean to the new Intervention Standards. If one thing is certain, it is that in 12 months time you will hear farmers boasting to each other about how they got some corn into Intervention – just as they used to boast about a particularly good malting sample a few years back.

Something will have to be done to reduce the amount of grain going into Intervention. It is costing the taxpayer too much money. The simplest solution is to raise the standards so high that not much grain can actually make the grade.

This is bad news for farmers, but wonderful for the people who manufacture grain cleaning equipment. It is lucky that we have a good drier because people who use ambient air may start to find life a bit difficult.

I will also try to find an agronomist to advise me. This may be hard because I'm so conceited that I don't really believe that anyone is good enough to advise me. But I am now reluctantly coming to the idea that the old days are now over. In the past anything you did to increase yield was – inevitably – sensible. This is no longer the case, so I shall have to be a lot more careful about inputs.

But the idea about paying a chinless wonder to tell me what a rep would do for free worries me. Besides, I have always felt that these crop consultants did about as much good as people who write articles in farming magazines. I am beginning to think that I am wrong, but I am looking for the best, toughest and most commercial agronomist in Great Britain. Where are you out there?

PS. I didn't mean that about chinless wonders. I was only joking. *Really. I promise.*

I did not, after all, hire an agronomist. It wasn't because I did not find any. On the contrary, every semi-qualified graduate in East Anglia seemed to write offering his services. But none appealed to me. It is crucial that you actively like your agronomist. Thus your first question is not whether or not he is skilled enough, but rather: do you want to have a drink with him after work?

Bad News from British Sugar

MAY 1985

All farmers are boastful but some are more boastful than others. The worst of all are those who write for magazines and tell the rest of us how wonderful they are. You know the sort. They usually begin: "I don't suppose the wheat will quite average the 10.72 tonnes a hectare, as it did last year. I tested 69 sample bushel weights yesterday and they are 3% lower than the 10 year average. Thus I should be able to expect at least 10.41 tonnes per ha across the farm. The plant counts were down by 8.5% so I increased the nitrogen by 3.6 kg per hectare and made sure we had 5.5% more urea than normal. Yesterday evening while doing my normal weed patrol, I saw three cleavers, one fumitory and a field pansy on the 45 ha I inspected. I noted their presence and will spot-treat them tomorrow with my knapsack sprayer."

It is not that I doubt these worthy geniuses for a second. I am just consumed by envy and guilt when I read of their never-ending triumphs.

At Thriplow it is not quite that simple. We have our fair share of disasters. Readers with long memories will remember our field of Longbow which yielded 37cwt last harvest. And for those sadists among you who have developed a taste for my misfortunes, I have some more good news. Our sugar beet last year was dreadful. In fact it is beginning to be clear that we are very bad sugar beet growers indeed. The final humiliating proof arrived in the post the other afternoon. British Sugar had the nerve to tell me how we compared to their other growers. It did not make pretty reading for someone as deeply competitive as me. [1] Of course, like all farmers, I have lots of excuses for this pathetic performance. Our light land never does well in a dry summer. Even more crucially, we had to re-drill all of our beet in mid-May so it never really stood a chance. But why was this necessary? We shall never know. ADAS, the chemical manufacturers and British Sugar all disagree. One thing is certain, however: good beet-growers do not re-drill in mid May.

I remember my sainted father saying that you only knew the herdsman was no good after you finally went bankrupt. Until then he would always have a whole variety of plausible excuses why the

- 229 -

herd's performance was so poor.

The silage wasn't good enough. It rained too much or too little. The winter had been too warm or too cold. The hay was musty. And so on and so on. We gave up milking in 1978 but we're still in the sugar beet business. Perhaps there is a lesson here.

Napoleon (you wouldn't catch him in a pair of Wellingtons) summed up the problem when he said: "There are a thousand reasons but no excuse." Thank you Napoleon.

Now I have proved beyond doubt that we are bad sugar beet growers, there remains the problem of how to improve. The solution may not be far away.

After decades of sleepy smugness, British Sugar appears to be waking up. And about time too. Like so many monopolies, it managed to combine arrogance and idleness in equal proportions. Take the fieldsmen for example. Here is a body of men who could be giving detailed help to each grower. They could and should be expert agronomists who act as clearing houses for the latest information. But instead they spend their days shuffling paper and trying to organise extra delivery permits. I cannot blame the fieldsman for being a useless appendage, since it isn't his fault. Instead I blame his bosses for failing to see his potential value.

But things look as if they're changing. Dear old British Sugar is beginning to set up consultancy groups in different parts of the country. Each group will consist of no more than 30 growers and 2000ha. Compare this to the 140 growers over 5500ha that some fieldsmen have to look after today.

If all goes according to plan, I shall join one of these groups and, for a fee amounting to 25p a contracted tonne, will receive all sorts of advice I never get from the fieldsman. For reasons that will now be clear, I need this advice more than most.

So thank you, British Sugar. I shall try to do better this year. In fact I've never seen the beet look so well. The plant is so thick we have to do some hand singling for the first time in ages. It brings a tear to my eye and a sugar lump to my throat.

> *We joined the Consultancy Group and remained in it for three years. It was not a success. At a cost of roughly £1000 per year, we received only slightly more help than we did in the old days when we had a fieldsman for free. Another good idea which never quite worked out.*

Buying a Combine

MAY 1985

Buying farm machinery is my favourite outdoor sport. I have never learned to shoot, do not wish to hunt and live too far from the sea to fish. So what could be better on a warm spring afternoon than to go out and buy a combine?

I had just spent a couple of hours having rings run round me by a bearded and talented seed merchant in Bury St Edmunds. As usual, I had agreed to miniscule premiums and outrageous seed contracts. I suppose I would have jumped out of a plane without a parachute if he'd suggested it. He's that sort of man. I looked at my watch and realised that there were two hours to kill before my next appointment – with the Ipswich Girl Guides. But time wasting in West Suffolk is never a problem for me. I just shamble along to Manns of Saxham and drool over shiny new Claas machinery. And that is precisely what I did.

The doors at Manns are the sort which open automatically when you approach. They make a lot of sense if you cannot afford a uniformed commissionaire. Life, after all, is hard in the machinery trade these days. Once inside, however, things start to move fast. I was immediately identified as a potential customer and smiles appeared on faces I had not even noticed before.

Within seconds, I was being whisked through endless anterooms containing glamorous secretaries. I could tell I was nearing my destination because the offices became bigger, the carpets thicker and the voices more respectful. Suddenly I was in The Presence. Far over in the corner of a magnificent office behind a desk which overlooked the car park sat The Man. The Americans would know him as the Head Honcho, to the French he would be Le Grand Fromage, but here in deepest Suffolk (to his face at least) he is just called Sir.

I sat in a comfy chair, drank a cup of tea and made scintillating smalltalk about life in general and the machinery trade in particular. They were having, I learned, a magnificent year. Sales in unit terms were up by a zillion percent and the outlook had never looked better. I could tell I was in the presence of a master salesman because before long I too was oozing optimism. And after my mauling at the hands of the seed merchant, that was quite an achievement.

The conversation continued to wander over diverse and witty topics until I remembered the real purpose of my visit. I was on the scrounge.

"Dick," (for that was his name) I said, "I have a favour to ask of you."

He winced visibly. There is nothing to make a combine salesman more dyspeptic than a big farmer trying to get something for nothing. But he soon managed to bring the wince under control and produced a beaming smile to take its place.

"What can we do to help?" he said, and in doing so gave an excellent imitation of a man who really wanted to help; provided it didn't cost too much.

I tried to sound casual and cool. I didn't want to scare him any more than I had already done. "I wonder if I could borrow a combine from you this harvest," I started.

The teacup shook only slightly in Dick's hand as his agile brain assessed the commercial consequences of this outrageous request. I could see he was still waiting for me to reveal my true purpose in greater detail, so I continued. "We've got this bit of hybrid wheat and we're going to have to combine some strips two metres wide. This could be a bit awkward with a Dominator 106 and a 17 feet header".

"Quite so." replied Dick. He was obviously playing for time. I suspected that he played chess professionally, or bathed with piranha fish for fun. Probably both. I felt hopelessly out of my depth.

There was a brief silence while I wondered what to say next. But I need not have worried. The businessman in Dick had taken over and, in a blur of speed and amazing physical co-ordination, he managed to put down his teacup and punch a button on the intercom. Within seconds he had ascertained that no such combine was available.

A black depression set in as I realised I had been wasting my time – not to mention his. But then, in another burst of entrepreneurial energy, Dick had solved the problem.

He located an old combine which was being traded-in against a new model. Twenty years old with a six feet header in working order. I could borrow it.

What could I do when faced with such generosity? The answer was simple: I decided to buy the combine. How much was it?

Another staccato exchange on the intercom. "One thousand pounds." A lesser man than I might have agreed there and then. But I didn't reach the dizzy heights I occupy today by being an easy pushover for combine salesman. Oh no.

"If you deliver it for that price you've got yourself a deal," I said aggressively. "You're on," said Dick. And that is how I came to be the proud owner of a 20 year old Claas Columbus combine last week.

You can keep your hunting, shooting and fishing. I'll stick with buying combines.

Dick Filbey, the Sales Director of Manns of Saxham, has retired now. He is one of the great men of the agricultural engineering industry.

The Bankrupt Farmers of Nebraska

JUNE 1985

The Platte River meanders slowly through the Nebraska prairies in a valley so wide and flat that you can see neither side from the river itself. One hundred years ago settlers moving west in their covered wagons travelled this route on their way to California. The plains were then full of buffalo and Sioux Indians. Thus Nebraska entered into the folklore of the west.

Today it is a quiet part of the world with rolling hills and big skies. Rusty barbed wire and ancient wind pumps lie derelict, reminding the passing motorist that livestock was once the most important industry. Now huge centre-pivot irrigators and articulated tractors show that arable farming has taken over Nebraska.

Dean Eberle is the all-american farmer. Forty-three years old, lean, tough and not afraid of hard work, he farms 2000 acres on the edge of the sand hills in central Nebraska. His wife works as a nurse in the nearby town and they have six children, two of whom are teenagers still at home. Their house is clean and spacious; their car is large and comfortable.

There is just one snag. Dean Eberle is bankrupt. The bank is about to foreclose. After three generations of Eberles, the farm will be sold and Dean will be looking for a job.

"We've been under a lot of stress for the past two years," says Mrs Eberle. "It's tough on Dean and on me, but it's worse for the kids aged 12 and 14. They don't know if they will be at the same school next month, or even if we'll be living in our own home. I don't feel bitter because we've had time to work it all out. I guess I just feel that God's will is done."

Dean is equally calm. "Sure I can blame the government," he says. "They put embargoes on our produce, they raised interest rates to 20% and the dollar is now so strong nobody can afford our corn."

But he admitted that he himself might have made matters worse. "When the banker said 'sell' I didn't. I dragged it out a little longer than I should have. Now I probably won't have any equity left when we finally sell the equipment and the land."

It didn't seem possible that a man like Dean could be bankrupt.

The reasons were far from clear. There was talk of his having to buy out his father and other family members, there was mention of high interest rates, there was the cost of running intensive beef and pig enterprises. But when I probed for the real reasons, I found – not surprisingly – that he was very unspecific.

Beulah Gocke is different. There are not many woman farmers in Nebraska. She was with her flock of Suffolk sheep when I drove into her windy farmyard in York County. Together with her 35-year-old son, Ray, she farms 440 acres and lives in the same wooden-frame house which her grandparents built 80 years ago. How long she will continue to live there is hard to say. "We've probably got only a few months before it is sold," she says.

Beulah and Ray Gocke run an intensive operation. As well as the 335 ewes, they have 100 sows and 35 suckler Simmentals. Most of the farm is irrigated, growing maize, sorghum, soyabeans and lucerne. But the cost of intensification probably caused their downfall. Unlike many other farmers who bought land, Beulah Gocke borrowed money to buy cattle and she now admits, "There's no longer any profit. The farm's been bleeding as if it had an ulcer."

The value of her irrigated land has halved in the past five years and has so eroded her collateral that the bank called in her loan. After two years of trying to get extensions, she and her lawyer have finally given up and she now faces the reality of seeing her land sold out from under her.

"I'll admit that we over-extended ourselves," she says. "But prices just haven't been high enough. The government is also at fault. High interest rates and embargoes made life impossible. When I asked the bank for an extension, they went into orbit". And yet Beulah Gocke remains philosophical throughout it all. "I'm not going to let bitterness ruin my life. If this is the way it's going to pan out, I guess we'll just have to make the best of it."

The town of Minden, Nebraska could be anywhere in the American Mid-West. It has a main street full of slightly seedy facades, a court house at the centre of a square, a red brick high school and a highway lined with neon-encrusted fast-food outlets and petrol stations. I was there to speak to the local bank president, Anthony ("Skip" to his friends) Hove Jr. It was a busy Friday afternoon in the bank and, while I waited, my eye caught a pile of papers which were lying carelessly on a table. They were all the same format: sale particulars of local farms.

Skip Hove, like any good banker, couldn't have been friendlier. He managed to appear both confident and concerned at the same time. Yes, many farmers were in trouble. So also were a few banks. In fact eight had gone bust in Nebraska during the past year. They had over-extended themselves by lending too much money to farmers and were now paying the price. "Bankers," he says, "make mistakes too. But no bankers ever rushed out into the streets waving dollar bills asking farmers to take out loans."

Had he ever foreclosed on a farm? "No. Well not exactly. We've been able to persuade the farmer to quit while he still had a bit of capital left." According to him, the causes were far from simple. It was not just that the price of land had come down sharply, it had been that the price of maize and soyabeans was lower than for the past three years. Nor was it because of the severe drought in some parts of the state last summer. All these events combined to make Nebraska farmers face their worst crisis since the Depression of the 1930s.

The problems facing Nebraska farmers are echoed in the neighbouring states. Doug Eckley is a salesman with John Deere dealer, Brook Equipment of Boone, Iowa. Standing beside a row of huge new tractors, he says, "I'm 31 and it's the first time I have ever seen anything like this. I just hope I never see it again." Sales have slumped as farmers have little money to spend. "Time was when farmers would call into this office and buy tractors or combines. Now we have to go out on the road and actually sell our equipment. It's tough and getting tougher."

But difficulty in selling new tackle is not the only problem Doug Eckley faces. "Even the secondhand market has collapsed. There are so many farm sales round here that our customers prefer to buy at the auctions rather than from dealers like us."

In the past few years the number of John Deere dealers in Iowa has fallen from 160 to about 100. "And for IH dealers it's been far worse. In the future there won't be so many dealers. Farmers will have to drive a heck of a lot further to buy their spare parts."

Fifty miles west of Boone, I found that Doug Eckley's predictions had already come true. Binns Equipment stands on the edge of a small town. Inside the showroom farmers were poking through piles of John Deere spare parts which were stacked on the floor under a sign proclaiming "Cash Sales Only".

"There comes a point in time when you've either got to go under or get out," says Kelly Shear. "We put this off for too long and I guess it's inevitable. We just couldn't make ends meet so we're closing the doors next week. The boss called us in and told us we'd better start looking for other jobs."

It had all been very sudden. "We used to sell 25 tractors a year, and 12 combines. But in recent months farmers started to come in and say, 'We're not going to buy anything until we see what crop prices are going to do'."

Across the road the West Central Co-operative silos were full. Inside the small office, the assistant manager, Jeff Dijody, was in sombre mood. He was offering $2.49 a bushel for maize compared with $2.75 a year earlier. Soyabeans had suffered an even sharper fall, down $1.50 a bushel to $5.51.

"The biggest difference I've noticed in the past year," says Jeff, "is that we're a lot tougher with credit. Last year we didn't ask questions if a guy wanted to buy fertiliser. This time, unless he's been approved, he will have to pay cash."

Had farmers changed their habits? "Some are selling their crop earlier so they don't get saddled with bank interest," he explained, "and others are looking about for ways to save on their herbicides. They go in for bandspraying instead of overall applications. And, of course, they look for cheaper products. A few farmers are even buying less fertiliser than they used to, but most reckon this is the last thing they'll economise on."

At this moment we were interrupted by the arrival of a customer. An old farmer had come in to check on prices. After a brief chat, he turned to go out of the door saying: "Things could get worse. At least we've got electricity now. The kids don't know what it was like in the Depression." It was my cue to leave. I was beginning to feel nostalgic for comfy old Cambridgeshire and the Common Agricultural Policy.

This trip made a deep impression on me. It was the first time I had ever actually met a bankrupt farmer. Instead of being derelicts who got up late in the morning, planted their corn too late and harvested their crops too late, they were actually good farmers. Far from being incompetent, their only mistake was to have been too keen. As a result, they borrowed too much money. I came back to England a very sober man. I too had borrowed a lot of money during the 1970s and early 1980s....

Pre-harvest Round-up

JULY 1985

A Sunday afternoon in late June. The rain is pelting down. Harvest is less than four weeks away and I am bored out of my tiny mind. Suddenly I notice the telephone sitting silently on my desk, half buried under a heap of circulars advertising seaweed-based fertiliser and growth promoters for lambs. Thank God for the telephone. My problems are solved. I decide to conduct a scientific survey of agricultural opinion throughout the world.

I start by phoning Loren Wehrenberg on his farm at Garber, Oklahoma, in the heart of the American wheat belt. The news from the prairies is not good at all. Until a few weeks ago he had been expecting an excellent harvest. Planting last autumn had been good and the intervening weather almost perfect. Until June, that is.

In the first three weeks of the month they had endured frequent hailstorms and a total of ten inches of rain. Prospects for an excellent harvest receded fast. The combines came out on about the fifth of the month and harvest will be over by the time you read this. Yields of hard red winter wheat are around 22cwt per acre, down from 26cwt last year.

But if Loren was disappointed about the yield, he was even more disappointed about the price, which had collapsed by 25% from last year's level. His local elevator was paying $3 a bushel (89 per tonne) compared with $4 in June 1984. He was thankful that he was able to store his crop and did not have to sell it immediately.

As I put the phone down, I reminded myself that Loren's wheat is hardly comparable with mine. At 12% protein, it is a lot higher quality. And since his farm is 500 miles from the nearest port, transport costs add a lot to the final price.

My next call was to Joe Linnell who farms in Summerbury, Saskatchewan, on the northern edge of the Canadian prairies. To most British farmers, there is little difference between America and Canada. But although Loren and Joe are on the same continent, their farms might as well be on different planets. One thousand miles to the north, Joe Linnell faces problems Loren does not even dream about.

Traditionally the Canadian prairies produced spring wheat, but in recent years there has been a move towards winter varieties. Last winter, however, in spite of good snow cover, "Most of the winter wheat in western Canada was a writeoff." Seeding, Joe told me, had gone well "after a beautiful April and May" and the Canola (oilseed rape) crop looked good too. But it is hard to be an optimist in that part of the world. Just as everything began to go well, they were invaded by swarms of grasshoppers. Some farmers have already sprayed five times against them, and it is still far from certain that these locust-like insects will be brought under control. And yet in spite of the fact that he expects prices to drop by about 10% compared to last harvest, Joe Linnell was quietly optimistic about prospects in Saskatchewan.

I had expected to find my continental friends deep in gloom but, as usual, I was wrong. Francis Cappelle farms near Laon in northern France. A Nuffield Scholar, he speaks perfect English and was keen to hear the gossip when I phoned him. The weather had been good – but a bit too wet for his tastes.

"Crops look pretty well. Cereals may not be quite as good as last year, but the maize and beet is better," he told me. Yes, he was unhappy about the prices which, he reckoned, would drop by at least 10% from last year. But with input costs up by 8%, he feared that his net profit would only be half last year's figure. What worried him most was the fact that in his part of France farmers owed their co-ops 25% more than they did last year. He reckoned that next year this amount would double again.

And yet Francis, like so many of the intelligent farmers I know, was quietly fatalistic about the future. Unlike so many French farmers, I got the impression that he did not feel that noisy demonstrations would really influence politicians or solve the problems facing the Common Agricultural Policy.

I turned my attention to Germany and began by ringing my favourite Bavarian, Christof Schwab, who farms on the banks of the Danube, near Regensburg.

The weather, Christof told me, had been unbelievable. Three hailstorms had given them no less than 300 mm in June alone. Most of the barley was flat on the ground. The wheat looked "far thicker than last year, but if we have high temperatures soon we could have problems." The rape also looked good. Only the maize (an important crop in this part of Bavaria) had not liked the cool, wet weather.

As far as prices were concerned, it was hard to predict but it looked as if they would be down by 8%.

Two hundred miles to the north on the flat plains of Lower Saxony, Hans-Heinrich Imholze manages the 2000 acre Schwarzenraben estate. It had been raining every day "with only a two hour break which was just enough to do some spraying". The crops looked very well in spite of some laid barley. He was worried about the possibility of fusarium because there is no chemical which will control the disease effectively.

When it came to prices, Imholze reckoned they would drop by 10% in spite of the efforts of Herr Kiechle★. "The man's not being realistic," he said. "He doesn't seem to understand what is possible. You simply cannot keep prices this high when the surplus is as big as it is."

It was still raining when I put the telephone down. My friends round the world seemed to be facing a harvest which ranged from good to excellent, even though prices are down by 10%. For their sakes I was happy, but it must be bad news for Brussels and the CAP, especially when confronted by a weaker dollar and a more aggressive export policy from Washington. I thanked heaven I was a farmer, not a politician, and wondered when the rain would stop.

An Open Letter to My Landlord

AUGUST 1985

Dear Landlord

You will not need me to remind you what a wonderful tenant I am. Not a weed is visible on the farm, gutters and roofs are in perfect condition, manurial values remain unexhausted and (this is the bit you really appreciate) I pay my rent on time. What is more, I am extraordinarily polite to your land agents, Messrs. Flatter & Deceive, and am positively unctuous to their partner, Nigel Unworthy-Smooth, whenever he comes to visit me, complete with his green wellies, cavalry twills, cloth cap, hip flask and black labrador. I tell you all this not out of conceit (me conceited?) but just

★   German Minister of Agriculture.

in case you think I am one of those constant whingers who belong to the Tenant Farmers' Association.

You will probably have read that the Common Agricultural Policy is in turmoil. Your land agents may even have told you about the over-production of cereals and the certainty that arable profits will continue to fall very sharply indeed. What is more, looking at the performance of the Stock Exchange in the past year or so, you may well have decided to get out of agricultural land altogether.

I believe you chaps call this "adjusting the balance of the portfolio". I call it "selling land and buying equities". Your keenness to sell will have been increased when you were told by Messrs. Flatter & Deceive that land values are falling fast. Mr Unworthy-Smooth will certainly have advised caution, and will have told you to "wait until the market bottoms out before reducing your holdings".

All of this may be bad news for you, but I am afraid that there is worse to come. What is more, I have reason to believe that your land agents have not dared tell you. Hence this letter.

In the past decade I have done very well as an arable farmer. But so have you as a landlord. Every three years Nigel Unworthy-Smooth put the rent up by at least 33%, and often more. Of course I squealed a lot and threatened arbitration, but at the end of the day I paid up as Nigel knew I would. High cereal prices and increasing yields enabled me to pay you and still buy a fancy car or two for myself.

You were – as I am sure you now accept – riding on the wave of cereal prosperity. But today the party is well and truly over. You are probably aware of this as a theoretical fact, but unless you know what it will mean to you in terms of hard cash, you are in for a most unpleasant shock.

My profits have come down for the past three years, both in real terms and in money terms. The future looks worse still because if Brussels is serious about reducing the grain surplus – and I believe that it is – it will have to lower prices not by a piddling 2 or 3% a year, but by 15 or 20%. Anything less would just make me try even harder to maintain my income by increasing yields. And if I succeeded in doing that, the surplus would actually grow rather than diminish.

Brussels knows there are only two ways of solving the problem. Either a lot of wheat producers will have to be forced out of farming, or we shall have to reduce our yields. In a perfect world, of course, I would simply lower my inputs of seed, fertiliser and sprays and produce less wheat. But there is a reason why I cannot do this. The reason is you.

Make no mistake about it, the rent I pay you is my biggest single fixed cost. If I came to you one day and asked for a rent reduction because I was being a good boy and producing less wheat, would you be sympathetic? Would you, hell!

Nigel Unworthy-Smooth will, of course, be unruffled when you show him this letter. "Don't worry", he will tell you, "all tenants talk like this as a rent review approaches. We'll get him up by at least 15% and I'll have a damned good crack at 33%".

Then he will say something which is absolutely crucial. You will find it splendidly reassuring but I believe it to be utterly and completely untrue. So be on your guard when he says, "At the end of the day if Walston won't pay the new rent, we can always re-let at far more than he is paying today. Why, only yesterday we opened some tenders for a farm in the Chichester area and the highest was £125 per acre."

Mr Unworthy-Smooth is correct as far as he goes. Tender rents are still very high indeed. There are still some maniacs around who are offering these fancy rents. They managed to survive in the halcyon days of arable prosperity, but with wheat likely to be around £80 a tonne next harvest, how is it possible for them to continue? They can't. Anybody who has done a cashflow forecast for the 1986 harvest knows exactly why. If you still don't believe me, phone the Farms department of Flatter & Deceive and see what they say.

Unless you accept that rents are going to come down roughly in line with cereal prices, you and your fellow landlords will bear some (not all) of the blame for the destruction of your tenants. You shared in our prosperity during the good days. I am afraid that you will also have to share the hardships of the bad days to come. What is more, Nigel Unworthy-Smooth (after a few gin and tonics) knows in his guts that I am right. So why not give Nigel lunch and talk it over in a civilised fashion? Nigel likes lunches.

Harvest 1985

SEPTEMBER 1985

Thank God it's over. I have never enjoyed a harvest less. And yet already the memories are beginning to fade. Today the drill is lost in a cloud of dust as the next year's rape goes into a dry seedbed.

It all began a week later than normal on July 23rd. I was full of optimism because our light land thrives on wet conditions and we were anticipating very big yields indeed – certainly more than last year which for us had been good but not miraculous.

The barley had at least managed to keep standing – even the Halcyon. But at the end of the day only the Panda did at all well, at around 65cwt/acre. The seed merchants were, fortunately, keen to get hold of the variety. Which is odd because last autumn it had not been a popular one. This year, however, was a very different tale. Nobody seemed to care about the embryo tests for loose smut – they just asked us to load their lorries. It never ceases to amaze me how fussy a merchant is when he doesn't want a variety.

Halcyon was a disappointment, averaging only 53cwt/acre. Good old Otter managed to produce 45cwt. This autumn we'll be putting our faith in Pipkin, hoping that it will succeed where Halcyon and Tipper have failed.

The rape was far more successful. We were growing the new variety Mikado for the first time. Throughout the season it had looked good, in spite of some scare-mongering about leaf scorch from winter frosts. We only put on 188 units of nitrogen which, in retrospect, was probably too little for such a short, stiff variety. Next year we shall increase the amount by 10%.

When the rape eventually ripened, I was glad that once again we had decided not to swath or dessicate but instead to combine it direct. The weather had been so bad that when at last the rain stopped, we began harvesting at 3pm and finished the 188 acres at dawn the next morning. The eventual yield after drying worked out at 28cwt/acre, which is better than we have done with either Jet Neuf or Bienvenu in the past. The oil content at 44% was also very good so we'll be sticking with Mikado next year.

If the rape and barley had been difficult to harvest, they were simplicity itself compared to the herbage seed. This, of course, is a crop which is hard to combine at the best of times, needing hot sunshine and a dry wind. This year we had neither, and so struggled through the wet and matted crop cursing our luck and wondering whether we should not abandon it completely. Eventually, after several attempts, we salvaged the early perennial ryegrass, Mantilla, and found that it had produced a dismal 8cwt per acre. The late ryegrass, Rathlin, did no better, but was at least combined in slightly easier conditions. One consolation may be that our thrashed ryegrass straw may be worth something this winter. Any offers?

The weather in the second week of August showed no signs of clearing, so we took the plunge and started combining wheat even though the moisture was 28%. Throughout the spring and early summer I had been full of optimism about this crop, but now I was becoming more gloomy with every passing day. Some fields were lodged, but most of the wheat was still standing. As a seed grower, I was particularly worried about sprouting grain, and kept a careful watch on the laid patches. I was amazed – to put it mildly – when we discovered that a standing crop of Moulin had started to grow in the ear.

This news made me even more impatient to get the wheat in the barn regardless of cost. During each brief gap between storms, the four combines dashed out and did what they could. At just over 12 acres an hour, it meant that we could cover a 50 acre field in just over four hours. The trouble was that this simply moved the bottleneck from the field to the drier as mountains of very soggy wheat occupied every corner of every shed waiting their turn before they went through the drier.

This harvest we noticed that the yield gap between first, second and third wheats was wider than ever, amounting to at least half a tonne. As far as the varieties were concerned, there was also a very great variation. Galahad had a wonderful year, averaging 75cwt over 255 acres. The sample was excellent. Longbow also did well at around 69cwt, and 200 acres of Brimstone impressed me with 67cwt even though it had been drilled late behind sugar beet. It had lodged more than most and the grain was not very pretty. Avalon achieved a creditable 70cwt on the first year field and 55cwt on its third year. Mission and Fenman both managed to scrape past the 60cwt barrier.

The disaster of the harvest was the one variety for which I had the highest hopes, Moulin. For the past two years it had done very well for us, but this year it had a miserable time. Our two fields, being grown behind herbage seed, did not quite average 60cwt, and a third year field shocked us all by producing a pathetic 42cwt. It was, as they say, one of those years for Moulin. To make matters worse, the Hagberg was a mere 67 so, in spite of the fact it was 12.5% protein, we could not even sell it for milling.

Durum wheat again failed at Thriplow, averaging just over 30cwt. I am prepared to admit that I must be a bad durum farmer because, I gather, other people have had good results this year. But at these yields we have lost money for the past two years – not to mention the enormous expense of rogueing offtypes from the crop.

If the wheat was giving us headaches, it was nothing to the problems we had with peas. Filby, the leafless variety, was particularly difficult. Weed control had been poor to start with and knotgrass wrapped itself round the combines' augers, fingers and elevators. At one stage I thought we might have to write off the crop, but eventually we managed to salvage a tonne an acre. Progreta did better at 38cwt.

Every harvest has its heroes. This year we had two: David (Spud) Speak and Oliver Johnson. Between them they manned the grainstore and drier for anything up to 20 hours at a stretch. They spent their waking hours covered in barley ails. They shovelled wheat which was so wet it would not flow. They cleaned bins of rape in the early hours of the morning. They moved piles of dusty grass seed and unblocked countless conveyors. So thank you Spud and OJ.

We eventually finished on August 31st, quite a week later than normal. Quite how we managed I shall never fully understand. Without the hard work and dedication from everyone we would still be bogged down in a sea of stinking, sopping, sprouting wheat. So thank you Dave, Ted, Fiona, Mossy, Brian, Chris, Dick, Will, Albert, Do, Stan, John, Lindsay, George, Philip, Stefan, Christof and Tim. Now for next year.

This simple and straightforward account of our harvest turned out to be one of the most provocative articles I ever wrote – to my amazement. Letters, and even phone calls, poured in from furious farmers in the North and Scotland who, far from finishing their harvest, had hardly begun. They abused me for having too many combines, employing too many men and (so they imagined) taking pleasure in their misfortunes. They were wrong, but it gives you some idea of what goes on inside some farmers' brains.

Talking to the Bank Manager

OCTOBER 1985

In the good old days – which lasted until yesterday – I used to love my Bank Manager. His regular presence throughout the year gave to my tedious and humdrum life a reassuring regularity. In the summer he would come out, have lunch and spend the afternoon looking round the farm. In the winter he might invite me to one of the posher restaurants in Cambridge. Regular readers of this column will remember that it is impossible to eat well in Cambridge (or in East Anglia, if it comes to that). And in the spring there was the Ceremony of the Cash Flow Forecast. This was far more enjoyable than the lunches because the ritual was so much more elaborate.

For two consecutive weeks Lionel Dawes, the retired Farm Secretary who now acts as statistician and sage, and I would pore over papers trying to find out how much we had spent on fixed and variable costs in the past year. Then would come the crucial moment at which we would predict what the inflation rate for the next year would be. Finally, we would make a wild but detailed (a fatal combination) guess as to when we would spend this money and hence how big the overdraft would be. The climax would come when I made the appointment with the Bank Manager, gathered up a thick volume of evidence, and put on a suit. At least I did to begin with. After a few elegant years I decided that no Bank Manager is ever fooled by the presence of a waistcoat, and so have recently taken to wearing my normal blue jeans and grubby denim shirt.

The interview normally lasted no more than 15 minutes and included at least one cup of tea. I asked for a small increase in the overdraft on last year's level, and backed up my request with a mountain of figures. The Bank Manager agreed, I said thank you very much – and another year had begun.

Today we use a computer to do most of the work, but Lionel's role remains as crucial as ever. However, this year things were rather different. For the first time in my brief, inglorious farming career, I began to feel that I should take this cashflow forecast seriously. In the past I had ignored it from the moment I left the Bank Manager's office. Such was my prosperity that I knew in my bones that there would be no problems. And there weren't. So I never bothered to check our performance during the year to see how it compared to the forecast. Being an arable farmer in the past decade has not been an arduous profession.

But the next decade will be very different. Very different indeed. So in addition to producing a forecast for the next 12 months, I thought it might be useful to look further ahead and see what would happen between now and 1989. This is a risky undertaking at the best of times because it involves not only guessing but – far worse – piling guesses on top of guesses. Being a profoundly stupid person, I was not deterred by all that.

I decided to concentrate on our most profitable crops, winter wheat and barley. I used as a base-line the costs I know we shall incur for harvest 1986. At this point life became a bit more difficult as it was now necessary to guess both quantity and price. I assumed we would achieve our three-year average yields and assumed (pessimistically) that the price of wheat would be £92 per tonne in September 1986.

From there I was entering unknown territory where only fools or blind men venture. I started to make sweeping assumptions with no real justification save for my own hunches. The price of wheat will fall by a further 5% a year until harvest 1988. Inflation will run at about 5% for most inputs. Wages will be held at their present level by not replacing people who retire. Rents and mortgages will fall before holding steady. And so it went on.

You may feel that I have been unduly optimistic by keeping fixed costs down too low. You may, on the other hand, think I have been too gloomy about prices. The conclusions are that wheat will remain profitable until after harvest 1987, after which time the smallest hiccup in either yield or price will cause us to lose money. Barley is a far gloomier picture altogether. If I really had the courage of my own convictions, I would stop growing it altogether.

But whatever happens, I stand by these figures even though they are based on nothing more substantial than today's facts and tomorrow's hunches. I am fully prepared to be seen as a fool by the time next harvest rolls around. It won't be the first time I have been entirely wrong. At least the exercise has made me realise for the first time both how well I did in the past and how grim the future looks. I shall watch that cashflow forecast very carefully this year.

My forecast was, unfortunately, far too optimistic when it came to yields. I had assumed a steadily rising output, albeit with falling prices. As it happens, we had two very bad harvests in 1986 and 1987. The prices were higher than I had anticipated, but the overall margins were worse. We gave up growing barley after the 1987 harvest.

Why I'm Not an Organic Farmer

DECEMBER 1985

Once upon a time I thought seriously about becoming an organic farmer. That was how I met Barry Wookey. He left a deep impression because he persuaded me to get on a horse and ride out over Salisbury Plain to look at his organic acres. Anyone who can induce me to get into a saddle must be an exceptional human being because I am a hopeless rider and am terrified of horses. I am also, by the way, frightened of flying, snakes, rats and making a fool of myself. But that, you will be relieved to hear, is another story.

Most organic farmers feel that they have not had a fair hearing in recent times. Some of the more neurotic ones even believe that there is a conspiracy between the chemical manufacturers, the fertiliser manufacturers, ADAS and the media to stifle their point of view. That is why I was so pleased to learn that Mr Wookey had addressed the British Crop Protection Council's conference at Brighton last month.

As a fully paid-up member of the "Slap-it-on-at-all-costs" High Input Brotherhood, I agree that the facts about organic farming should be brought out into the open. No longer can we afford to giggle about "Muck and Mystery" farmers and proceed to carry on as if nothing had happened. It is time to take a long, hard look at our inorganic system of farming and see whether we can't learn a thing or two from Mr Wookey and his friends.

I have long since given up any ideas that I myself could join the ranks of the organic farmers. Two reasons were uppermost in my mind. First, I do not feel passionately in my guts that it is Right with a capital R. Second, I simply could not afford to be an organic farmer.

Ask any farmer why he farms the way he does, and he will immediately start talking nonsense. He will tell you it is because his father taught him, or because he has tried umpteen different systems, or because the local ADAS man or chemical rep or private agronomist or land agent advised him. The articulate ones will even cite trials or results to prove their point until your mind goes numb under a deluge of figures. But after all the verbiage comes to a halt, the fact is that the farmer farms in the way he feels (repeat, feels) is best. This is even more true of organic farmers, all of whom feel desperately that organic farming is right, good, sensible, proper, intelligent and (this is where I start to feel nauseous) moral.

Like the early Christians being persecuted in the catacombs of Rome, organic farmers today band themselves into a tightly-knit group of self-righteous men. They see the rest of the farming world conspiring against them, and talk darkly about the wicked role of the agrochemical companies.

They know, without any doubt whatsoever, that they are good whilst the rest of us are, at best, ignorant heathens who one day will see the light. I regret that I simply do not possess the burning certainty necessary to be a true believer or, if it comes to that, a true organic farmer.

But neither could I afford to be an organic farmer. Oh yes, I won't dispute that the gross margin on organic wheat sometimes compares favourably with high input crops. It's the years which come in between the wheat crops which worry me. I pay a commercial rent of £53 per acre, and have an overdraft and a mortgage on top of this. I simply could not afford the sort of rotation that Mr Wookey practices. He, you will recall, starts with a three year ley and, of course, uses no nitrogen other than legumes. Even forgetting that there is already a surplus of milk and meat in the EEC today, I simply could not come up with a livestock system which would pay my fixed costs as well as leaving me a profit at the end of the year.

Barry Wookey then grows winter wheat which, I am prepared to admit, may make as good a profit – albeit at lower costs and yields –

than I can right now. But then once again he returns his land to grass and takes a hay cut off it. A third winter wheat follows the hay and then he plants winter oats.

This rotation may make sense if you pay neither rent nor mortgage nor bank charges. But how I could hope to meet my fixed costs after growing three years' grass and using neither Nitram nor weedkiller mystifies me. Perhaps all organic farmers are so rich that they own their land outright and are free of all debt. If so, I must congratulate them on their excellent management and even better fortune. But it just ain't relevant to most real farmers who live in the real world with real debts. Question to the organic farmers: What are your fixed costs?

In East Anglia there are other factors which have always made me shy away from organic farming. It would mean, for example, that I would have to stop growing sugar beet altogether. Unfortunately, British Sugar will not pay me a premium for organic beet and, with no herbicides permitted, I would have to use hand labour to keep the weeds down. So my costs would be up and my output down. Not a pretty sight. Oilseed rape would also disappear from my farm as I cannot imagine it growing remotely economically without any nitrogen whatsoever. Question to organic farmers: How do I grow sugar beet or oilseed rape?

No, I shall have to continue with my chemicals and my fertilisers. But I shall resist the temptation to close my tiny brain completely. Instead I shall watch the organic chaps closely because the day may come when I change my mind. In the meanwhile I wish Barry Wookey and his friends well. I also wish I weren't so scared of horses.

Organic farming is today enjoying something of a revival, not only in the countryside, but also in Whitehall. The government has realised that the system has two splendid advantages over conventional agriculture; it costs less and it produces less. At a time when subsidies and surpluses are both mounting, this makes organic farming most attractive to hard-pressed politicians. But the fact remains that organic arable farming is still a rich man's folly. No ordinary farmer with bank interest, mortgage and rent to pay could possibly afford to have half his land down to grass and clover on which he grazes a few animals.

New Year Wishes 1986

JANUARY 1986

Being a simple – and very modest – son of the soil, I don't want much in 1986. I can survive without a new combine, I might even be able to struggle through with my two-year-old car and I suppose I could just forsake the continuous diet of caviar and champagne, which all of you readers think I have for each meal. No, all I want in 1986 is to have a few simple questions answered.

My problem is that while I know the questions, I haven't yet found anyone to whom they should be addressed. In the hopes that the readers of this journal are cleverer than I, here is a brief sample of what I have in mind.

1. Will there be a cereal quota this year? How will it work?

2. Will I have to take land out of production? How much? When?

3. Will the Intervention System survive at all? What will happen to the quality standards?

4. Will there be a market for either feed wheat or feed barley? Wouldn't it make more sense to grow only bread-making and malting varieties?

5. What will happen at my rent review this year? Will my landlord be understanding if, in a year or two, I am forced to take some land out of production?

6. Does high input cereal production still make sense? If not, what sort of cutbacks should I make?

7. After the dry autumn and the very backward crops, is my cashflow forecast hopelessly optimistic?

In my mercifully brief farming career, I have never before been this uncertain about so many different things. The snag is, of course, that I cannot blame anyone other than myself – and all you other farmers too. We are now paying the price for our prosperity this past decade. It is we who have produced too much, and have received too high prices.

To survive the next few years, we shall need to be both better farmers and better businessmen than we have been in the past. But we shall also need to be better with our public relations. No longer can we farmers afford to live in a make-believe world.

So, in addition to having answers to these questions, I would also like to see a new NFU emerge from the shambles which is Agriculture House. Here, at least, I am optimistic. Simon Gourlay is the one chap who might be able to bring us back into the real world. Of course, he'll make a lot of enemies in the process. But in addition to being bright and tough, he has a secret weapon which is almost unique in farming – a sense of humour. You think I'm exaggerating? When did you last meet a funny farmer?

In France the Lunatics Run the Asylum

MARCH 1986

The Department of the Allier in central France is not on the road from Norwich to St Moritz, so there is no reason for East Anglian farmers to know where it is. But put your finger on the middle of a map of France and you've found it. The countryside around the old city of Moulins is too pretty for a crass sugar-beet-loving clod like me. Somerset farmers, however, would feel very much at home among the gently rolling hills dotted with Charolais cattle and the occasional field of cereals.

The farms in the region are small, averaging no more than 100 acres. They appear to be moderately prosperous, even if they do lack a BMW in every driveway. But the farmers of the Allier are deeply unhappy. Unlike their British counterparts, who either pass resolutions at the Annual General Meeting, or form Action Groups in Dyfed, these men are a little more drastic. They vote communist. Indeed, it has been estimated that as many as 60% of the farmers of the Allier actively support the Communist Party. The local FNSEA –roughly the equivalent of the NFU – is, I was assured, today controlled by the communists. Imagine the Somerset County Branch of the NFU being run by men with pictures of Marx and Lenin behind their desks. Whatever would Sir Henry (God bless him) Plumb think?

I was there on the day of the recent election, and spent some time in the village hall watching French democracy in action. Life was complicated by the fact that they were voting not only for the National Assembly (House of Commons) but also for the regional government. Instead of marking a ballot paper with an X, the French voter is confronted with sheets of paper containing a list of the candidates from each of the parties. Where I was there were no fewer than sixteen different candidates, since eight parties were contesting two elections.

The voter takes these papers into the ballot box and throws the ones he will not vote for into the wastepaper basket which has been thoughtfully provided. The list of candidates for which he does wish to vote is stuffed into an envelope and then placed in the ballot box.

After a day in the district, I began to realise that for farmers in the Allier, East Anglia is about as relevant as the Gobi desert is to me. What is even more disturbing is that they seem to believe that they have a God-given right to farm their land. Whether or not anyone in the world can actually afford to buy their produce is utterly irrelevant. If I can grow wheat cheaper in Cambridgeshire, it's no concern of theirs. If the politicians in Paris don't see things this clearly, maybe a mass demonstration will change their minds.

When it comes to the problems of surpluses, or even the Common Agricultural Policy as a whole, their attitude is simple and direct. Every farmer must be kept in business regardless of any other consideration.

And maybe the farmers of the Allier are right after all. The newly-appointed French Minister of Agriculture, Franois Guillaume, is none other than the previous boss of the FNSEA. His blind insistence over the years that French farmers should be protected from economic reality makes Arthur Scargill seem like a moderate. Only in France could this bizarre event have happened. It's as if Simon Gourlay were suddenly appointed by Mrs Thatcher to take over from Michael Jopling. In French agriculture today, the lunatics are running the asylum. Heaven help the rest of us.

Gluttony in Paris

MARCH 1986

Of all the seven deadly sins, give me gluttony every time. Or almost every time. There are, it is true, the occasional moments when a bit of lust is just what I feel like. But in Paris recently, where I went to celebrate my wife's birthday, gluttony left the other six standing. This is odd because the average moronic Brit becomes a sex maniac the moment the ferry docks at Calais. He thinks that French women are nymphomaniacs at best and tarts at worst. Hence the embarrassing cries of "Ooh la la" when the inhabitants of the day excursion bus first catch a glimpse of a French female.

So much for lust. Gluttony does no better. Our charming British visitor makes straight for the dockside bar and proceeds to drink himself stupid on imported Watney's Red Barrel. He knows that French food is inedible, because the natives eat only garlic and frogs' legs. So he sticks to ham rolls or fish and chips. On the return journey he passes the time vomiting and listening to his mates singing bits of "Mademoiselle from Armentiers".

Farmers Weekly readers are, naturally, not even distantly related to the aforementioned yobs. They are all sophisticated connoisseurs of European culture. So when you are in Paris for the agricultural show this year, I suggest you take time off to visit the Eiffel Tower. These days you don't just go there for the sightseeing. You can also eat one of the best meals in Paris on the second floor of the tower. A new restaurant, called the Jules Verne, opened there recently.

Barley barons like me (with more money than sense) will love it. The food is exceptional, the decor high-tech chic and the view sensational. It will probably be fully booked for dinner, but try phoning for a table at lunch. You won't regret it, even though it will cost you thirty quid a head.

But the euphoria of a Paris weekend didn't last long. Back on the farm I've never (repeat, never) seen the crops look worse. We have had little snow so the frost-scorch has been severe. As if that weren't enough, the cold spell just after Christmas produced some very damaging frost-lift. One field of late-drilled winter barley lost about 60% of the plants. There's nothing I can do except whinge about my misfortune and hope that the rest of you feel sympathetic.

However depressing it is to be a farmer these days, it must be a lot worse if you happen to be an agrochemical retailer. Not many people bought chemicals last autumn because it was so dry. And now, with crops a month behind a normal season, we have done no spraying at all this year.

The machinery dealers aren't having an easy time of it these days either.

If it's tough being a salesman, imagine what it must feel like if you are a wheat breeder at the PBI or a sales executive with the NSDO. After two years of what Princess Anne would call naffing around, Mrs Thatcher has finally decided to sell the whole outfit. By this time morale is, I assume, terrible. Many of the most talented boffins hung up their white coats and have gone off to breed wheat for other masters. Good luck to them. It is particularly poignant that the Government, which pays lip service to the idea of efficient capitalism, could have made such a mess of a simple commercial transaction.

But today there is one group of people who should be feeling far more uneasy than any I have mentioned so far. The odd thing is that they are splendidly unaware that their profession also faces a crisis. I refer, of course, to those charming triple-barreled men in their green wellies, the land agents. Spare a thought (and maybe even a tear) for them as they sit around Mayfair waiting for the phone to ring. For the phone is ringing with growing infrequency. Which isn't surprising since fewer people are either buying or selling land these days. What is worse, the traditional indoor sport of land agents has also lost all of its old fizz. In the good old days Algy, Archie, Bobby, Berty, Charlie, Dicky, Gerry, Henry, Rodney, Roly, Tommy, Timmy and Willy (not forgetting Nigel and Rupert) used to sit round comparing rent settlements to see who had managed to screw his tenants up the highest. The winner paid for the G and Ts and the Pension Fund paid for the winner.

So when, like me, you sit in dismal weather and look round a dismal farm at dismal crops and read the dismal news in the dismal newspapers, remember that it could be worse. You could have been born an agrochemical dealer, or a tractor salesman or a plant breeder or even (heaven forbid) a land agent.

Bad Debt Nightmare

APRIL 1986

As the screw tightens on farming, I worry more about bankruptcy. It's not my own imminent demise which concerns me (not much, anyway) but I am becoming very nervous about the grain trade.

In common with most farmers, we only deal with a handful of merchants. If one of these went bust, we would be in serious trouble. Naturally, when I talk to a merchant he assures me his company is in splendid health. But, in the immortal words of Mandy Rice-Davies, "He would, wouldn't he?"

My worries are hardly new. Three years ago I became so concerned at the prospect of bad debts that I took out a very expensive insurance policy. I used the services of Trade Indemnity, which specialises in this sort of cover. But as the pressure on costs grew, I began to look for ways of reducing my overheads. The

£5000 a year I spent with Trade Indemnity looked pretty vulnerable. Recently I took the plunge and cancelled the policy. So here I am, after saving £5000 a year on my insurance bill, totally exposed to the risk of a customer going bust.

There are two possible solutions to the problem. The first is to insert a little clause into the agreement I have with the merchant. It says that the title to my grain does not actually pass until I have been paid in full. This means – in theory at least – that if the merchant goes bust, the chap to whom he has sold the grain should pay me and not the receiver. In practice, however, it may not be quite so simple. Nonetheless, I shall include this clause in all my grain contracts.

The second solution is one I am reluctant to adopt. There are some companies which are so big and powerful that the risk of their going up the Swanee is almost non-existent. If I really wanted to be safe, I suppose, I would sell all my grain to Dalgety, Cargill or Kenneth Wilson. I would avoid all the country grain merchants and do business only with the multinationals.

The snag is that, while it might make financial sense, life would become boring. And, of course, I would have to accept a lower price per tonne. If I insist on trading with fascinating, stimulating, glamorous men who pay a little more, I shouldn't be surprised that the faceless men from the multinationals pay less and are less fun.

Maybe I'm wrong again and those huge organisations are stuffed with chaps who, like my grain merchant friends, run spoilered white Mercedes cars, pay fancy prices for ordinary grain and throw in a case of 1966 vintage port from time to time just to keep me happy.

So my message to the grain trade is clear and loud. Please make sure you don't go bust until after you've paid me this autumn. Or, better still, don't go bust at all.

Don't Buy Certified Cereal Seed

MAY 1986

I make money growing cereal seeds. So if I were at all sensible I should never encourage farmers to save their own seed. Every bag they save means one less bag sold by the friendly (or otherwise) local seed merchant. And every bag the local seed merchant does not sell means one less bag he wishes to buy from me.

You don't need to be a genius to realise that if I knew what was good for me, I'd be telling the world to buy more seed – not less. I would, of course, be acting on the ancient principle so beloved of farmers that what is good for my farm must also be good for the rest of the world. This is baloney.

You would assume that the seed trade is now taking steps to ensure that seed is as cheap as possible. You would be wrong. Instead they are showing all the initiative of the Gadarene Swine as they rush headlong towards the cliff.

Take the plant breeders, for example. I love plant breeders. Their new varieties have done wonders for my bank balance over the years, and I am entirely in favour of plant breeders' rights. So I am all the sadder when I see what their commercial chaps have been doing recently. Plant breeders' income comes from royalties. This money finances their very expensive breeding programmes. Like mine, their costs have risen sharply in recent years. But, unlike me, they were able to raise their prices at the stroke of a pen. Since 1983, while the price of wheat has fallen by 27%, the royalty charged by the breeders for C2 seed has risen by 9%. Lucky plant breeders.

Wouldn't it be wonderful if the rest of us could decide to raise prices regardless of the pressures of the marketplace? The trouble is that if plant breeders continue on this short-sighted course, they will damage not only themselves but their customers. If they persist in ignoring the fact that the price of wheat and arable profits are falling, they will soon price new varieties out of the reach of ordinary farmers.

Another example of what might politely be called "odd" behaviour was seen last year when a leading plant breeding company introduced a new winter wheat. It is an excellent variety which should do very well on British farms. But so keen was the company to make money fast, that it devised a unique marketing scheme. Any seed merchant who ordered seed to multiply was told that he would have to pay a levy (in addition to the normal royalties) of 1925 for every tonne of seed ordered.

What made this arrangement extraordinary was that the levy would have to be paid even if the crop failed and no seed was actually multiplied. A consequence of this bizarre policy would have been to pass on the costs to the farmer. But it all went wrong. Last summer the poor old variety ran into purity problems and instead of being released as Basic Seed, most of the crop was downgraded to C1.

The levy was quietly forgotten. But gossip in the trade suggests that this year other wholesale seed merchants have been inspired by this example and are planning to release new varieties using the same method. I hope I am wrong about this. I shall keep you informed.

A small section of the seed trade, however, is having a wonderful time. The chaps who operate the mobile seed–cleaning plants are multiplying like aphids. And who can blame farmers for using them? They are cheap, quick and efficient. Mind you, there are rumours that a few of these operators break the law by selling uncertified seed instead of just cleaning the farmer's own material. If this is happening, I wouldn't be at all surprised. No wonder some established seedsmen are getting nervous. But before blaming farmers, governments or even cowboy operators, the seed trade should take a close look at itself. It is not a pretty sight.

That levy cost a lot of merchants a lot of money. The variety concerned did actually manage to get onto the NIAB Recommended List, but sales of this (and other new varieties) were poor and, as a result, the seed trade suffered greatly. I suspect the originator of the idea will quietly drop it. I hope so.

An Open Letter to Patrick Tory

MAY 1986

Dear Patrick Tory*

We haven't met so I hope you won't mind if I write you this rather public letter. You are asking all cereal growers to vote for a levy which will amount to a maximum of 20p per tonne. The money is going to be spent on three different projects, Food from Britain, cereals research and that old pipe-dream of your predecessor, Rowan Cherrington – a body to market British cereals abroad.

You have, I am told, already got the support of the whole of the farming establishment – those crusty old men in Agriculture House who prefer sitting on committees to tractors. Thus I have no doubt that you will win the vote comfortably. I shall be in the minority because I intend to vote against Food from Britain and UK Cereals Exports. Perhaps you would like to know why?

I shall support the levy on cereals research and am happy that 8.4p per tonne will be deducted to make up the reduction in Government spending. This is a sensible idea from which all cereal growers will benefit. I wish I could say the same for your other two proposals.

Food from Britain does not deserve a single penny from any cereal grower. It has been a failure from the very beginning, has achieved absolutely nothing in spite of spending millions, and will do absolutely nothing to help cereal growers. For me to give 1p on every tonne I produce simply to help this moribund organisation stagger on for a few more years would be a total waste of money. I am sorry to appear so harsh and unfeeling because the chaps in Food from Britain have worked hard and have done their best.

The idea for a UK cereals export development body deserves even less time than Food from Britain. I realise that this will be an unpopular opinion. Marketing, like high-fibre diets and low ground pressure vehicles, is something we are all in favour of these days.

I know your arguments (or some of them). I realise that the Americans have US Wheat Associates, the French have SOPEXA

* At the time Patrick Tory was Chairman of the NFU Cereals Committee.

and other countries have other bodies which are supposed to "market" their grain. I am very far from convinced, however, that these important sounding groups actually do any good at all. In theory, of course, US Wheat Associates in Cairo persuades Egyptian flour millers to buy American wheat instead of European wheat. But do they really? Can you prove it? I doubt it. In the good old days of the 1970s, it is true, US Wheat Associates did play an important role in persuading people in the Third World to change their diets from rice to wheat. Hence all the hamburger joints from Morocco to Manila.

Don't get me wrong. I'm not against marketing itself, but it only makes sense when the housewife is the purchaser. The success of Danish Bacon and French Apples are two examples of good marketing. Even Food From Britain occasionally does well too. The other day I found myself eating English honey in an expensive Paris hotel. It had been marketed well, on its taste, quality and (most important of all) snob value. But – and this is a crucial point which you chaps are overlooking – the Egyptian flour miller to whom we hope to sell our wheat is not concerned about such details. All he wants to know is how much does our wheat cost, how high is the quality and when will it be available?

The money you raise from cereal producers will be spent – so you assure us – on persuading this Egyptian miller to buy our wheat. To do this you will organise what you rather grandly call an "inward mission". What this means is that you will pay his airfare to Britain, show him the port facilities at Southampton, take him round a farm or two and finally give him a night on the town in London and a lot of glossy brochures. Will you go further, perhaps? How about providing him with an escort (not the car) or making him comfortable in other ways?

Don't take my word for it. I am, after all, just an ignorant farmer. Speak instead to the people who actually sell wheat to Egyptian flour millers. Talk to the multinational grain companies and see if they think that UK Cereals Exports will be cost-effective. They just laugh. Politely, of course, because international grain dealers are polite chaps.

What really matters, say the men from the multinationals, is not marketing but having the right wheat in the right quantity at the right place at the right time. I agree with them, and that is why I shall be voting against the levy next month.

I lost. The cereals growers of Britain, supported by the entire agricultural establishment, voted in favour of all three propositions.

No More Cereal Surpluses

(An open letter to Agricultural Commissioner Andriessen)

JUNE 1986

Dear Mr Andriessen

How would you feel if the following four events happened:-

1. The output of cereals in the EEC fell dramatically.
2. The cost of growing these cereals also fell.
3. The quality of these cereals increased.
4. The administrative cost for the above was nil.

It sounds like a fairy story doesn't it? Are you still interested? Or have you already dismissed me as yet another of those mad and opinionated farmers who bombard you with idiotic schemes?

The solution to your problems with the cereal surplus is simple in the extreme. All you need do is to copy the grouse-shooting fraternity in Scotland. They, you will recall, forbid anyone to shoot grouse until August 12th. You should adopt the same principle for planting winter cereals. You should pass legislation which divides Europe up into four arbitrary zones, each of which would have a Drilling Dateline. Thus, for example, if you farm south of 44 degrees lattitude (i.e. Toulouse–Florence) you would not be allowed to start drilling before November 5th. For those south of the line Paris–Stuttgart the date would be October 27th. People like me who farm south of the Edinburgh–Copenhagen axis would not be allowed to start drilling before October 21st, and the date for the few farmers north of this line would be October 15th.

These dates would be simple to police. No satellite photographs would be needed. No bureaucracy would be necessary because neighbouring farmers would do it all for you. A quick (anonymous) phone call to the local Ministry of Agriculture office would ensure that people did not cheat. Of course, penalties would be harsh for those who did.

The result would be that fewer winter cereals would be grown. Those that were planted would certainly produce lower yields because of the late drilling date. There is an old tradition in my part of eastern England that yields drop by 125kg per hectare (1 cwt per acre) for every week drilling is delayed after October 15th. In my own experience the difference is usually far greater than that.

Of course, more spring cereals would be grown, which is good news for you because not only are yields lower than winter corn, but in general the quality is higher. What is still more exciting is the savings which would be made on fertiliser and chemicals. It is, of course, much cheaper to grow spring varieties than winter ones. And as if these were not enough, imagine how popular you would be with the Green Movement if you could show that fewer chemicals and fertilisers were being used. They might even give you a medal or, worse still, ask you to speak at a convention. The agrochemical lobby would not be happy, but you might just be able to tolerate their tears and tantrums.

The whole policy of Drilling Datelines also has the enormous advantage of being extremely flexible. If one year the harvest was very poor and EEC stocks fell to a dangerously low figure, you could increase output quickly in the following year by moving the Drilling Datelines forward – or even abolishing them altogether. Conversely, if output did not fall by as much as you had intended, you could always set the Drilling Datelines even later.

Of course there would be objections. Farmers unlucky enough to find themselves living on the southern side of a Drilling Dateline will feel aggrieved that their neighbours on the northern side of the line are allowed to get their drills out a week earlier. But that, I am afraid, is always a problem of living near any border. Likewise, farmers on heavy land will complain bitterly that with a shortened drilling season they are at a disadvantage compared to people on light soil who can get on the land more easily. True again, but there is nothing in any book of rules, from Genesis to GATT, which says that all farmers on all soil types should have an equal chance to grow any crop they wish to. I might just as well complain that it is unfair that I cannot grow celery on my thin chalk soils whereas a few kilometres down the road on the black peat of the Fens, they make a fortune with the crop.

Of course I realise that you and your colleagues in Brussels will dismiss the whole idea of Drilling Datelines out of hand. It is too simple. Too simple to understand. Too simple to administer. It has another crushing disadvantage; it is too cheap. Your advisers will instinctively distrust anything which is simple and cheap. Instead they will insist on more co-responsibility levies, more Intervention Boards, more set-asides, more quotas, more paperwork. Or am I wrong? I look forward to hearing from you.

I never heard anything from Comissioner Andriessen – or from anyone else if it comes to that. But I still think that a system of Drilling Datelines is the only sensible, practical and cheap method of solving the problem of Grain Mountains in the EEC. I wonder why it is that whenever I try and persuade someone about this scheme, they simply look embarrassed and change the subject.

Noble Savage

JULY 1986

Once upon a time the world was a better place. Knights lived in Castles and spent their time jousting, carousing, rescuing damsels or rushing off on Crusades. In the interests of Romantic Rubbish, we forget the disease, filth, pain and general foulness of life in the Middle Ages and call this period The Golden Age of Chivalry. At the same time lots of black people lived in Africa in a state of total bliss. They were ecstatic because they had neither Coca-Cola, the BBC World Service nor Kalashnikov rifles. Once again we carefully ignore all semblances of reality by forgetting that life was mean, brutish and short. This was The Age of the Noble Savage.

To these two periods, we must now add a third, The Age of Balanced Farming. It was, you may be surprised to hear, not very long ago. They were the days when there were no grain mountains, when farmers were loved by an adoring public, when governments worried that we were not receiving enough taxpayers' money and when we could do no wrong. Of course, we did not use inorganic fertilisers, herbicides consisted of a man (probably a gang of men) with a hoe, fungicides were unheard of and tractors were rare. Everything was in perfect balance and harmony. No finite fossil fuels were being used, the fertility of the land depended on clover and horse manure, and butterflies and birds flourished in every hedgerow. Remember hedgerows?

I grew up in such an age. Well, almost. As a child I remember Suffolk Punch horses being backed between the shafts of a cart by old Sheldrick. The three Jersey herds on the farm produced Tuberculin Tested milk and won prizes each year at the Royal Show. The other enterprises consisted of an Aberdeen Angus beef herd, pigs, chickens, turkeys, sheep, Arab horses and even a grass drier. On the 1800 acres we farmed then, we needed 80 men to run the place. They all lived in the village of Thriplow. The word "commuter" had not even been invented.

In those days there were seven farmers in Thriplow (there are now three), and about the same number of tractors. The summers were invariably hot, the winters cold and the men sang as they stacked the sheaves and drank beer in the harvest field. They all carried 18 stone sacks on their backs and milked cows by hand before dawn. They all lived in (tied) cottages with hollyhocks growing by the door. They were happy to be without running water, lavatories, washing machines and colour TV. The working week was long, holidays were short, pay was bad, education poor and health care no better. This was The Age of Balanced Farming.

The reason it is important to understand about the Noble Savage and the Golden Age of Chivalry is not just to pass History O Level examinations. It is because there is a small (but noisy) body of opinion in (and outside) Agriculture today which thinks that all our problems would be solved if we could once again return to the Age of Balanced Farming. These splendid but naive people claim that if we return to Low Input farming the following things will happen:-
1. The surpluses will disappear. 2. We won't use up finite resources. 3. We won't pollute the world with chemicals. 4. We shall all eat better food and be healthier. 5. The landscape will become prettier as the "prairies" (bad) are replaced by the "patchwork quilt" (good). 6. The flora and fauna will increase. 7. There will be more jobs on farms so the rural economy would improve.

This is, I regret to say, what my American farming friends would call Hogwash. And my American farmer friends are an important part of the reason why. If one day a Government told me that I had to limit my output of wheat, rape and sugar beet, and that I would have to use less (maybe none at all) fertiliser and chemicals, what would I do? Would I revert to the days of my childhood and once again have a truly Mixed Farm at Thriplow? Would you see dairy herds springing up all over East Anglia, not to mention hordes of free-range chickens? Would the number of farmworkers suddenly increase as we all took on extra staff to milk the cows and feed the chickens? Would the commuters be squeezed out of their leafy mod con-encrusted, carriage lamp-bespattered pseudo-Georgian timbered bijou residences? No.

If the day ever does come when I am forcibly restricted from using High Inputs, I shall copy my American farmer friends. I shall, in short, farm like they do in Kansas. I shall continue growing arable crops but will ensure that they are all combinable. I shall alter my own lifestyle drastically and spend a lot of time sitting in the air-conditioned cab of a 300 horsepower tractor. I shall employ another two people on the 3000 acres at Thriplow and together we shall run the farm. The machinery will be vast and so will the fields. Nobody should be surprised if the landscape also resembles Kansas. People who complain about the "prairies" of East Anglia clearly have never seen a real prairie farm. Compared to today, the standard of agriculture will be poor. Yields will be low, and so will my costs. But I shall survive. Which, when you come to think about it, is what farming is all about.

Most conservationists have a vague notion that if only farmers like me stopped using chemicals, all of our problems would be solved. They are right in some respects, notably that we would produce less, pollute less and consume less. But what they never seem to think about is what effect this would have on the countryside. I wrote this article in a (probably fruitless) attempt to make them realise that there are also some less attractive consequences of their policies.

The Ministry Cocks It Up
(An open letter to Michael Jopling)

JULY 1986

Dear Minister

It can only be described as a CUBAB★.

I refer, of course, to the arrangements your Ministry has made for the Cereal Co-Responsibility Levy. Perhaps nobody in your Department has had the raw courage to tell you what has happened, so let me perform this most unsavoury task.

The objective was worthy – albeit unimaginative. Make the cereal producers contribute to the cost of getting rid of the stuff. No problem with the Theory, but when your Civil Servants came to the Practice they started to realise that it wasn't as simple as it seemed. Unlike milk, which can all be kept track of when it is bought by the Milk Marketing Board, grain moves in a mysterious way.

The Italian Ministry of Agriculture, when faced with the same problem, took an intelligent decision. They hoisted a white flag and surrendered completely. Instead of trying to organise an unorganisable scheme, they simply offered Brussels a lump sum of 15 million on behalf of Italian farmers and promptly forgot the Co-Responsibility Levy completely. Everyone was happy. Brussels got the money it wanted and the Italian grain trade did not have to lose any siestas messing about. The Italian farmers were also excused the inevitable CUBAB. Lucky the Italian farmers.

Pity the British farmers – and the British grain trade – when faced with the rules your Ministry has devised. Let's just take the case of the man who grinds his own corn on his own farm and feeds it to his own livestock. He will not have to pay the Levy. But a farmer who uses a Contractor's mobile Mill & Mix machine to grind his own corn for his own stock will have to pay the Levy. Why? Because he does not actually own the machinery and employ the operator. The

---

★   CUBAB = Cock-Up Beyond All Belief. Not to be confused with a FUBAB, which is infinitely more serious. Examples of the latter include the Groundnut Scheme, the Coal Strike and Food from Britain.

solution, Minister, is simple in the extreme. The farmer will purchase the machine from the Contractor – but only for the day. He will, in other words, agree to "buy" the Mill and Mix outfit at 8am and "sell" it back again to the Contractor at 6pm. In doing so, he will also employ the operators for the day. As a result of this patently ludicrous manoeuvre, the farmer will not be liable for the Levy and will save himself £3.37 on every tonne he grinds. By the way, how are you going to police this particular measure? Follow every Mill & Mix onto every farm?

But worse is to come. Take the case of the farmer who sells some wheat for £100 per tonne (just to keep the sum simple) to his friendly merchant down the road. He will only receive £96.63 per tonne because the Merchant will deduct the Co-Responsibility Levy of £3.37 per tonne. The merchant, however, then sells the wheat to a non-levyable customer (like a large and integrated livestock company). No Levy is due on this transaction so the Merchant is obliged to refund the farmer the Levy he has already paid. But, of course, it isn't as simple as this. The Merchant cannot possibly keep track of every parcel of wheat he buys and so has no idea whose wheat it was he sold to the livestock company. What does he do with the Levy which he has received from the farmer? Does he give it to the Government? Does he donate it to the Send a Tonne appeal? Or does he quietly forget it and put the lolly in his own pocket? We shall never know for sure but I myself have a pretty shrewd guess.

Then there is the problem which worries me as a cereal seed producer. Your Ministry decreed that cereals destined for seed should not pay the Levy. Thank you for this generosity. You decided, however, that the screenings should pay the levy. I sell 100 tonnes of seed wheat to my friendly seed merchant and no levy is deducted from the price he pays me. But within a few days I shall receive a letter saying that the screening losses were a dismal 22%. Could I therefore pay the levy on 22 tonnes? Knowing the seed trade as I do, I shall believe them implicitly, because they are all honest men. But how will I ever know what the screening losses really were? The opportunity for the seedsman to line his own pocket is, I am afraid, considerable.

No, Minister. Your staff have made CUBAB of the Co-Responsibility Levy. It is impossible to police, will make life miserable for farmers and the grain trade, as well as giving some sections of the industry an unfair advantage over others. If Brussels persists in the idea of a Levy at all, can you please ensure that there are absolutely no exemptions next harvest? Anything for a simple life.

The Tenants' Revolt

AUGUST 1986

It was a cold grey January afternoon. I was sitting in the farm office worrying about my fixed costs. With a rent review due at Michaelmas, I suppose it wasn't surprising that my thoughts turned to rent. For the past 50 years rents have risen remorselessly. As a result I, like most tenants, have become punch-drunk with the regular increases every three years. But now things are a wee bit different. The price of land has dropped by around 50%, the price of everything I produce on the farm has also dropped, whilst the cost of most of my inputs has risen. It was obvious that rents could not be allowed to go against the trend and continue rising. But however convincing I personally might have found this proposition, it was hard to see that a landlord would agree.

I wondered if my rent was higher than that of my neighbours, and as I did so, it occurred to me that I hadn't a clue what anyone else in the area was paying. Maybe my rent was, in fact, extremely low. In that case I should clearly shut up and keep smiling. But it was equally likely that it was far too high. However much I knew about the cost of agrochemicals, fuel or seed, I realised that when it came to rent, we tenants were extraordinarily ignorant. Of course it was our own fault. No tenant ever talked about his rent for fear that his neighbour might gain some advantage. But now the competition for land was slowing down, attitudes were changing fast. Francis Bacon had once said that "Knowledge is Power." The corollary must surely be that "Ignorance is Weakness."

The next day I was talking to a nearby farmer who was also a tenant. I suggested that we prepare a brief questionnaire which we could give to our neighbours. The objective was simple: what rents were being paid in our area of south Cambridgeshire? We were not interested in other parts of the country where the conditions were different, but we needed to know what similar farmers on similar land were paying.

The questions were as follows:-

Acres rented?
Rent per acre?
Full repairing and insuring?
Bare land?
Date rent agreed?
Landlord?
Landlord's Agent?

The deal was that anyone who filled in the questionnaire was entitled to receive a copy of the Rent Survey which resulted. If they did not want to provide the information, they could not receive the survey. No names were to be mentioned so that confidentiality would be maintained.

The response was amazing, as the news of the survey spread throughout the area. Within four weeks we had received over 60 replies covering nearly 30,000 acres from Baldock in the west to Newmarket in the east.

It became all too clear that tenants' attitudes had changed drastically during the past year. Whereas at Michaelmas 1985 they would have been happy (nay, overjoyed) at a prospect of a nil increase in their rents, now they had realised that there had to be a decrease.

Meanwhile some of the more acute landlords had also come to the same conclusion. As a result, they had "forgotten" to serve Section 12 Notices on their tenants last year. These tenants, who had been overjoyed by what they took to be their landlords' incompetence, now realised that for rents to remain unchanged was very far from being good news. This profound change of mood is the reason why the Cambridgeshire Rent Survey has been such a success, but would have failed had it been attempted even 12 months earlier.

At the Group's first meeting, attended by over 30 tenants, it soon became clear that everyone was as worried as I about the level of rents. But they were also concerned about what to do. There was a lot of vague talk about arbitration, but none of us actually knew what arbitration involved, how much it cost and whether it was even practicable. Still less did we understand the intricacies of landlord and tenant law, or the details of serving a Section 12 Notice. It was for these reasons that we decided to find a land agent who was not inextricably tarred with the reputation of being "a landlord's man".

Robert Arnold of Cambridge fitted this bill and came to the next meeting. He made his position very clear he would be happy to advise the group on an informal basis, and would be even happier to represent individual members on normal professional terms. Those members who were already represented by land agents should remain that way, and he would happy to co-operate with these agents. He did not insist on representing every tenant in the survey. He felt strongly that if the group was going to achieve anything at all, it would have to act in concert. Nobody should agree a new rent without first clearing this with Arnold. All information about negotiations should also be passed through Arnold so that no single tenant could be "picked off" and used as a comparable to increase rents in the area. We should, he felt, show the sort of solidarity which has been all too rare among tenants in the past.

After some discussion, we decided not to formalise the group. A few people were already members of the Tenant Farmers Association, and most were members of the NFU. We did not want to compete with either organisation. Hence we decided there would be no committee, no officers, no subscription and hence no formal membership. Instead we would simply remain a loose-knit group of tenants whose sole purpose was to exchange information about rents.

Those were the objectives. But there is a big difference between talking and acting. Many questions remain. Does the fact that a group of tenants in a small area know what rents are being paid really make any difference at all? Will the group show the solidarity necessary to present a united front to the landlords? But the biggest question of all concerns arbitration. If one of the group decides to go to arbitration, will the other members provide financial support by helping with the expenses? This sort of co-operation remains a distinct possibility if the landlords insist that rents must not come down this Michaelmas. The tenants of south Cambridgeshire await developments with – to put it mildly – greater than usual interest.

A Year of Fiascos

SEPTEMBER 1986

It's not much fun writing a column like this. If I talk about the good news, farmers from all over the country (but mostly from the Scottish Borders) accuse me of boasting. If I tell the bad news, members of the Ramblers' Association from deep in the Muesli Belt tell me that I am whingeing.

What follows will go down well in the Tweed valley but may not find favour among the wine bars of Kentish Town. This year has had more than its fair share of fiascos and absolutely no triumphs. It will be good for my soul if I share some of them.

Back in March, you may remember, Franois Guillaume was plucked from the Presidency of the FNSEA and dropped into the hot seat of the Ministry of Agriculture in Paris. He immediately struck up a cosy relationship with his German counterpart, Ignaz Kiechle. All this excitement coincided with a slack time on the farm so I decided to investigate what was happening in Europe. Thanks to the generosity of Anglia Television, I found myself flying out to Brest where Guillaume was addressing the FNSEA's annual conference.

This brief excursion gave me a taste for the agricultural bigwigs of Europe. I determined to interview Mr Kiechle in Bonn. An appointment with the great man was duly made and a few days later, armed only with a notebook and an inflated ego, I set off at dawn from Stansted in the shoebox which flies to Amsterdam.

Beside me sat an architect who, at 7am, consumed three vodkas with the reheated omlette which was our breakfast. At Schipol I changed planes and flew to Dusseldorf where I rented a car and drove down the autobahn to Bonn.

I arrived at the Ministry of Agriculture, straightened my tie and composed my most pompous expression, as befits someone as profoundly important as me. A lady opened the waiting room door after ten minutes. I rose and made a brief but moving speech about how good it was for the Minister to see me at such short notice. My oration continued in full flood, even though I noticed that her lips were moving. It soon became clear that she was trying to say something; I naturally assumed that she was welcoming me. When

I eventually brought my peroration under control, I began to hear what she was saying.

The minister could not see me. She was very sorry. Something about being summoned by Chancellor Kohl because of last night's American raid on Libya. Before I had time to collect my thoughts, I was back in my Opel heading north towards Dusseldorf. The journey back to Thriplow was very long indeed. And it was not cheap either.

Later in the spring I realised that the price of wheat this autumn was going to be very low. I checked the Futures prices and saw in a flash that those idiots on the Baltic Exchange had got it all wrong. With all the decisiveness of Napoleon before Austerlitz, I phoned a broker and sold wheat forward for September at £99.20 per tonne. I then sat back to watch while the rest of the world realised how stupid they were and how incandescently intelligent I was.

Six months later, when the price had risen by £6 per tonne, I had lost a heap. The moral is clear. Leave the Futures Market to the experts, whoever they are.

On the farming front things have been no better. The ryegrass drilled last autumn did not look all that special when it came through the winter frosts. But, I consoled myself, all would be well after a bit of nitrogen and a few warm nights. There were also a few weeds which would have to be dealt with.

Eventually the warm weather did come, and so did the nitrogen. We applied it in liquid form and immediately put on a dose of the herbicide, Ally. Within a few days I noticed a browning of the leaves which, in my profound knowledge of such matters, I ascribed to liquid nitrogen scorch. But the browning became blackening and the leaves began to wither and senesce. (You can always tell the trendy progressive farmers. They say "senesce" instead of "die".)

Even I became dimly aware that, as they say in cheap thrillers, something was not right. In holy and righteous indignation I phoned Tony White, the man who provides us with both advice and agrochemicals. After describing the symptoms (premature death), I asked Tony what was the matter. "What herbicide did you apply?" he asked. "Just what you recommended," I replied, "Ally."

There was a gurgling noise at the other end of the phone as if Tony was pretending to be a bathtub. "No," he said with some vehemence, "we never suggested you use Ally. That happens to be the one product which we recommend to take ryegrass out of cereals. I'm not surprised you've killed your crop. You should have used MCPA."

So I kissed goodbye to 100 acres of herbage seed this year, not to mention a lot of money lost on the futures market. But neither of these would have hurt half as much if only Mr Kiechle had shaken my hand.

What made this year so exquisitely painful, was the fact that every other farmer in Britain enjoyed a magnificent harvest, only slightly less memorable than the vintage of 1984.

Harvest 1986

NOVEMBER 1986

Like Queen Victoria on breakfast cereals ("We are not a Muesli"), I did not find harvest funny this year. It was one to forget. But that won't be easy as it was the worst we have known since the drought of 1976. Meanwhile, the rest of the country – if Ministry figures are to be believed – was having the second biggest crop on record. Quite why we did so badly is not easy to explain, but I do have various excuses with which I reassure myself whenever the poor undernourished ego needs a fix. Last autumn, you may remember, was very dry. Regardless of when it was drilled, nothing actually germinated until mid November.

As if that were not bad enough, we then had a very hard winter. The resulting frost lift on our chalky land thinned out the plant population which was already too low. To complete the process, the drought and very high temperatures in June gave us shrivelled grains.

The winter barleys were uniformly disappointing, averaging a pathetic 48cwt/acre. Halcyon and Pipkin (a variety for which I had particularly high hopes) were not much more than 40cwt/acre, and the occasional field dropped below this level. Their malting quality was (to put it politely) appalling.

Dear old Maris Otter, which we were growing for the last time after 21 consecutive years, found the struggle too much and collapsed to 44cwt/acre. Even Panda, a variety which has yielded as much as 80cwt/acre on this farm, could only manage just over 50cwt this time.

If the barleys were bad, the wheats were even worse. It is probably a mistake trying to grow third wheats on our sort of land. When the variety concerned is Brimstone, the results are nearly catastrophic. Over nearly 400 acres Brimstone averaged 41cwt/acre. And to add insult to injury, nobody wanted it for seed either. I can't say I blame them.

Avalon, Galahad, and Longbow all turned in yields which hovered around 50cwt, while Moulin and Brock did only slightly better. Slejpner, on the other hand, behaved almost respectably – but that was probably because it was all first year. With an average of 65cwt, it did at least make us some money this harvest.

The two varieties for which I had the highest hopes proved to be very surprising. We were growing Apollo for the first time; a German feed wheat which has done exceptionally well in trials across Europe. Admittedly, our seed rate of only 90lbs per acre was on the low side, and the field in which it was planted (after two years herbage seed) was one of our poorest, but I had not anticipated how badly it would do. One hundred and forty-two tonnes from 60 acres works out at a truly dreadful 47cwt/acre.

My other great hope, a variety called Hornet from the Plant Breeding Institute, provided the only success of the entire harvest. A direct comparison with Apollo is unfair since the seed rate was our normal 1cwt/acre and the field was one of our best. Hornet yielded just fractionally under 80cwt/acre and the bushel weight was excellent. If only the other wheats had done anything like this well, I would be a happy little chap today.

Among all the gloom one tiny ray of happiness emerged. After two disastrous years, we finally succeeded in growing a crop of durum wheat which made a profit. The Capdur managed 44cwt/acre and was a good sample too. If I were going to grow durum again (which I am not) I would treat it as a spring variety and drill in March.

It was not just the poor yields which made last harvest such a nightmare. We experienced a problem which has been getting progressively worse in the past two years, and this year reached crisis proportions. As seed growers, we have to use a strict rotation of break crops between the wheats and the barleys to prevent admixtures.

This year, however, the whole system appeared to break down. First-year barleys were so plastered with volunteer wheat from two years ago that we lost 350 acres of Pipkin for seed production. The story with the wheat was identical, but at least it was possible to rogue out the barley – albeit at a cost of up to £50 per acre. The problem was the same regardless of the break crop which intervened. Sugar beet, peas and rape all appeared to be equally ineffective at preventing this explosion of volunteers.

Why it happened remains a mystery. I have a horrible suspicion that it was caused by our decision to give up burning two years ago. Instead we have incorporated the straw (and the ungerminated grains too) before ploughing them all down to ten inches. A year later these same seeds are ploughed out again when, thanks to "Sod's Law", they germinate and grow mightily amidst the following crop.

We shall try to solve the problem in the future by not incorporating straw. Instead of mixing it into the top 4 inches of the soil before ploughing, we shall use a set of discs to create a very shallow tilth which will encourage germination. If this does not work we shall have to seriously ask whether we can afford to remain in the cereal seed growing business. One thing is certain we cannot afford a harvest like this year's very often.

Admittedly, the herbage seed was a fiasco, but the other crops all did fairly well. The Mikado rape, which had looked so dreadful after the winter, did a respectable 28cwt. The Progreta peas, at 40cwt, were the best we have ever grown, and the sugar beet looks like averaging around 20 tonnes per acre. But at the end of the day we live or die by our cereals.

As a result it looks as if we shall lose money for the first time since I started farming some 15 years ago. Contributions (no flowers please) to the Editor, who will forward them to me – or his favourite charity. I wonder if there is any difference.

We did lose money. And I lost face too, which is more painful but less important to the Bank manager. Little did I realise then that we would also lose money in the following year. Ouch.

Managing to Survive . . . or Surviving to Manage?

NOVEMBER 1986

There hasn't been anything like it for five thousand years. That was the day when a man (or probably a woman) first planted a seed in the aptly-named Fertile Crescent. Since then, farmers have enjoyed prosperity and poverty as cycles came and went. But nothing in this whole period could possibly have equalled the riches enjoyed by European arable farmers in the eleven years after 1973. Cereal growing was, as Lord Thomson once described the TV business, "a licence to print money".

Today, using the hindsight for which we have become famous, farmers can recognise how fortunate we were throughout the 1970s and early 1980s. But at the time we sang a very different song. Did the agricultural press echo with grateful farmers thanking the politicians and the taxpayers for their generosity? Did the NFU admit to its extraordinary good fortune? Did anyone in the entire industry have the grace – or even the commonsense – at least to keep quiet? No. On the contrary. Throughout this Golden Age of Arable Farming, the loudest noise in the countryside was the sound of farmers bemoaning their fate. With each succeeding year the agricultural lobby grew ever more vociferous as it told a bewildered public that unless prices were raised the industry would go bankrupt and Europe would certainly starve. The campaign was brilliantly successful; Intervention Prices (which had been devised to provide a safety net to prevent widespread bankruptcy) crept ever upwards until, at the end of the period, they were actually above the market price. In the lunatic asylum called the CAP, the floor had become a ceiling; the world was upside down.

Prices were not the only cause of British farmers' discontent. There were the usual wails about the bad weather, the unfair competition from abroad and impending disaster from a multitude of sources. Of course, our ideas about what was unfair needed a bit of explanation. It was, for example, perfectly fair for a farmer to buy cheap Dicurane from France, but it was grossly unfair for cheap French poultry to be sold to English housewives. Grey imports of tractors from Belgium were considered well within the norms of free enterprise, but Danish Bacon and French Golden Delicious apples were objected to as a violation of free competition. To a farmer, fairness has always been a very flexible concept.

Today, with the benefit of history, we can look back nostalgically to an age when even the worst arable farmer could make money. The good ones made small fortunes and the excellent farmers became very rich indeed. Incompetence alone was not a reason to lose money. No, to do this with any certainty, you needed to be more than just incompetent. You also needed to have an extravagant wife and an addiction to roulette. Provided a man got up before midday, managed to scatter a few seeds in the autumn, and was prepared to harvest the crop the following summer, there was no way an arable farmer could fail to make a profit.

What caused this explosion of farming prosperity right across Europe? Three main reasons.

1. Nations, scarred by the experience of the war, were desperate to ensure that never again would Europe depend on outside sources for food. Self-sufficiency was the altar at which all postwar politicians worshipped. They were also acutely aware that, in the 1940s and 1950s at least, the farm vote was still crucial. Keep the peasants happy and you also enjoy social stability. Thus was born the EEC and the Common Agricultural Policy with its guaranteed high prices.

2. The continued failure of the Russian agricultural system – caused, of course, by the unbroken run of bad weather they have had ever since October 1917 – allied to rising living standards in the USSR, meant that they needed vast quantities of grain. This reached a peak in The Great Grain Robbery of 1972 which boosted world prices to unheard-of levels.

3. An agronomic revolution in which the yield of cereals doubled in a decade. This was caused by another three main reasons, none of which would have happened without the prosperity brought about by the Common Agricultural Policy. These were (in no particular order):–

A. Plant Breeders Rights gave an incentive to spend time and money breeding new varieties of cereals. Maris Huntsman from the PBI was the classic example of this.

B. Chemists began to come up with a range of fungicides to

control cereal diseases which no farmer had even heard of. Bayleton, the penicillin of arable farming, was the first of these.

C. New techniques, developed largely (but not exclusively) by Laloux at Gembloux and the Schleswig-Holstein Landwirtschafts Kammer*, showed cereal farmers that they could intensify their systems by using more fertiliser, more chemicals and more care.

I entered farming in 1972. In the following decade I could not understand the old fuddy-duddies who were constantly harping back to the Bad Old Days of the 1930s. Farming, for me anyway, was a doddle. I should have realised that human beings' attitudes are invariably formed by their early experiences. Thus the men who had grown up in the '30s remained cautious and pessimistic for the rest of their lives, while I – a child of the booming '70s – was optimism personified. And for a decade or so I had figures to show that I was right.

At Thriplow, wheat yields rose from 5 tonnes per hectare to nearly 9 tonnes per hectare in less than ten years. At the beginning of this period, I used to have arguments with my Father about spraying Calixin on a field of Maris Otter winter barley. The discussion consisted of whether the damage done to the crop by the sprayer wheelings would be greater or less than the good done by controlling the mildew!

Then in 1977 came my conversion. It took place not on the road to Damascus but in the middle of a wheat field between Kiel and Flensburg on the Baltic coast of Schleswig-Holstein. I had spent an entire day on the back of a Unimog driving through (not round) the sort of cereal crops I had not even dared dream about. I returned home full of enthusiasm for prophylactic spraying, tramlines and all the other paraphernalia of intensive cereal production. I became obsessed with counting and quantifying everything so I could talk knowledgeably about seeds, plants and ears per square metre. Split nitrogen applications, split growth regulator applications, sequential fungicides, pre-emergent herbicides, insecticides in the autumn against barley yellow dwarf virus and in the summer against aphids; all these became part of my normal life. Each year I went to ever more learned conferences at which clever people (mostly paid by the chemical companies) proved conclusively that if I were to put

---

* Chamber of Agriculture, roughly the equivalent of ADAS

on still greater inputs, my profits would rise. And, I have to admit, they were usually correct.

The enthusiasm was contagious. Farmers became infected overnight as lengthy (and sometimes heated) debates broke out between the advocates of Laloux or Schleswig-Holstein. For a couple of years it was even possible to spot the "infected" farms from a car or train. Tramlines stood out in the landscape like the scars on a drug addict's arm. Within a very short time, this tiny island of ours with its 56 million people became a net exporter of cereals.

I was lucky. I came into farming as the dawn of this new age was breaking. Unlike my father's generation, who were certain that once again farming was going to fall over the precipice into bankruptcy and ruin, I knew that things could only continue to get better as a grateful and hungry world pressed us to "plant from fencerow to fencerow".

My biggest problem was what to do with the profits I kept making. The solution was simple. I converted them into machinery by taking advantage of the 100% tax write-offs we were allowed. Of course, there was one disadvantage; the bank overdraft kept rising as I borrowed more and more to fund the purchases of bigger and bigger equipment. Tractors, combines, grainstores, grain driers came in profusion. Just as I felt I should stop investing and concentrate on reducing my borrowings, along came Brussels with the FHD Scheme★ which gave me even bigger capital grants to encourage still more investment. As a result, I bought lorries and tractors with even greater abandon, safe in the knowledge that I was doing what the EEC wanted. No wonder the machinery trade had to ration tractor deliveries as other farmers competed with me to buy everything the factories could turn out.

But I was not content simply to spend money on machinery. That was too easy. I also realised that it was crucial to own more land and so managed, over an eight year period, to buy 300 neighbouring acres. As the price rose from £1000 to £2400 an acre, I knew I had made the right decisions. Not only did these purchases increase the size of my farming enterprise, but they also proved to be spectacularly good capital investments. My shrewdness never ceased to amaze me.

★ Farm and Horticulture Development Scheme. Dreamt up by Brussels to encourage farmers to become more efficient, and hence to pay workers higher wages. It was, in practice, counter-productive because only the big farmers could face the paperwork involved. The small (and inefficient) farmers ignored it.

In November 1986, what I have just described above seems almost like a fairytale, or at very least like the ancient history of a distant planet. In less than three years, the whole farming landscape has altered immeasurably. I find myself faced with a problem, not of how to spend my profits, but how to survive. It is not a pleasant feeling, but it is not an entirely new one either.

I first came face to face with agricultural hardship when I visited Nebraska and Iowa three years ago. I had made a special request to the Farm Bureau (roughly the equivalent of our National Farmers Union) to meet bankrupt farmers. Hearing that there were severe problems in this part of the States, I felt it would be instructive if I could actually speak to people who had failed to keep their farms afloat. I expected, of course, to meet a bunch of incompetents; a group of people who never got out of bed before 10 in the morning, who planted their seeds a few weeks later than their neighbours, who forgot to spray for weeds and who never managed to combine the crop before it rained. In other words, I expected to meet some spectacularly bad farmers.

As usual, I was wrong. The bankrupt farmers of Nebraska were clearly above average. They were energetic, keen and had good track records. It was not their farming which was faulty, it was their enthusiasm. Such was their desire to expand their farms, to put up a new silo or milking parlour, to buy more land or a bigger tractor, that they had borrowed too much money. They were, in the jargon so beloved of Americans, over-leveraged.

Today, after an extremely poor harvest, the view before me at Thriplow almost (but not quite) resembles Nebraska. I owe the Agricultural Mortgage Corporation a whole heap for the land I have bought. I owe Barclays Bank another heap for all the machinery I have bought. I owe the leasing companies a whole heap for more machinery and I owe my landlord rent of £53 an acre. It is not a pretty sight.

Will I survive to manage my farm? Yes, but it will not be easy – at least not compared to the balmy days of the 1970s. But I shall succeed, without any doubt at all.

There are some things which I shall not do. I shall dispose of these before going any further.

A. I shall not try to increase output – any more than I have been doing for the past decade. I shall not increase my inputs to chase that last ounce of output. I must admit, however, that I shall continue to use a very high-input system in an attempt to produce as much as is practicable from each acre of land.

B. I shall not diversify into new-fangled crops such as lupins, evening primrose or borage. I may increase the acreage of legumes and it is not impossible that over the next few years I might even dabble with linseed. But I shall remain primarily a cereal producer since this is what my farm is best suited to grow.

C. I shall not extensify by adopting a Kansas-style of farming. This is the system whereby dad and son run 3000 acres with the help of two huge tractors, a set of discs and a couple of combines. They use little or no inputs and produce (in a good year) two and a half tonnes of wheat to the hectare. I could only make this Low Input system work if I also had Low Input Costs. Unfortunately, I do not. Like poor old Sisyphus, I have to expend a lot of energy simply to stay where I am. My Fixed Costs (of which more later) dictate that I have to go flat out for maximum production.

Of course, if my Bank Manager, landlord and other creditors all let me off my obligations so I could wake up one morning free of all debt, then I would be mightily attracted to a Kansas-style way of farming. But until this miracle comes to pass, it will remain a dream.

D. I shall not convert to organic farming. Even with the high prices being offered for organic wheat, I simply could not afford to have over half the farm down to clover, lucerne and grass. I have a strong (but unproven) suspicion that every organic arable farmer in Europe is either an owner-occupier paying no rent, or a tenant paying very low rent. I would be happy to be proved wrong, and even happier to meet an organic arable farmer whose landlord, like mine, expects to receive £53 per acre.

E. I shall not intensify the farm by introducing more livestock. At least I don't think I shall. I am not a good stock man temperamentally, and my experience with our old Jersey herd has given me a deep-seated prejudice against cows.

F. I shall not be unduly concerned about controlling variable costs. Of course I shall continue trying to buy my inputs as cheaply as possible. In common with most farmers, I happen to think that I am superb buyer. Whether I really am is another matter altogether, but you should allow me a few illusions. Nevertheless, the fact remains that I am almost powerless to control the Variable Costs. If fuel or fertiliser prices fall, I enjoy the benefits, and if agrochemical prices rise, I pay the increase. Either way I am virtually impotent.

If I do Manage to Survive, I shall Survive to Manage simply by controlling my Fixed Costs. These hold the secret to my future as a farmer, and it is on Fixed Costs that I shall now concentrate.

Last year (i.e. Harvest 1986) we incurred total Fixed Costs of £480 per Hectare. This year I hope to reduce this by 14% to £414 per Hectare. I shall achieve these savings in the following main areas:-

1. Perks. The single most difficult economy to make is to your own lifestyle. Nevertheless, I am certain that before I ask anyone else on the farm to make any sacrifice whatsoever, I must first be prepared to lead the way. Thus my beloved Porsche has been sold and my Private Drawings must be cut by 25%. You might be surprised how difficult it is to sell a fancy car. The reason is not just that nobody ever likes to have fewer luxuries, but one's pride rears its ugly head too. What will the neighbours think if they see me selling my car? Will they think I'm going bust? Will the local tradesmen refuse me credit? Will I lose face? These and other doubts must be stamped on firmly.

After reducing one's own perks, the next hardest task is to reduce those of one's father. As with most family farms, the elder generation depends on the farm to provide some (often all) of the cash for old age. But if the farm can no longer afford to provide these goodies, then the recipient must be told firmly that he (or she) will also have to tighten up on perks or cash.

An (almost) painless economy is to stop paying money into the Self-Administered Pension Fund which was set up a few years ago to make provision for the future – and to siphon off some of the profits of the good harvests.

2. Labour. The Christmas Bonus is the first casualty. It had grown sturdily over the last decade and there is no doubt that some people had forgotten that it was a Bonus (i.e. a reflection of prosperity) and not part of the salary. But mucking about with a Christmas Bonus will not be enough. We shall be employing 33% fewer people than we did two years ago. This has been achieved largely by what Personnel Officers usually call "natural wastage" since of the five people who have departed, three did so in the course of retirement. One other chap left of his own accord and, unfortunately, one was made redundant.

3. Insurance. For the past 70 years my family have dealt with one of this country's leading insurance companies. The service we received was excellent and, as a result, we were Happy and Satisfied Customers. Every year I would go through the policies with the local manager and the premiums would rise. This year, however, I decided to get some competitive quotes from a Broker and from the NFU Mutual. I was flabbergasted to see how expensive my insurance had become simply because I had never bothered to obtain a quotation before. As a result I have saved 33% on the cost of the premium, amounting to over £7,000. The moral is clear; customer loyalty is not to be underestimated, but in 1986 it may be a luxury we can no longer afford. The same will also apply to all the other things we have traditionally bought from a single source who happens to be "an old chum" or a "nice chap".

4. Property repairs. I enjoy the doubtful benefits of a Full Repairing and Insuring Lease and so I am always liable to receive a visit from my Landlord's Agent who will remind me to repair that gutter or paint that cottage. Hence I will not be able to save a great deal (if anything at all) on the cost of property repairs. However, when it comes to making improvements, there is a lot of money to be saved. No longer will we be spending £7,000 a year on putting central heating into houses or building extensions to enlarge the cottages. This was all very well in the halcyon days of the 1970s, but it will have to be cut right back this year. Hence we can save around £5,000 a year (4 per ha) by not carrying out improvements.

5. Rent. As I write this, I am engaged in the final delicate stages of a Rent Review at which nothing has been settled. However, regardless of the outcome of my own particular Rent Review, there can be no doubt whatsoever that rents must come down and will come down this year. This will not be a simple task, but will be made much easier if the following tactics are used:-

a. Arm yourself with knowledge. The days when tenants could afford to keep quiet about their rents is long since gone. Find out what other tenants in your area are paying – and tell them what you are paying. That way you will know whether or not your rents are high or low. If they are the latter you should clearly keep quiet, but if they are high, you will need all the help you can get.

b. Use a Land Agent. I happen to be deeply prejudiced against the race of Land Agents which has, like aphids, gone forth and multiplied over the past decade. I must, however, admit that since we farmers have prospered, there is no reason why Land Agents should not have done the same thing. (And they have with a vengeance.) But I have recently had to swallow both my pride and my prejudice when I realised that tenants who did not use Land Agents to represent them at Rent Reviews invariably ended up with higher rents than those who did use Land Agents.

This fact emerged from the south Cambridgeshire survey. I am ashamed to admit that the highest three rents (and I was among them) were paid by tenants who had trusted their own negotiating skills and had not paid a Land Agent to act for them. This autumn all three of these tenants have seen the error of their ways and have made use of a Land Agent!

By taking action on the five headings listed above, I hope to reduce our fixed costs by 15% this year. However, this alone will not be enough to make any real impact on the problem. I shall have to take a far more drastic step if I am to succeed in bringing down my costs in a big way. This solution, unfortunately, can only be a temporary one.

6. Capital equipment. As mentioned earlier, one of the hallmarks of the Golden Days of Arable Farming was the very high level of capital investment. Indeed, last year I managed to spend almost £200 per hectare on machinery. This consisted of £118/ha on outright purchases and £80/ha on leasing. I can no longer afford such a very high level of investment. This year the figure will be reduced by no less than 80% to a measly £34 per hectare. In doing so, I shall save £200,000. Or, to be more accurate, I shall not spend £200,000 .

However spectacular these economies may appear – and to reduce expenditure from £240,000 to £40,000 in a single year is pretty impressive – I cannot maintain them for very long. It is the equivalent of going onto a crash diet of warm lemon juice and lettuce. You may lose a stone in a week, but if you keep it up for much longer you become very ill and die soon afterwards.

Within a year or two I shall, of course, have to start replacing my machinery again. But it will give me a breathing space during which I can reduce my borrowings and put my finances in some semblance of order. Thank goodness all the machinery on the farm is as new as it is. We shall suffer no hardship for the next two years if we limit our replacements to the bare minimum.

The remaining fixed costs I can do very little to control, other than by keeping a wary eye on expenditure. Here I am helped by having a computer and a good budgeting system. I spend a lot of time at the beginning of the financial year working out a cashflow forecast and a budget. It is time well-spent because we are able to monitor these forecasts every month and thus get early warning if something is going seriously wrong. In today's tighter financial climate the computer has at last come into its own. Instead of being an amusing toy with which one could impress the neighbours and a few reps, it is actually a cost-effective tool which enables me to keep a far closer control over the finances than I could possibly hope to do with a conventional manual accounting system.

Many farmers will undoubtedly accuse me of, at best, overreacting or, at worst, simply panicking. Many will blithely assume that our industry's problems are no more than just a little temporary hiccup in the farming cycle. The surpluses will go away as quickly as they came and, once again, we shall be asked by politicians to produce as much as we possibly can. All that needs to be done today is to persuade the Bank Manager to give a slightly bigger overdraft than he did last year, and we can "ride this one out".

To do this is to confuse what one wishes to see happen with what one thinks will actually happen. A common but fatal mistake. Many farmers will convince themselves that little or nothing need be done on their farms other than to ensure that the crop is planted, fertilised and harvested on time. They are partly, but not wholly, right because there will never be any substitute for old-fashioned good husbandry. You may be the cleverest businessman with the best computers and biggest tractors; if you neglect the farming you will still be a failure. The boss's foot will always remain the best fertiliser, but survival as a farmer will require more than simply being to the manure born.

All I Want Are Some Greengages

JANUARY 1987

Greengages – not milling wheat or malting barley. Not double-zero rape. Not two tonnes of peas an acre. Not 20% sugar beet. Not 1.8 lambs a ewe. No, what I want most in 1987 are greengages. It won't happen, of course. The bullfinches will, as usual, eat the buds in the spring and I shall spend the summer eating tasteless lumps called Victorias, Czars and Early Rivers. My requirements for this year are simple: an enormous crop of greengages. Come to think of it, I'd even settle for a small crop.

It would also be helpful if we got some decisions out of Brussels. Their indecision has long since ceased to be a joke and is now becoming dangerous. It is all rather reminiscent of the platoon marching towards a cliff. With only a few paces to go before the precipice, a soldier can stand it no more. He shouts to the sergeant major: "For God's sake say something, even if it's only goodbye." One of these days the EEC will have to stop talking about reforming the CAP and actually do something. Meanwhile, we farmers will just have to hope that the cliff edge is still a long way off.

As I become ever more middle-aged, flabby and self-satisfied I should not be entirely surprised that I find myself less irritated by the Farming Establishment. Temperamentally I might be happier if the NFU were run by a crowd of useless buffoons, but, in practice, I admit this wouldn't help. In fact the Gourlay/Naish axis is the best leadership we have had for ages. It is firm, forward-looking and yet has a light touch, a sense of (perish the thought) humour and a realisation that things in the big world outside the farm gates are not quite as simple as many of the members used to feel.

I don't envy Simon Gourlay his job. He's pulled in different directions by horn and corn, by landowner and tenant, by north and south, by east and west, by big and small farmers, by conservationists and chemical manufacturers and by vegetarians and carnivores. No wonder he is so long and thin.

One of the things I want to know as soon as possible this year is who is going to own British Sugar. It won't make a twopenny damn's worth of difference to me as a beet grower, but the industry can't go on in this state of uncertainty much longer. I happen to have a sneaking preference for Tate and Lyle. Not because they are better than Gruppo Ferruzzi and Riccardo Butler (they aren't), but simply because they paid for me to go out to America and look at their sugar beet operations in Montana. Don't ever underestimate the power of freebies on someone as corruptible as me. Give me an air ticket and I'm anybody's.

Talking of takeovers, I hope that ICI succeed in buying the Plant Breeding Institute. It was, of course, a staggeringly stupid decision of the government to privatise the world's best wheat breeders in the first place. If only I'd had a bit in the petty cash tin this year, I'd have liked to buy PBI myself. I've always wanted to be a plant breeder. And a test pilot. And a brain surgeon.

I hope that this harvest will see the first real signs of a successful hybrid wheat. Both Rohm and Haas and Rothwell Plant Breeders have put an enormous effort into hybrids and it is time they began to enjoy some success. Of course, if hybrid wheats ever do appear, they will make the European grain surplus even bigger. But that is not my problem as a farmer. I shall continue to go flat out for maximum yield and quality while I let the politicians decide how to control me.

On the farm this year I would like to find a herbicide which really kills sterile brome. This weed appears to be immune to every combination we throw at it, and it seems unaffected by ploughing. I am a wee bit optimistic because I gather that Bayer has got a new chemical which is just waiting for government clearance. It can't come too soon.

Perhaps I am being too greedy, too optimistic and too naive. Perhaps none of these wishes will – or even can – come true. I would happily surrender them all for a basket of home-grown greengages – and a bottle of ice-cold sauternes.

Glory of glories, 1987 turned out to be the best greengage year we have had for decades. I got my basket full and my bottle of sauternes, so I can't really complain too much. It just happened to be a lousy harvest.

Wunderbar – If You Happen to Be a German Farmer

JANUARY 1987

I'm a pretty typical farmer. Quiet, modest and happy enough if I'm left alone to get on with the job of growing a field of wheat or two. I'm not the sort of chap who regularly attends his local NFU branch meetings, still less do I march in demos or protest by overturning lorries. I haven't a clue about the CAP, and all this fuss about the Green Pound being devalued leaves me befuddled. At least it did before I took my family to Germany for the New Year.

I left Harwich as the relaxed and lovable old peasant readers of this column know so well. One week later I returned in a very different mood. It wasn't the food that had done the damage (that was excellent) or the climate (a bit wet) or the traffic on the autobahns (very heavy). What transformed me from being one of nature's gentlemen to a sulphurous yob was a single piece of information which I discovered during my stay in the Fatherland. German farmers are today receiving 40% more for their wheat than I am. I would not have been surprised had this figure been 5%, and even 10% I could have stomached. But 40% is simply outrageous.

Their costs are, it is true, slightly higher than ours, but however you do the sums, it is abundantly clear that they are making a great deal more money than we are. Take, for example, Hans–Heinrich Imholze who manages 2000 acres in Lower Saxony. He is today being paid no less than £162 per tonne (455 dm) for feed wheat ex farm. And for milling wheat he is receiving £170 per tonne from his local merchant. These figures shook me to my thermal underwear. I could do with an extra £47 per tonne myself. In fact it would make the difference between profit and loss this year.

(For connoisseurs of German agricultural details, I should stress that these prices do not include the VAT which German farmers receive, nor do they include the Co-responsibility Levy. Hence they are directly comparable with our prices in the UK.)

Of course I don't begrudge (much) Herr Imholze the money, but in my own bumbling way I had always assumed that we were all in a Common (repeat Common) Market. Being a fairly sophisticated sort of peasant (I can, after all, chew straw and walk at the same time) I realise that life is never quite as simple as it may appear. That is why they invented the Green Currencies and those ludicrous Monetary Compensation Amounts (MCAs) which nobody except Don Patterson (Dalgety's export expert) really understands. These financial gadgets would, the bureaucrats assured us, iron out the glaring inequalities so that I could compete with Herr Imholze, Herr Schwab, Herr von dem Bussche and my other German farmer friends on roughly equal terms.

So much for my naive belief that Brussels had everything under control. I don't pretend to understand why feed wheat fetches 47 per tonne more in Lower Saxony than it does in Lower Cambridgeshire. However, a part of the cause is because Sterling is so weak against the Deutschmark. A year ago I could get 3.54 marks for one pound. Today I can only get 2.74. Anybody who has thought about buying a Claas combine or a Porsche car recently knows what effect this has had on prices.

However bad the news may be for me, and for all the other emaciated Barley Barons who can still totter round East Anglia, there is one group of men who are extremely happy. I refer, of course, to those wonderful chaps in the grain trade. They have found that because British wheat is the cheapest in the EEC it can be exported very easily indeed. Hence the millions of tonnes which have poured out of this country since last harvest. You can pick out the grain exporters across a crowded room at an agricultural conference these days. They're the ones with the big smiles buying everyone drinks at the bar. But why should I be surprised? Merchants and farmers have always been on opposite sides of the fence since farming began. And they always will be too.

It is, however, one thing to discover a glaring injustice, but quite another to know what should be done about it. The possible courses of action are many and varied. I could, I suppose, write to my Member of Parliament (a decent but plodding example of lobby fodder if ever I saw one). I could try to persuade the Caxton and Melbourn branch of the NFU to pass a Resolution. I could even speak to my important friends on the County Cereals Committee and see if they would like to pass an even more weighty Resolution. I could phone Simon Gourlay late at night at his Kensington flat. I could organise a sit-in at the Ministry of Agriculture. I could park the farm lorry across the entrance to Ipswich Docks. I could even take my wife's advice – and go on hunger strike. Or I could write an article in *Farmers Weekly* and hope that it is read by someone important and influential. It's nearly lunchtime now – so almost anything is better than a hunger strike.

The gap in prices caused by the Green Currencies was clearly greater than any politician had intended.

SSSI Dream

FEBRUARY 1987

I hadn't been sleeping at all well; my nights were punctuated by bizarre dreams. Amongst these, one stands out with an awful clarity. I was sitting in the farm office on a cold, bright January morning minding my own business when there was a knock at the door. In walked two ladies who introduced themselves as Jenny and Sarah from the Nature Conservancy Council.

I offered them cups of coffee and made small talk for a while before Jenny, the senior member of the two, cleared her throat and began, "We would like to talk to you, Mr Walston, about one of your fields." Being a man of enormous intelligence and sensitivity, I immediately realised that she was about to broach a delicate subject. I smiled that cool yet serious smile which I keep in reserve for just such an occasion. "Please go on," I said in a tone which I hoped showed my total sincerity.

"Well," began Jenny, "you have a field which we would like to designate as a Site of Special Scientific Interest, or SSSI as you probably know them. It is a very important site because, as far as we know, it is one of the very few habitats in the whole country for both a very rare animal and an even rarer grass."

By now I was beginning to regret that I had offered Jenny and Sarah the coffee. There I was facing falling grain prices and rising costs (not to mention a nervous bank manager and an omnipotent landlord) while these two women were proposing to turn one of my fields into an SSSI.

"Don't worry," said Sarah soothingly, "it isn't a very big field. In fact it's only nineteen acres." I began to feel better as I had been picturing a couple of hundred acres of wheat being converted into an adventure playground for the muesli-belt brigade.

"You'd better tell me why this field is so important," I said, trying to conceal both my anger and my fear. "Certainly," said Jenny. "Your part of the county is interesting because it has collapsed pingoes. These were once lens-shaped chunks of ice which were later covered by soil from the glaciers. When they eventually melted they created small depressions which today are damp hollows in a naturally well-drained chalkland landscape. Two of these collapsed pingoes exist on your field and they are what we are interested in. They provide the habitat for a very rare grass called *Lythrum hyssopifolia*, otherwise known as Grass Poly, and a tiny freshwater shellfish called *Chirocephalus diaphanus*, which is commonly known as the Fairy Shrimp. Both are in danger of extinction and an SSSI on your field would help to preserve them."

"Thank you for the Botany and the Biology lesson," I said, trying (but probably failing) to keep the sarcasm from my voice, "but I happen to be a working farmer. I suppose you'll insist that I graze a few Jacob Sheep on the field, put up a Portaloo and a car park and sell organic buns and butterfly nets to the visiting Volvo-owners." I realised I had gone a bit too far. Both Jenny and Sarah had been friendly, polite and highly professional. I should have followed their example so, taking a deep breath, I came to the crunch. "Are you going to lay down conditions? What do you want me to do?" I asked.

"Well," said Jenny, "we thought you would probably ask this question and, to be truthful, it's all a bit embarrassing. You see, both the grass and the shrimp appear to survive – even flourish – under your system of farming. If they didn't, they wouldn't be there now. So we are going to insist that you continue farming this field using the same intensive arable rotation that you have been for the past few decades."

"You mean," I stammered, "that I shall be obliged to grow high input cereals on this SSSI?"

"In a nutshell, yes," replied Jenny.

As I recovered my composure, I spotted where my advantage lay. "But what", I demanded triumphantly, " would you say if one day I saw the light, and instead of being a wicked intensive arable farmer, wished to become a lovable organic dog-and-stick farmer? I would put the field down to grass and simply graze it with a few sheep? Or," I said, warming to my task, "what would happen if – when Setaside comes – I set this field aside and simply fallow it?"

Sarah did not even blink. "In that case," she said, "we would have to enter into a Management Agreement with you and actually pay you to grow wheat on an SSSI."

I woke up with a start and rubbed my eyes. I was not in bed and it had not been a dream. The conversation described above actually did take place a few weeks ago. Any similarity with actual events is entirely deliberate. The names of individuals have not been changed to protect the innocent. Thank goodness for the collapsed pingoes, thank goodness for the Fairy Shrimp and Grass Poly, thank goodness for Jenny and Sarah. Roll on Setaside, I'm ready for you – at least on nineteen acres.

> *This fairy (shrimp) tale is absolutely true. Our SSSI now appears to flourish with regular doses of agrochemicals. I am happy, the conservationists are happy. What a perfect world we live in.*

Open Letter to Jonathan Porritt – Friend of the Earth

APRIL 1987

Dear Jonathan Porritt

You've been pretty rude about farmers during the past few years. You've called us all sorts of names and have lost no opportunity to go on telly and remind the rest of the world what an unpleasant bunch we are. This activity is called farmer-bashing and, I must admit, you have learned the trade well and now show great talent.

It is, of course, true that some of us have deserved your attentions. The man who bulldozes a hedge to convert a one hundred acre field into a 200 acre field deserves no sympathy. The man who sprays Roundup on Marsh Orchids so his daughter's pony has better grazing is not my idea of a hero. But these types are far from typical – even though you have given the impression that they are normal.

Such has been your success that today even the most idiotic

farmer now agrees Conservation must be taken seriously. But you are in danger of forgetting some important facts. Let me remind you of a few.

1. Protecting endangered species is a rich man's luxury. There is little or none of this sort of conservation practised in impoverished Eritrea. In that country starvation hovers over the land and farmers fight an endless battle to survive.

2. You can preach against insecticides in Britain, but just try the same message on a Somali farmer whose crop has been wiped out by locusts.

3. England's greenish and not unpleasant landscape was created (and preserved) not by poor peasants but by prosperous men. The rich landowners protected their hunting and shooting, and – often by chance – also protected the flora and fauna.

4. During the 1930s, when agriculture atrophied and bankruptcies littered the landscape, no farmer ever thought about conservation. They were too busy trying to survive.

5. Today, after 15 years of the CAP, farmers are prosperous. Some of them (not all, I admit) have spent a lot of money on conservation.

6. If you win your argument and the CAP is castrated, I may go bust because I am a high-cost farmer. But restrain your cheers. The land I occupy today is perfectly suited for arable crops and will certainly be farmed by someone else.

7. Contrary to your dreams, the man who follows me will not be a bird sanctuary warden. He will be a working arable farmer. To survive he will be forced to produce wheat at a low world market price. He will have to compete with Kansas. To succeed, he too will have to farm as they do in Kansas. This fact contains some good news and some bad news for you. The good news is that he will use fewer chemicals and fewer fertilisers than I do today. He will also produce less wheat per acre than I do.

8. The bad news is that the rural economy will suffer terribly. Naive visions of farm workers flooding back into the villages is so much bunkum. Likewise, your earnest wish that farms will become smaller will not actually happen. The low-cost farmer of tomorrow will inevitably employ even fewer men than I do today. If he must

produce wheat at a low world price, he obviously cannot employ lots of men. And when it comes to conservation, he will spend as much as farmers do in Kansas today. That amount is, I am afraid, zero.

The message must by now be clear. The only farmers who will ever do anything about conservation are prosperous farmers. Of course, it does not inevitably follow that all prosperous farmers are also conservationists.

So when you and your colleagues are girding your collective loins for yet another bout of semi-hysterical but wholly self-righteous farmer-bashing, it might be wise if you paused for thought. Restrain your baser instincts even though this approach may lose you friends (and subscriptions) in the muesli-belt.

When you next lobby the politicians and, in doing so fulminate against the Common Agricultural Policy and the rich farmers it has created, stop a moment and reflect. You may feel that farmers have

not done enough for conservation in recent times, but consider what would have happened had agriculture been left to rot, as it was in the 1930s.

It may come as a shock, but Friends of the Earth needs a prosperous agriculture if it is to protect the countryside. So forget your old prejudices and I shall try and persuade the more reactionary farmers to forget theirs too (this may be a struggle). We are in this together and the sooner we realise it, the better it will be for the Dartford Warbler, the wetlands – and for farmers.

> *For Friends of the Earth, farmers occupy a special place, somewhere between dumpers of nuclear waste (who are worse) and big game hunters (who are less bad). I resent being placed in this category of wreckers of the ecosystem.*

Garbage from Britain

JULY 1987

I have some good news for you and some bad news. First the good news. You have just been appointed to a very well-paid job. Now the bad news. You are the Managing Director of a company selling Sudanese computers and Bulgarian tractors.

If you'd got any sense you would quit immediately and go back to farming. But I suppose if you are a really talented salesman you could always find a few customers for the clockwork Khartoum KK-1 microcomputer (complete with abacus and worry-beads in case of emergencies). You might even be able to locate a farmer who will buy a Bulgarian tractor, even though the tyres don't match and the sump is slightly cracked.

Most of us would resign after the first day at the office because we would realise the hopelessness of the task ahead. But there are some people in this world who relish a challenge. Among these must be Mr Walter Goldsmith, who has just stepped into Nick Saphir's shoes as boss of Food from Britain.

He is obviously a talented and brave man. And he'll need to be. It's not just that farmers are mean and bloody-minded about contributing to FFB (and I am), it is that British food is so bad. No, it's worse than bad. It is terrible. You think I'm exaggerating don't you? You think I'm just prejudiced?

Go to any stall in any market square in any county town in any part of the United Kingdom and open your eyes. Look at the rubbish they are selling. Look at the bruised fruit hiding under the polished specimens on the trays. Look at the tired vegetables which were badly prepared, unevenly sorted and disgracefully displayed. Ask the stallholder if you can select your own fruit and he will become positively indignant at the idea. He will tell you that you will get what he serves you and if you don't like it you can go elsewhere.

Now move to the nearby butcher and repeat the process. The meat does, admittedly, look pretty because of the clever lights which even make a semi-albino like me look tanned. But here again the quality is uneven, the packaging is primitive and it is a matter of luck whether you buy a chunk of meat or a slab of tasteless pink water-injected hormone-implanted plastic.

Get in your car and cross the Channel. We all know the story. Well-grown, well-presented, well-graded grub in profusion. Even in countries like Holland and Germany where, goodness knows, the standard of actual cooking is no higher than in Britain, at least the ingredients are a whole heap better.

Once upon a time Food from Britain decided to correct all this. They invented the Foodmark which was intended to be a guarantee of quality. Whenever you saw it on a packet of anything (so the story goes) you knew that what you were buying was going to be damn near perfect. It was a smashing idea but it failed miserably. Why? Firstly because the big supermarkets refused to help.

These chainstores had gone to enormous lengths to sell only the best possible food. Why should they allow a Foodmark sticker on their fresh lettuce when the same sticker might also appear in the mouldy little greengrocers round the corner selling the usual garbage? Far from raising the standards, the supermarkets found that Foodmark idea actually blunted the quality image that they were trying to produce.

Secondly, the Foodmark was handed out by Food from Britain to producers who simply didn't deserve it. Instead of being a rare accolade given to only the very best of British Nosh, it was just another sticker on a lot of third rate stuff. No wonder the housewife took no notice.

If I were Mr Goldsmith today I would have a lovely time. I would start by announcing loud and clear that, with a few notable exceptions, British food stinks. I would recommend that British housewives should, as a general rule, buy foreign vegetables, Danish bacon and French apples because they are better than our own. I would thus admit what the rest of the world has known for ages. Starting from this tough and uncompromising position, I would then try and rebuild Food from Britain.

If the British food industry objected to this approach and refused to contribute to Food From Britain, that would be their decision and they would have to take the consequences. They could, once again, go back to their old ways of producing rubbish and hoping that the ignorant and tasteless British housewife would not notice. But time is not on the industry's side. You only have to look at the success of Marks and Spencers, Waitrose, Sainsburys and even good old Tesco to see that the buying public are beginning to wake up to the importance of quality.

Having established the truth, I would then re-launch the Foodmark (albeit with a different name). But this time I would ensure that it was given to only a tiny handful of products which really were as good as (or better than) the best of the foreign imports. Of course, it would take a long time for the idea to catch on because there would be so few products which would be worthy of the new Foodmark. But eventually the idea would bear fruit. And the fruit might even bear the Foodmark.

Of course, Mr Goldsmith won't have the courage to do this. He will tell us how wonderful British Food really is. He will ignore the facts and instead be forced to suck up to the industry just to get some cash from them to keep his empire running. It's very sad. What Food from Britain really needs are a few greedy people who care what they eat and don't mind offending all the other growers and processors who don't know the difference between greengrocery and garbage. In the meanwhile I shall continue to shop at Marks and Spencer, who have done more for British food in the past few years than everyone else put together. Mazeltov.

A torrent of angry letters arrived on the Farmers Weekly *editor's desk. Some suggested that if I didn't like British food I should emigrate, while others insisted that British food was the best in the world and the article showed I had no taste.*

Harvest 1987

SEPTEMBER 1987

Harvests are like General Elections. When you know what happened at Torquay, Billericay or Cheltenham, you know who is going to be the next Prime Minister. Just give me the yield of the first field of winter barley and I'll tell you what sort of a harvest it is going to be.

So you won't be surprised to hear that I was a pretty optimistic little chap back on July 28th when we cut our first field of winter barley. It was third year Pipkin and it yielded exactly 59cwt to the acre. I was, to put it politely, smug. And as the rest of the barleys came in, I knew we were in for one of the better harvests of recent years. The worst Pipkin did 54cwt, the Halcyon slightly better, the Panda managed 64cwt. It was only lethargy which stopped me ordering a new Porsche.

If the barley had been good, the Mikado rape was even better. The rain fell continuously and the dessicated crop began to sprout. Then one morning the sun came out and, like Montgomery before El Alamein, I decided that this was the moment for the Decisive Move. We started combining at 11am and continued non-stop for the next 27 hours, by which time we had done 240 acres. After doing a spell while the regular drivers ate supper, I went to bed early. The next morning I got up at 4.30 am, had a quick cup of coffee, and took over a combine just as the sun was coming up at 5am. Nine hours later we finished. The yield worked out at 31cwt per acre, which was better than any individual field of rape had ever done before. The only problem was that, as if to compensate for the yield, the price had fallen by 25% since last harvest and so the financial result was not as good as I had hoped.

The monsoon continued, which made me glad we had done our combining marathon, but meant that the next crop, herbage seed, was a nightmare. A slimy mush had formed beneath the surface and green regrowth made things even nastier. The combines struggled in conditions for which they had never been designed. The eventual yield of Brenda, an early perennial ryegrass, was poor, at around 7cwt, but was at least better than last year when we killed off the entire crop by applying the wrong herbicide. Our other variety,

Lamora, did slightly better at about 8.5cwt per acre.

In a normal year we would expect to harvest the peas between herbage seed and wheat. But normal year this wasn't. The Progreta, which had done so wonderfully last year, looked worse and worse with each succeeding downpour. Earlier in the season I thought they had never looked better, but now, flat on the ground, soggy, sprouting, stained and – worst of all – with a lot of pods but not many peas, they looked awful. I decided that we should concentrate on the wheats and forget the peas until we had salvaged the rest of harvest.

But at least the wheats still looked good. None had lodged and the plant populations were pretty fair. How could I have known that the weather during flowering had been so bad that only about 75% of the grain sites had filled? One afternoon I found myself in our best field of Hornet which I was showing off to John Bingham, the man who had bred the variety. I was bubbling with optimism and said that it would certainly yield 75cwt per acre. Bingham rubbed out couple of ears and said, very quietly, that we would be lucky to reach 60cwt. I put this gloom down to professional caution. But in the event the breeder was nearly correct. That particular field did 66cwt and Hornet as a whole was, for the second year running, our best wheat with an average of 64cwt per acre. Slejpner just broke the three tonne barrier and Mercia impressed at 55cwt with a good sample. The surprise of the year was Brimstone, of all varieties, which nearly made up for an appalling performance last year by averaging 53cwt even though it was all third wheat. Galahad and Apollo were disappointing at under three tonnes per acre. All in all, the wheats averaged 56cwt per acre which was about half a tonne less than I had been confidently predicting at the beginning of harvest.

I exclude our 70 acres of Moulin from these figures because this variety was in a class of its own. When we eventually combined the crop it produced 13.4 cwt per acre of unsaleable black, sprouted ergot-laden wheat. A tragic end to a variety which could have been the most significant since Maris Huntsman.

The Progreta peas were eventually salvaged in the second week of September, but only at enormous cost to the combines and everybody's tempers. The yield worked out at 18.6 cwt per acre of some of the ugliest pulses it has ever been my misfortune to see.

So much for my theory about General Elections and Harvests. This one, which started so well, got steadily worse as the weeks passed. It eventually turned out to be only slightly better than our disaster of last year. It also disproved the old cliche (on chalkland anyway) that a late harvest is a good harvest. But one farming truism has been reinforced powerfully. It will be a long time before I count the crop before it is in the barn.

Salaries for All

NOVEMBER 1987

A little local revolution took place at Thriplow this spring. We abolished hourly pay and overtime. Everybody on the staff went on to salary.

It had long struck me as stupid and archaic that Dave, the Manager, and Ted, the Foreman/Fitter, were on salary but the rest of the staff still were stuck in an antiquated pay system. In the bad old days when Managers managed and didn't get their hands dirty, a salary went with cavalry twill trousers and tattersall shirts as an essential status symbol. In those days we used to employ 80 people on the farm, and have a formal management structure consisting of umpteen different levels of authority. The year was even punctuated with Foremen's Meetings which enabled the NCOs to find out what was happening on the rest of the farm – and (if absolutely necessary) to air a few discreet grouses.

But today, thank heavens, we live in a different world. Gone are the beef cattle, the dairy, the pig unit, the poultry, the Arab horses, the grass drier, the carpenters, painters and gardeners. Instead we employ five men on 3000 acres, together with Dave, Ted and Elaine in the office. The labour force has not only been shrinking rapidly during the past five years, it has also become much younger, with an average age today of 35. Yet the seasonal nature of modern arable farming, with its long hours in late summer and autumn, contrasts starkly with the slack period between November and July when it is sometimes difficult to find work on wet days.

Arable farming has changed, and with it the old divisions between workers and management have become very blurred indeed. Dave does a lot of the drilling, Ted finds himself sitting on a baler or a combine for long hours at a time, and even I – complete with soft white hands and a tender behind – spent more time on a tractor last year than I did in the previous five.

Why, I wondered, did it somehow made sense for Management to be expected to work without overtime, but the rest of the staff were not trusted to do this? Was it solely because farm workers were so underpaid that only with the carrot of overtime could they be induced to put in more than 40 hours a week? Or was it because a salary was a form of perk which, like the key to the Executive Washroom, was given to the most important employees? Or was it a combination of both these reasons together with a tradition which started long before the Tolpuddle Martyrs and has continued down through the ages, fostered by distrust between employers and employees. Piecework was, after all, a system whereby the employer ensured that he only paid for a job when it was done – and hence got more value for money from his men. Today piecework has been largely discarded by arable farmers and only exists in a few murky backwaters. But whatever the reasons for today's structure of wages, it seemed to be the time to abolish this stupid distinction between white and blue collars.

But it was one thing thinking these noble thoughts and quite another putting them into practice. The new system could only work if the people on the farm trusted me to pay them enough to compensate for the loss of overtime. I would also have to trust them to do the hours necessary when the work needed to be done.

Eventually we came up with a formula which seemed to make sense to everybody. We took each man's earnings last year (not basic pay), added 10%, and called it salary. The whole scheme would be reviewed in 12 months, and anyone would have the right to revert to being hourly paid if he felt that he had received a raw deal. I too, as employer, would have the same right to terminate the experiment if I felt that it had not worked out satisfactorily.

The only sticky point was that I had to convince everyone that this was not a subtle scheme to get more work for less money. I was not, in other words, expecting them to put in any more hours than they had in the previous year. But, by the same token, I would be unhappy if they all decided to do fewer hours. No timesheets would be kept so the precise number of hours worked would never be recorded. Once again, the success of the scheme would depend on trust.

Six months have now passed. During one of the most difficult harvests we have ever known, there was not even a tremor of trouble. Far from feeling that I was being ripped off, I got the strong impression that everyone actually worked longer and harder than they ever had before. The absence of timesheets and overtime meant that nobody looked at a clock until the job was done. But for one member of the staff, it did not seem such a good idea after all. He began to miss the sight of his Basic and Overtime earnings on his monthly payslip. So he has reverted to the old system (and the old level of pay) while everyone else remains salaried.

I must, however, end with a a cautionary footnote to the saga. What we have done at Thriplow is, it now seems, illegal. We have managed to contravene the Agricultural Wages Order. The following example will show the problem.

Jack (of all trades) is a Craftsman. The Agricultural Wages Board lays down a Basic minimum wage for a 40 hour week of £114.08 and overtime at £4.28 an hour. If, during the busy autumn season Jack puts in 20 hours overtime, the AWB says he should earn at least £199.68. But Jack is now salaried and so receives no overtime. Instead he earns £164 for every week in the year. Nevertheless, I am assured that in this case the Ministry of Agriculture (or Jack) could sue me for underpayment.

Of course, like all salaried employees, Jack realises that while for maybe twelve weeks in the year he will do worse by being salaried, for the remaining 40 weeks he will do better. That's probably why Jack hasn't sued me. But the Ministry could feel differently. By next harvest I may be in Bedford Jail doing porridge.

A Born-Again Whinger

JANUARY 1988

The strain is beginning to tell. For the past decade or more I have been cheerfulness personified. Happy about the state of agriculture, grateful to all those generous taxpayers, I wandered the world informing anyone foolish enough to listen that farming was wonderful. If my mood ever faltered for a second, I had the perfect antidote: buy a new combine.

But lately I have began to find the pressure of being cheerful more than I can really take. The constant forced smile on my chubby features has made my jaw muscles ache. As yields, prices and morale continue to fall, I am beginning to find it difficult to tell the Bank Manager that everything is still splendid. So in 1988 I have made a new resolution. I shall become a born-again whinger. I shall, in short, join the ranks of all you farmers out there in readerland who have been complaining ceaselessly – and very noisily – since you left school/the army/the City/Cirencester/ University (delete the inapplicable) to join Daddy on the farm. You have known all along what I preferred to overlook, namely, that however good things appeared to be in agriculture, they were only a brief passing phase between long periods of gloom and despondency. I apologise. You were right and I was wrong. Mea culpa, mea culpa, mea maxima culpa.

The snag is that I am so unaccustomed to the role of whinger that I don't really know either the words or the music. So I'll have to make it up as I go along.

For a start I'm getting royally fed up with the agrochemical manufacturers who have yet again put up their prices. Overall this autumn the cost of chemicals rose by around 4%, and for some things like oilseed rape herbicides it was nearer 20%. I know the manufacturers and the retailers had a lousy autumn, but so did we whingers (sorry, farmers), so they can't claim to be in a more parlous position than we are. It is about time someone put the squeeze on the chemical manufacturers. I would dearly love to be that person, but since they no longer have big price differences between France and England, I can't get into the farm lorry and go to Calais any more. So come on, Bayer, Ciba-Geigy, ICI, Monsanto and all you other multinationals. You're not doing yourself any good by hurting your customers. Lower your prices. Or else. Please.

And the same applies to plant breeders who feel that they can raise the royalty rates as they please. No wonder the sales of certified seed are falling. So they jolly well should.

But above all in 1988 I would like some good weather. For me on light land this means, I'm afraid, lots of rain. But not too much in June so that the wheat does not pollinate. After 1987 I have learnt again what I spent a decade forgetting. No matter how clever a farmer you are, no matter how many chemicals you have at your disposal, no matter how wonderful the variety is, you are still utterly dependent on the weather. It is a sobering thought for one so conceited as me. But, as a born-again whinger, I must blame someone. Can one of you fellow whingers tell me who?

Index

ADAS, 26, 33, 57, 74, 106, 138, 211, 249
Agriculture (Miscellaneous Provisions) Act, 95
Agricultural Mortgage Corporation, (AMC) 117, 281
Am Stra Verter, 93
American Farm Bureau, 226
Andriessen, Frans, 262
Anglia Television, 103, 224, 272
Anglian Water Authority, 173
Animal Farm, 215
Apple computer, 97, 98, 99

Bank Manager, 246–248
Bankruptcy, 256, 281
Barclays Bank, 281
Batchelor, Hughie, 152, 172, 199
Bay Wa, 144
Bean Electronics, 98
Bell, Dr., 23
Beste, Hermann, 58, 59
Bilborough, Dick, 19
Bingham, John, 301
Boddy, Jack, 179
Body, Richard (later Sir), 133, 179
Bowen, Michael, 66
British Agricultural Supply Industry Scheme (BASIS), 106, 145, 146, 147
British Agrochemicals Association (BAA), 145, 147
British Sugar Corporation, 1, 13 factory cutbacks, 44
Brooke, Rupert, 188
Bulk buying, 154
Bush Hog discs, 39
Butler, Sir Richard, 179, 181

Cambridgeshire, 11, 17, 44, 45, 133, 177, 237
Canadian farmers, 160
Canadian Wheat Board, 162
Cannabis, 62, 63

Canola, 165
Capital Transfer Tax, 45
Cappelle, Francis, 197, 239
Cargill, 257
Cereal Seed Growers Association, 24
Cheddar cheese, 84, 85, 86
Cherrington, John, 71, 72, 73
Cherrington, Rowan, 260
Chewton, Lord, 84, 85, 86
China visit, 29
City Institutions, 122
CLA *see* Country Landowners Association
Claas, 10, 62, 65, 67, 141, 142, 231, 233
Common Agricultural Policy, 101, 115, 278, 294, 295
Communist Manifesto, 43
Commuters and farming, 136
Computers in farming, 52, 97, 126
Co-operatives, 143
Co-responsibility Levy, 267
Corn merchants, 167
Country Landowners Association, 46, 95, 96, 97, 120, 152
Cresson, Madame, 115
Crop drier, 32, 33
Cytozome Stubble Digester, 201

Dalgety, 257
Dalsager, Mr, 83
Davies, Brian, 211
Debessai, Jonas, 220
Direct drilling, 37, 38
Dover, 102
Dowdeswell ploughs, 10, 11, 38, 212
Drilling Dateline, 262, 263
Dronningborg, 67

Eritrea, 217–224
Eritrean People's Liberation Front (EPLF), 217, 219, 221, 222
Eritrean Relief Association (ERA), 217

Fahr, 67
Farm Bureau, 281
Farm & Horticultural Development
    Scheme (FHDS), 101, 280
Farmer-bashing, 191
Fiddian, Bill, 40
Filbey, Dick, 233
Firebrace, James, 214
Fisher-Humphries, 67
FNSEA, 114, 252, 253, 272
Food from Britain, 260, 296, 297
Food from Our Own Resources, 13
Friends of the Earth, 296
Fungicides, 40

Gaudery, 170
Geldof, Bob, 215
German Agricultural Society (DLG),
    8
Goldsmith, Walter, 296, 297
Gourlay, Simon, 181, 252, 253, 287
Greytak, John J., 182–185
Guillaume, François, 114, 272

Hallsworth, 170
Herbage seed, 299
Hubbard, Ken, 36
Hybrid wheat, 203–205, 288

ICI, 57, 139
Imholze, Hans-Heinrich, 240, 289
International Harvester, 66, 141
Isoglucose, 17

Jersey herd, 32
John Deere, 65, 67
Jopling, Michael, 253, 262

Kansas, 117, 191, 203, 294
Kenneth Wilson, 257
Khartoum, 218
Kiechle, Ignaz, 272

Laloux, Professor, 26, 71, 119, 279,
    280
Land agents, 55, 56, 57, 122, 133,
    240–242, 284
Land prices, 21
Lardenois, Petrus, 4
Laverda, 67
Linnell, Joe, 238

Lower Saxony, 36, 58
Lucerne, 33, 53, 69, 88
Luther, Martin, 65

Manns of Saxham, 65, 231
Mao Tse-tung, 30
Marijuana, 62
Massey Fergusson, 62, 65, 67
Maynard, Joan, 34
Milk Marketing Board, 85, 267
Ministry of Agriculture, Fisheries and
    Food (MAFF), 106
Mississippi, 60, 61, 191
Mole Valley Farmers, 102
Montana, 182–185

National Farmers Union, 1, 20, 49,
    57, 78, 95–97, 103–106, 111,
    114, 118, 120, 129, 133, 152,
    153, 157, 180, 225
National Institute of Agricultural
    Botany (NIAB), 23, 24, 34, 40
National Trust, 45
Nebraska, 234
Nerayo, Doctor, 219
New Holland farm machinery, 65,
    67, 164
New Zealand, 80
NFU *see* National Farmers Union
Nickersons, 42, 203, 204, 205
Nix, John, 95
NSDO, 42, 57, 74, 75, 255

O'Cathain, Detta, 85
ODA, 216
OPEC, 32
Organic farming, 49, 50, 248–250
Owner-occupation, 15
Oxfam, 143, 214, 215
Oxford Farming Conference, 15

Paris, 8, 113, 123
Patterson, Don, 290
Payment in Kind Program (PIK),
    140, 150, 151
PBI, 23, 43, 255, 275, 288
Peart, Fred, 14
Pension Funds, 54, 128, 129
Pesticide Safety Precautions Scheme
    (PSPS), 145, 146, 147
Plant breeders, 40

Plumb, Sir Henry, 252
Porritt, Jonathan, 293
Port Sudan, 218
Powell, Enoch, 133

Ransomes, 6, 10, 11
Reagan, President, 150
Rent Review, 284
Rents and tenancies, 269–271
Richardson, David, 200
Rockwell Aim computer, 97
Rohm & Haas, 203, 204, 288
Rosen, Anthony, 19, 49, 101
Rothwell Plant Breeders, 288

St Paul, 68
Sanderson Rough Terrain Truck, 54
Saphir, Nick, 296
Saskatchewan, 161–167, 191, 197,
    238
Scargill, Arthur, 133
Schleswig-Holstein, 26, 49, 71, 75,
    119, 189, 198, 279, 280
Schluter, 39, 59
Schwab, Christof, 197, 239
Scudamore, Paul, 98
Seed growing, 23
Seed merchants, 157
Seed trade, 258
Send a tonne to Africa, 194–196,
    214–224
Sheep, 68, 87
Shoard, Marion, 77, 93, 161, 199
Smythe Drill, 172
SOPEXA, 260
Sites of Special Scientific Interest
    (SSSIs), 153, 172, 291–293

Spraying, 27
Straw, burning, 76, 92, 187
    incorporation, 187, 211
Stubble digesters, 201–202
Suffolk Punches, 5
Sugar beet, 1, 4, 17, 82

Tenancies, 120
Thatcher, Margaret, 48
Thriplow, 64, 124, 141, 172, 192,
    194, 201, 266, 291
Tipper, Brian, 127
Tory, Patrick, 260
Trade Indemnity, 167, 168
Tramlines, 280
Truman, Harry, 31

US Wheat Associates, 260
UKASTA, 157
Urea, 138

Velcourt, 170
Virgil, 16

War on Want, 194, 214
Watt, Hew, 31
Wehrmann, Professor, 36, 37
Wehrenberg, Loren, 196, 198, 238
Weisswurst, 190
Weyburn Inland Terminal, 163
White, Tony, 273
Williams, Tom, 14
Wookey, Barry, 248, 249
World Food Programme, 216

Young, Hamish, 63